LIGHON

QUA TY

Please return by the last date or time shown

LIGHT-SPEED, GRAVITATION

AND

QUANTUM INSTANTANEITY

Anthony D. Osborne
&
N. Vivian Pope

Published by

 **PHILOSOPHICAL ENTERPRISES**

Swansea, U.K.

Published in 2007 by

 **PHILOSOPHICAL ENTERPRISES**

ISBN 0-9503790-6-9

Printed and bound in Wales by

Dinefwr Press, Ltd.,
Rawlings Road, Llandybie,
Carmarthenshire, SA18 3YD

Cover photograph and portraits of authors by Gareth Llewellyn Williams,
ZOOMSCAPE, Swansea

Cone model by N.V. Pope

TABLE OF CONTENTS

LIST OF ILLUSTRATIONS

ABBREVIATIONS AND ACRONYMS

CERN	European Centre for Research (Geneva)
DST	deep space time
EPR	Einstein-Podolski-Rosen
GR	General Relativity
IAAAD	instantaneous action-at-a-distance
MOND	Modified Newtonian Dynamics
MST	Minkowski space-time
NR	Normal Realism
POAMS	the Pope-Osborne Angular Momentum Synthesis
SLT	special Lorentz transformation
SR	Special Relativity
VLBI	Very Long Baseline Interferometry
WIMP	weakly interacting massive particle

FOREWORD

One of the most important principles of science is attributed to the fourteenth century philosopher William of Ockham and known as *Ockham's Razor*. It is the methodological principle of ontological parsimony: when presented with alternative explanations always opt for the simplest, the one with the fewest possible causes, assumptions or variables.

This book is an appeal to Ockham's Razor, for it offers a much more economical account of Special and General Relativity than is present in the traditional development of relativistic physics. In fact, the extent of the simplification of Relativity offered by Anthony D. Osborne and N. Vivian Pope is such that a theory which could hitherto be fully appreciated only by those with advanced university-level mathematical training can now be understood with, for the main part, little more than A Level Mathematics. But in this book, simplification is not the same as 'dumbing down'. Osborne and Pope present a rigorous, scholarly and philosophically coherent re-appraisal (a *synthesis*) of the fundamental tenets of both Newtonian and Einsteinian physics and of some of the consequences of that physics for both quantum physics and cosmology.

That reappraisal has consequences which go far beyond an incremental re-working or adjustment of existing results. If the approach presented in this book turns out to be correct, it would presage a paradigm shift in physics that would not only challenge the academic establishment but also change the way that ordinary people think about the material world. Let me give an example. Newton's First Law of motion states that every object in a state of uniform motion tends to remain in that state of motion unless an external force is applied to it, in other words, that the 'natural' state of motion is in a straight line. Osborne and Pope propose an alternative first law of motion: the natural (*i.e.*, forceless) state of motion is *orbital*, not rectilinear, *i.e.*, that bodies orbit one another freely unless an external force is applied to prevent them. Now the universe is full of orbital motion: from the micro-scale – 'electrons in orbit around nuclei' – to the macro-scale – moons around planets, planets around stars, rotating galaxies, *etc.* If this alternative first law is true, then there is no need to propose an *in vacuo* force of gravitational attraction to account for orbital motion. This is compelling, not least because it leads to a simpler and more elegant explanation. It also explains why, despite vast efforts and millions of dollars worth of research, no empirical evidence of any *in vacuo* 'forces', 'waves' or 'particles', has yet been found to explain how 'gravity' propagates or acts at-a-distance. A commonsense objection to this idea is 'Well, if there's no such thing as gravity, then what is it that sticks us to the surface of the earth? Why don't we just float off into space?' The answer, according to Osborne and Pope, is that the natural (forceless) orbital radius for our body's mass is far down towards the centre of the earth below where we stand. So there is a force that means that you weigh something. It's just *not* a mysterious *in vacuo* 'force of gravity'. It is the *real* force exerted by what restrains you from orbiting freely, *i.e.*, the ground under our feet.

The world of science is, of course, full of alternative theories. One reason why Pope and Osborne's synthesis deserves to be taken seriously is that aspects of it are experimentally testable. One such test is conceptually simple. Take a spinning mass; spinning in the same direction and same plane as that of the earth it should weigh a little more than when at rest on the earth's surface, and when spinning in the opposite direction it should weigh a little less. The problem it presents is not conceptual but practical: the change in weight predicted by the theory is very small (about one hundredth of a milligram for a 175 gram disk spinning at 18,000 revolutions per minute). Thus the experimental apparatus would need to be both very strong to cope with the energy of the spinning disk, and very sensitive accurately to measure the predicted weight-change. The proposed experiment is certainly difficult, but not impossible with today's technology. Indeed, related experiments have already been performed in Japan and indicate a change in weight due to spin. What is important here is that

Osborne and Pope are not asking for the ideas presented in this book to be taken on faith. As presented, their synthesis can be supported or rejected by means of such experiments.

This book deserves to be read and to provoke controversy. The work is not 'popular science'. It is the culmination of a twenty-year collaboration between Osborne and Pope, and a fifty-year intellectual journey by Pope (quite literally, a life's work). To anyone who cares about the truth in physics, I commend this book.

Alan Winfield
Hewlett-Packard Professor of Electronic Engineering
University of the West of England, Bristol
June 2007

PREFACE

This book represents the output of a close collaboration between the authors which has lasted for over twenty years. It is unusual book in that it combines expertise in philosophy and mathematics in the spirit of what is traditionally known as Natural Philosophy. Our intention has been to produce a *synthesis, i.e.,* a conceptually economical, logically and philosophically coherent re-appraisal, of the apparently disparate theories of Newtonian dynamics, Special and General Relativity, and the study of physical phenomena at the micro-physical level. As such, this book presents not just another physics *theory* to replace any of these existing theories but a wholesale *philosophy of physics.*

The following chapters are by no means intended to be deliberately controversial. Indeed, readers familiar with Newtonian dynamics or Special Relativity for example, will find many of the conclusions the same. At one level, much of the material in this book represents simply a novel and, we believe, simpler approach to Special Relativity, Newton's theory of gravitation and General Relativity.

However, on another level our synthesis will be controversial since it depends on a fundamental shift in philosophy regarding the interpretation of the behaviour of light in particular. In our radical alternative approach, light is *not* something which travels in space, it is simply pure information, in all its direct and indirect instrumental manifestations, from which the whole relativistic scenario of matter, space and time, and hence the notion of travelling itself, is projected. Hence, our approach represents a paradigm shift which has far reaching consequences in the way we conduct physics.

The second part of the book, from Chapter 6 onwards, is concerned particularly with the role of angular momentum. In our approach, we claim that there is no need for Newton's *in vacuo* 'gravitational force' to explain the paths of the planets for example, if a proper account is taken of conservation of angular momentum. Similarly, we show in Chapter 7 that if a proper account is taken of *spin* angular momentum at the micro-level, then it is possible to obtain the standard parameters of the hydrogen atom without the need for an *in vacuo* 'electrostatic force'. We demonstrate in Chapter 8 how some of the consequences of General Relativity can be obtained by combining conservation of angular momentum with the time-dilational result, normally associated with Special Relativity. Chapter 9 contains a critical review of some of the more fanciful speculations in modern science, and as such, is bound to be seen as contentious.

We have tried to ensure that the material in this book is as self-contained as possible and very little previous knowledge of physics is assumed. At times, and especially in Chapter 8, some of the mathematics is of degree level standard but for the most part, only a knowledge of mathematics a little beyond A Level is required. However, it is our hope that readers with a more limited background in mathematics will still be able to understand the *ideas* presented and in many cases, a non-mathematical summary is provided. In short, rather than being an advanced academic text, it is our greatest hope that this book will be read and appreciated by the widest possible audience.

We would like to thank Mary Pope and Penny Gower for reading the manuscript, making useful suggestions and spotting a number of typographical errors. We would also like to thank Alan Winfield for reading the manuscript and writing a Foreword. Finally, our thanks go to Gareth Williams for taking the photographs and to all the staff at Dinefwr Press Ltd. who helped to produce this book.

Anthony Osborne

and Viv Pope

Penclawdd, August 2007.

PROLOGUE

The origins of the ideas leading to a new lateral thinking approach to modern physics described in this book go back to 1954. This was when a young telephone engineer was first introduced to Einstein's Special Relativity at an astronomical society meeting in Swansea, UK. Finding that the Theory was every bit as abstruse as it was reputed to be, he naïvely wrote to Einstein asking him how it was logically possible that observers in different states of relative motion endured at different rates. How can it be, he enquired, that a pair of twins moving relatively to one another could each end-up both older and younger than the other. He received an encouraging reply to his carefully worded letter, saying that his question was 'well formulated' and that (naïve though it was) it was one which, under the title of 'the clock paradox', had worried even professional physicists.

Einstein's reply was that there is, in fact, no such paradox [1][2]. The only 'paradox', as Einstein's letter eventually convinced his correspondent, lay in the conventional but unjustifiable preconception that 'time is the same everywhere'. This got the young engineer thinking. What, he wondered, had been the logical warrant for that conventional precept? In physics, what else can *time* be – that is, *real* or *physical* time – other than simply what is measured by clocks, as opposed to the tacitly assumed, utterly mysterious 'universal' time, or cosmical 'God's-time'? In that case, since the only means of reading distant and fast-moving clocks is by means of light signals, and since the periods of those light signals (the ultimate 'clocks') are extended with motion away from us and shortened by motions towards us (the well-known 'Doppler effect'), then it seemed to him pure commonsense that the times registered by those distant and sometimes fast-moving atomic clocks have to be systematically different from those we read on our own observatory clocks and spectrometers in the way that Einstein had demonstrated. Experiments with geometrical diagrams [3] and logical arguments with others finally convinced him that Einstein was right. There was no paradox.

Puzzling over the practical and philosophical implications of this led him to continue his studies and, eventually, to give up his occupation as a telecommunications engineer (lineman) for an academic vocation as a lecturer, researcher and writer in Philosophy of Physics. This was with special emphasis on an objective and critical study of the origins of the customary conceptions of space and time.

This young telephone lineman was Neville Vivian (Viv) Pope. The first intimation that he was to develop a version of Special Relativity differing from Einstein's was when he tried to represent space, time and motion geometrically. He discovered that with a geometrical scale constant of 186,000 miles to the second he could derive Einstein's time-dilation formula on the basis of Pythagoras' theorem alone, without having to mention the 'speed of light *in vacuo*'. Unfortunately, despite his discovery being verified by mathematicians and physicists at his local university, it would be many years before he could find a way of publishing it [4].

Meanwhile, he applied his critical eye to other widely held tenets of physics. One of these was the Einstein-Podolski-Rosen (EPR) paradox, the notorious cause of disagreement between Einstein, the author of Special Relativity, and Bohr, the leading exponent of Quantum Theory. In Einstein's theory, nothing can travel faster than the speed of light, c. But this was seriously at odds with quantum instantaneity. Pope's unconventional (indeed, heretical) solution to the paradox was simple. It was, on grounds of conceptual economy, to jettison the conventional interpretation of c as being a speed and treat it in the way he had done in constructing his Pythagorean facsimile of Einstein's formula; that is, simply as a *constant ratio* between units of the conventional measures of observational length and time in the constructing of space-time diagrams.

This led to the development of the Pythagorean 'cone model' of space-time geometry described in Chapter 3 of this book and illustrated on the cover [5]. With the help and advice of a teaching colleague, Dr. John Hopton, at Burton-on-Trent Technical College, Pope devised this graphic depiction of the dual aspect of time, combining quantum instantaneity and relativistic time-delay as the two 'cinematic' components of quantum interaction between atoms. It was at about this time (1984) that Pope was introduced to Dr. Anthony Osborne at the Department of Mathematics, Keele University, UK. Having graduated at The City University, London in 1976, in 1980 Osborne was awarded his doctorate on 'Gravitation & Dynamical Systems'. Intrigued by Pope's ideas, Osborne offered his collaboration in writing their first joint paper, giving a fuller mathematical expression to these bare and rather unsophisticated ideas of Pope's. Not only did this corroborate those ideas but it also made them more presentable in the standard language of the scientific community. Thus began a rare meeting of minds between a free-range philosopher and a mathematician, and their joint venture has since become known in many conferences and publications as POAMS (the Pope-Osborne Angular Momentum Synthesis) [6].

The first Pope-Osborne publication presented the geometrical (geometro-temporal) Pythagorean cone model construction of relativistic time-dilation, which portrays proper time and relative time together as orthogonal, front and side elevations of the rectangular time-cone [7]. In the Citations Index of that time, this was ineptly described as 'a modelling approach to relativity'. The fact that it was fundamentally different, in that it had been derived without Einstein's axiomatic interpretation of the constant c as 'the speed of light *in vacuo*', had escaped the notice of the reviewer, who had failed to see that the 'New Approach' had profound philosophical implications for the conduct of physics. Had the reviewer been more perceptive, he would have seen that these philosophical implications are radically different from any that might be drawn from Einsteinian Relativity, being more in line with the Relativistic Philosophy, or Phenomenalism, of Einstein's philosophical mentor, Mach.

Prior to his meeting with Osborne, these philosophical implications had been systematically explored by Pope in cooperation with a fellow student, G. Arwyn Evans, on a degree course in Philosophy at the University of Wales, Bangor. This was with the help and support of a former telecommunications colleague, Alan M. Smart. It involved a critical analysis of language, along the lines pioneered by Wittgenstein, of our classical conceptions of distance, time and motion. This led to a new paradigm of scientific philosophy which they decided to call *Normal Realism*. However, when Pope submitted this as a thesis for a Masters Degree at Bangor it was rejected because it crossed too many academic boundaries. 'Philosophers,' he was told, 'should not try to tell physicists what they should and shouldn't do'.

However, the development of the offending philosophical approach to the problems of modern physics continued extramurally right up till the time of Pope's meeting with Osborne at Keele, where the Head of the Mathematics Department invited the Philosophy Department to oversee Pope's philosophical input to the Pope-Osborne collaboration, for a doctoral thesis. This was declined on the grounds that no-one in the Philosophy Department 'felt competent to assess the mathematical-science aspect of the work'.

Nevertheless, a rare interdisciplinary collaboration between Arts and Science had been established in the Mathematics Department at Keele, albeit as an academically unclassifiable, administrationally uncomfortable project. This novel philosophical approach to the problems of modern physics is described in the following chapter, and it is this same approach to specific conceptual issues of physics that is mobilised throughout this book. It reveals, by logical analysis, the presence in current theoretical physics of a mess of conceptual redundancy, which needs to be eliminated if conceptual progress in theoretical physics and common understanding are to be resumed. We would say, therefore, that the aim of our intended *aufklarung* is to reveal what, over the centuries, bare nature has been trying to tell us behind all the intellectual noise.

The discussions that led to the philosophical articulation of Normal Realism had also involved long dialogues in correspondence with the philosophers, Karl Popper, Gilbert Ryle (Editor of *Mind*), Rom Harré, and Alfred Ayer. There was also correspondence and, eventually, a meeting, between Pope and the eminent scientist, Herman Bondi, clinching their agreement over the redundancy of Einstein's interpretation of c as a 'speed *in vacuo*' and the validity of a much simplified version of Special Relativity based on the non-speed interpretation of that constant [8].

Pope and Osborne together continued to explore the mathematical physics implications of their agreed radical reinterpretation of the constant c as a *dimensional constant* instead of the conventional 'speed of light'. This resulted in a paper, published in *Physics Essays*, entitled 'Instantaneous Relativistic Action-at-a-Distance'[9], followed by another paper entitled 'Instantaneous Gravitational and Inertial Action-at-a-Distance'[10]. These two publications led to Pope being invited to co-edit a compilation of international papers under the title of *Instantaneous Action-at-a-Distance in Modern Physics: Pro and Contra* [11].

One of the early proponents of instantaneous action-at-a-distance (IAAAD), Professor Peter Graneau, a contributor to the aforementioned book, later suggested that the 'Pro' lobby (which, as it transpired, was larger than the 'Contra') should hold a Workshop with a view to reaching consensus on action-at-a-distance instantaneity. This Workshop was duly convened at the University of Wales, Swansea, in July 2001. That was followed, in April 2002, by a second Workshop at the same venue [12]. It was as a consequence of these Workshops that another book was published, edited by Pope, Osborne and Professor Alan F. T. Winfield, all three of whom were contributors to the Workshop [13]. The association between Pope and Winfield, Professor of Electronic Engineering at the University of West of England, Bristol, UK, dates back to the 1970s when, as a schoolboy, through an initial friendship with Pope's daughters, he became interested in Pope's radical ideas. He regularly attended seminars held during these and successive years and, as a lecturer at the University of Hull, helped to refine and promulgate these Normal Realist ideas. He has since become a leading figure in the POAMS group.

In its combining of expertise in philosophy and mathematics, this book does not present just another *physics* theory. It provides a glimpse of how the current runaway eclecticism, or random proliferation of physics theories, may be curbed. That is to say, it provides an example of how some conceptual economy and logical coherence might be restored to physics along the lines of what used to be called Natural Philosophy, the name by which physics was originally known. It also presents an account of the details and achievements, so far, of the POAMS Paradigm. This suggests a new conceptual compass bearing for the future course of a logically and mathematically coherent physics – or, rather, a resurgent Natural Philosophy. In the next chapter, as preparation for what follows, we describe in some detail the philosophical basis of the whole new way of thinking about the physical world (a new paradigm) to which we are logically committed by the radical shift in interpretation of c from a 'speed' to nothing more than a dimensional scale constant.

Notes and References

[1] It was later learned that Einstein did not often reply to his correspondents.

[2] This letter from Einstein is stored in *Philosophical Glimpses*, a seventeen volume record of private correspondence held by the Swansea County Hall Archives Dept., ref. D/D NVP/1-17, Volume 1, page 5. http://www.swansea.gov.uk

[3] See Figs. 3.1 and 3.2 in Chapter 3.

[4] Pope, N. V. and Osborne, A. D.: 'A New Approach to Special Relativity', *The International Journal for Mathematics Education in Science and Technology*, **18**, 2 (1987).

[5] This space-time conic depiction is not to be confused with the 'light-cone' of Eddington.

[6] The most recent of these publications, to date, are as follows:-

1) Pope, V: *The Eye of the Beholder: The Role of the Observer in Modern Physics* (**phi** Philosophical Enterprises, Swansea, 2004). See the Welsh Books Council website, www.gwales.com

2) Pope, N. V., Osborne, A. D. and Winfield, A. F. T. (eds.): *Immediate Distant Interaction and Correlation in Modern Physics: The Balanced Universe* (Edwin Mellen Press, New York, 2005). Website: www.mellenpress.com

[7] *Op. cit.* reference 4.

[8] This interpretation was corroborated by Herman Bondi in his book, *Assumption and Myth in Physical Theory* (Cambridge University Press, 1964) and in correspondence between Bondi and Pope. (*Art. cit.* reference 2, vol. 8, pp. 2970; 2980-2981, http://www.swansea.gov.uk .)

[9] Pope, N. V. and Osborne, A. D., *Physics Essays*, **5**, 3 (1992), pp. 409-421.

[10] Pope, N. V. and Osborne, A. D., *Physics Essays*, **8**, 3 (1995), pp. 384-397.

[11] Chubykalo, A. E. , Pope, N. V. and Smirnov-Rueda, R., (Nova Science, New York, 1999).

[12] Both of these Workshops were organised and directed by Mary (A. M.) Pope in collaboration with the university authorities.

[13] *Op. cit.* reference 6, No. 2.

CHAPTER 1

Philosophical Basis and Background

1.1 Introduction

A criticism sometimes levelled against particular conferences on theoretical physics is that those who present their theories at these conferences scarcely, if ever, state where, philosophically, they are 'coming from'. Too many of these presenters simply set out their theories on the basis of a fanciful assumption that their premises automatically conform to philosophical principles on which all right-minded people are agreed, so that any talk of 'philosophical underpinnings' is unnecessary, hence to be avoided. They see no more *philosophy* in the way they think than fish see water.

However, even the most minimal attempt at philosophical analysis of their presuppositions all too often reveals a lack of awareness of how insecure may be the philosophical assumptions they take for granted. Undoubtedly, this is why so many theorists at these conferences fail to understand, far less agree, with one another. It might well explain why there has been, in recent years, so little real conceptual progress in this area.

Most people, most of the time, just do whatever they do without thinking – far less philosophising – about it. They scarcely, if ever, wonder *why* they think and act the way they do. Yet a moment's reflection is sufficient to reveal that the ideas we customarily entertain, and the language in which these ideas are couched, are seldom our own. In practically every case, they have a lineage stretching far back into the past, way beyond our own personal compasses of experience. What is it, then, that shapes these basic ideas and forms of language, since it is not we ourselves? It is, of course, the culture in which we are born and raised.

Any notion, then, we may entertain that as individuals we are free to think and act as we like is false. Cultures differ, sometimes very radically. And to the extent that our cultures differ so do we from one another as individuals. Since not everyone's social ambits are the same, even the most local differences may create confusions in communication which are little short of disastrous. In such cases, when communication breaks down, the solution, surely, should not be to coerce others into accepting our arbitrary ways of thinking with taunts or political persuasion, far less with physical force. Ideally, it should be to sit down and carefully analyse, on the *philosophical* level, the lineage and logical efficacy of our respective idea-systems. This should be with a willingness to make radical logical adjustments wherever necessary in our habitual employments of language, as opposed to seeking simply to inflict our own philosophically unexamined ideas on others. This applies, not least, in what we fancy is our most 'objective and dispassionate' science, where the clashes between different belief-systems are often on a par with those of politics and religion. A prime example of this sort of implicitly philosophical conflict is that between the God's-eye-view 'Realism' of Einstein and the 'Positivism' of Bohr over the issue of whether or not 'God plays dice' with events at the ultimate quantum level.

In this book, as a safeguard against this unconscious dogmatism, we start with a brief logical analysis of the philosophical underpinnings of current scientific convention. Without this precaution, what we prescribe for the philosophical future of physics will inevitably fall foul of the confusion caused by interference from pervasive and persistent relics of long-abandoned philosophical notions that should have – but unfortunately have not – been discarded.

1.2 God's-eye-view realism

Do we perceive things as they are or only as we think they are? How can we tell? When we see an 'electron', what are we seeing? Is it the real object, as it is 'in itself' – whatever that may be – or is it only an arbitrary or conventionalised interpretation of observational data? One of the founders of what we now know as physics, was the French philosopher, René Descartes (1596-1650). He argued that all we ever see or sense are our 'ideas' of physical objects, never those objects themselves as 'God' may be presumed to see them. For Descartes this was no problem, because, as he devoutly reasoned, the God who made those objects is the same God that made the senses by which we perceive them; and since God, by definition, is Infinitely Good and Perfect, 'He is no deceiver'. So for Descartes it followed that what our senses tell us, in the best and plainest, most standard of sensory situations, must be true. Thus, he concluded, what we perceive in those paradigm circumstances is an exact replica of, hence as real as, what God sees. This presumed, fundamentalist or absolutist 'God's-eye-view' of things is the basis of what has since become known, in modern physics, as *Realism*. Being so plainly false, this reasoning of Descartes' was bound, sooner or later, to create a reaction, which it did, a century later.

1.3 The Phenomenalist reaction

Philosophers after Descartes, not surprisingly, saw his argument as fallacious. The fallacy is that it creates a kind of built-in conceptual schizophrenia. As Descartes' critics saw it, the argument splits our minds in two. In the one part are our ideas of what things are 'in themselves', as we presume 'God' sees them, and in the other are our ideas of what those things are as 'we' see them. And then we have yet another set of ideas as to how those two separated sets of ideas in our minds are connected, which Descartes conceived as a linkage provided by an infinitely non-deceitful God. The plain fact that these different sets of arbitrarily separated ideas were *entirely his own ideas* was lost on Descartes. So, as it transpires, this splitting-off of a presumed 'God's-eye-view' of physical objects from our perceptions of them created a false dichotomy. Called *Cartesian dualism*, this split Natural Philosophy in two. The 'God's-eye-view' half became physics and the other half, the 'Man's-eye-view', became psychology, the science of Mind. This dichotomy between 'Mind' and 'Matter', introduced by Descartes over three centuries ago, has held sway in Western thinking right up to the present time.

1.4 Subjective Idealism

In this split-minded way, Descartes had inadvertently set a trap for future philosophers. Among the first to fall into this trap was the highly influential philosopher, Bishop George Berkeley (1685-1753). Berkeley reasoned that since we cannot presume to be God, we can have no knowledge as to how God might perceive things. There was no point, therefore, in this splitting or duplicating of our idea-systems into, on the one hand, our ideas of what things are 'as *we* perceive them' and, on the other hand, as we presume '*God* perceives them'. So, Berkeley concluded – catastrophically, as it turned out – everything that *is* exists '*in the mind of the observer*'.

The Cartesian fallacy was therefore compounded. It was as though some crafty person had cut a bar of chocolate in two and conned someone into accepting the one half as the whole bar. However, some people thought this was a good logical answer to Cartesian dualism. Among these were the prominent philosophers, David Hume (1711-1776) and Immanuel Kant (1724-1804). With modern hindsight, this answer to Cartesian dualism can be seen as a disaster which threw academic philosophy way off course for nigh on three centuries.

In this way, Berkeley's truncated 'idealism', fallacious though it was, became the basis of what was subsequently known as *phenomenalism*, which many thought, mistakenly as we shall see, to be a theory of reality based entirely on appearances. In that constricted, half-minded way of thinking it was made to seem that there can be no reality in anything other than that of our own sense-impressions. This was the view known in philosophical circles as *Subjective Idealism*. In its logical extreme this becomes the calamitous view called *Solipsism*, the notion that the 'mind' in which everything exists is, ultimately, one's own mind, so that there can be no objective distinction between dream and reality. To be trapped in this solipsistic way of thinking indicates a psychiatric disease.

The infamous dictum which launched this subjectivist view was Berkeley's statement: *Esse* is *percipi* (to be is to be perceived). For centuries, this was taken to be some kind of truism. Indeed, it is not too much to say that from Berkeley's time on, practically all the energy that went into the pursuit of academic philosophy was squandered in pursuing vainly contrived ways of escaping that solipsistic consequence.

But then, at the beginning of the 20th century, a Cambridge philosopher, George E. Moore (1873-1958), decided to subject Berkeley's dictum to a method which was to become known as *Linguistic Analysis*. In what way, Moore wondered, can that statement of Berkeley's be true. It is not true by definition, like 'A bachelor is an unmarried man'; nor is it factually true, like 'All traffic stop-lights are red'. In what sense, then, can it possibly be true that in order to *be* or *exist*, an object has to be seen or perceived? The result of Moore's Linguistic Analysis was that there is simply no warrant for that statement whatsoever; that it is a form of language which has no true meaning.

1.5 The rise and fall of the 'Linguistic' movement

This 'Linguistic' movement in philosophy actually starts with an essay of Moore's entitled 'The Refutation of Idealism'. Published in *Mind*, 1903 [1], that one small essay quietly changed the whole course of Western philosophy. Following Moore's Linguistic Analysis of Berkeley's dictum, other writers began to seek, in similar manner, to purge the common language altogether of what they perceived as other relics of Cartesian dualism. These new writings and teachings were by philosophers such as John L. Austin (1911-1960), Gilbert Ryle (1900-1976), and many others including, not least, the eminent Ludwig Wittgenstein (1889-1951). Consequently, in the twentieth century, philosophy took off in a radically new direction. The aim of these Linguistic philosophers was, by means of the process of Linguistic Analysis that Moore had pioneered, to purify and restore to 'normality' a common language which they saw as contaminated throughout by the theoretical relics of Cartesian dualism. This they aimed to achieve by nothing more than an insistence on 'proper usage' of what they thought of as 'Ordinary Language' – inevitably the 'King's English' of these Oxbridge scholars.

However, just as with Berkeley, in their reactionary zeal to apply this new method to language as a whole, these philosophers committed yet another fallacy. This was similar to Berkeley's Idealist fallacy in that it was made to seem as though, in Wittgenstein's memorable words, 'The World is Language'. If this was meant to restore to language its original commonsense basis, then it failed. For commonsense scientists this 'Linguistic' philosophy was no advance on Subjective Idealism. It was too much for practically minded people to think of what is revealed to us by microscopes, telescopes and other instruments such as voltmeters, particle accelerators and so on, as just 'bits of language'. This was where the dualistic fallacy of Descartes eventually led to a final parting of the ways between modern 'Realistic' (Fundamentalist) Science and 'Idealistic' Philosophy in the Arts/Science split lamented by the likes of C. P. Snow [2].

The high point of this conflict came in the 1960s. This was due to the indiscriminate, reactionary dismissal by the 'Linguistic' philosophers after (the later) Wittgenstein, of all objective modern scientific language as incurably polluted by the jargon created by Cartesian dualism. This jargonised language they disparagingly dubbed 'Scientism'. The trouble was that in their reactionary zeal, these philosophers rejected scientific language as a whole, thereby (to use a well-known simile) throwing out the 'baby' of developing science with the murky 'bathwater' of Cartesian dualism.

What these 'Linguistic' philosophers had argued, however, was not entirely false. Quite obviously, in our commonsense and scientific observations of the world, nothing comes labelled by nature as, say, an 'electron', a 'quark', a 'quasar' … or whatever. It is, undeniably, *we* who do that labelling or naming, and it is *we* who arbitrarily assign these objects to their various language classes and categories, such as 'animal', 'vegetable' 'mineral' and so on with the various sub-categories and classifications, such as 'fish' 'potato', 'salt', *etc.* This, of course, defines the normal creative, ongoing process of concept-construction and revision that we generally know as *language*.

But, of course, no language, in and of itself, can guarantee, at any stage in its development, that whatever it suggests to us is 'real' is *in fact* real. The mistake these 'Linguistic' philosophers made was to assume that there is some 'pure' form of language (metalanguage) which, by virtue of nothing but its own formality, constitutes an eternal and 'incorrigible' template into which all the scientifically discoverable things and processes of nature automatically fit. As these 'Linguistic' philosophers conceived it, apart from its most practical uses in advancing pure technology, this would make all science as such redundant. A grammatical and semantic study of a tidied-up version of 'Ordinary Language', they assumed, would do it all. In the end, all distinctions between reality and illusion, they imagined, would be revealed to us in 'proper usage of Language'.

But of course, there is no way in which our finite *human language* may, by its own internal efforts, hoist itself as if 'by its own hair', into absolute certainty in that imagined way. This is why, after flourishing for a decade or so – in academic circles, at any rate – 'Linguistic' philosophy eventually died a death, taking with it, in many instances, the very name 'Philosophy' with which it had become too closely and intimately identified. Since then, all other subjects, including physical science, have been left to go their various eclectic ways, practically bereft of any awareness of the insecurity of their own unspoken and un-analysed philosophical underpinnings.

Plain commonsense, however, tells us that there has to be something else, beyond human language, with reference to which the efficacy or otherwise of that human language may be judged. But what is that external, extra-human language? A glance through our scientific/philosophical history answers this question.

1.6 Science and language

The Greeks had a word for what, nowadays, we would approximate to 'language'. This was the secular word *logos*, which meant something in the nature of things that was beyond human language (including that of logic and mathematics) but whose forms it was the end-aim of all our best scientific uses of language to emulate. This was recognised by Science at its very inception. Even nowadays, the sciences remain classified as divisions of *logos*. For example, Geo-*logy* signifies the language (or *logos*) of earth-study; Bio-*logy*, the language of the study of living organisms; Psycho-*logy*, the language of the study of mind, spirit or consciousness; Palaeonto-*logy*, the language of the study of fossils … and so on. And not least, of course, is *Logic* on which all scientific and other rational communication is based. All these different departments of science signify, by their common titular appendage '-*logy*' that they were originally conceived as different categories and divisions of *logos*.

However, the word *logos* has since accumulated all sorts of 'supernatural' connotations. In this book we bypass these sorts of associations and concentrate on the plain fact that human language is never self-sufficient as a means of assigning absolute truth and reality to our perceptions of things; that at every stage in its evolution its efficacy has to be judged with reference to a something superior to it, something which is super-lingual but not divisive in the Cartesian way and which does not necessarily – although for some it might – have theological implications.

1.7 Normal Realism

Normal Realism is the paradigm of Natural Philosophy which is the logical result of removing from contemporary physics all vestiges of both the Cartesian and the Berkeleyan fallacies. This resurgent Natural Philosophy is largely a modern offshoot of both classical phenomenalism and modern linguisticism whilst being identifiable with neither. Essentially, it exorcises, along the lines pointed by Moore, the spectre of Subjective Idealism that has persisted in phenomenalism and its off-shoot, linguisticism, until quite recently.

The result of this analytical clearing-out of historical fallacies is a *radical empiricism* in which there is no 'God's-eye-view' presumption of intuiting the 'absolute' existence of entities underlying all our direct and instrumental perceptions of them. By complete contrast, in Normal Realism, scientific knowledge of the physical world rests, not on absolutist, God's-eye-view intuitions or precepts about underlying realities (the so-called 'Realism' of classical Physics) but always on our very best logical interpretations of *phenomena*. These *phenomena* are not the subjective 'pale shades' of those 'underlying realities' that in Cartesian dualism are known directly 'only to God'.

They are the one and only physical reality which is manifest in all the observational (*i.e.*, sensory and instrumental) categories articulated by the barest, most economic use of communal language. The main difference between this *Normal* language and the incorrigible 'Ordinary Language' of the 'Linguistic' philosophers (dubbed the 'Language Police') is that the language of Normal Realism is not fixed and immutable, as 'Ordinary Language' was supposed to be. Language, in Normal Realism, is essentially developmental, evolving as our communal experience evolves, hence always, in principle, essentially revisable in the face of natural uncertainty, as befits our finite position in the scheme of things. In Normal Realism, the end-aim of this empirical or developmental scientific language is, by the process of free and continual logical elimination of error, to winnow out from contemporary scientific language, the true *logos* of nature from all the fanciful theoretical chaff. In short, the mantra of the Normal Realist might well be: 'I have no idea what Ultimate Truth is; but by the careful use of logic I sure enough know what isn't!'

What this book sets out to demonstrate is that in applying its method as much to philosophy as to physics, Normal Realism logically integrates the two. This it does by removing the last relics of the Cartesian separation of the observer from physical reality. Not least of these persistent relics is the classical 'speed of light' interpretation of the dimensional constant c in Special Relativity, which separates the object observed from the observer of the object in the Cartesian way. Thus, the classical Cartesian separation has become what is currently called 'Einstein separation', the logical fallacy of which is the same as in Descartes' separation of observational reality into objects as we perceive them and those same objects as perceived by 'God' [3]. Thus, despite there being no possible way known to empirical science in which the light by which we see things can be observed or detected 'travelling *in vacuo*', we nevertheless assume that our ideas of what a thing is 'in itself' and our ideas of 'how we perceive it' are fundamentally separated, as in Cartesian dualism, by this metaphysical agency of light travelling in the way the second axiom of Special Relativity asserts [4].

Normal Realism is unique among the current approaches to modern physics in that by removing this last relic of Cartesian dualism from relativity, it eradicates the notorious conflict between extant Relativity and Quantum Theory over the issue of direct (*i.e.*, instantaneous) *versus* delayed atomic interaction. Note that the word 'normal' in Normal Realism was carefully chosen at its inception in the 1970s. This was so as to be taken, not as synonymous with 'usual', or 'conventional' but as *normative*, or *prescriptive*, as opposed to purely descriptive. The *norm* or standard of scientific language thus prescribed is that of the best possible use of rational or logical language, the most conceptually efficient, most wholesome and least theoretical usage in describing ongoing experience.

In this way, Normal Realism is an articulation of the *normal*, logical way of thinking and use of language which extends the Wittgensteinian method of 'purified commonsense' beyond ordinary everyday experience to integrate with experience in areas such as those of modern physics and cosmology. Its aim, in this respect, is to offset the current trend towards theoretical over-elaboration in these areas. As part of the ordinary language resurgence initiated by Moore, it makes a seamless join between scientific ideas and commonsense-logical realism. In this way, Normal Realism is by no means hostile to physical science, as was the scholastic 'Ordinary Language' of Linguistic philosophy. But neither is it purely passive towards, or descriptive of, what scientists do, as used to be the mandatory agenda of academic Philosophy of Science [5]. Instead, it is normative, or prescriptive of science, in the classical manner of the natural philosophy from which, originally, all physical science sprang. In short, Normal Realism is no more nor less than a resurgent *Natural Philosophy*. That is to say, it is a philosophy that is *involved* in science, whereas, since Descartes, philosophy has been shunted – not undeservedly, one might say – into an academic *cul-de-sac* where it has little or no relevance to the affairs of science or, indeed, any other sector of practicality.

In this book, we demonstrate how this Normal Realist agenda works in practice as a basis for producing a conceptually cleaned-up and philosophically articulated quadripartite synthesis of Newtonian physics, relativity, quantum physics and cosmology. This is based on phenomenalism as pioneered by Ernst Mach (1838-1916) blended with the commonsense anti-idealism of Moore, also including elements of the 'Linguistic' philosophy of the likes of Austin, Ryle and Wittgenstein. The result, as already pointed out, is not some new theory to add to the already intolerable burden of intellectual contrivances in modern theoretical physics. In complete contrast, Normal Realism [6] is no more than an extension of ordinary commonsense language and mathematics into matters of purely observational modern science. It replaces what has been described as 'an eclectic mish-mash of theories-upon-theories-upon-theories' with a unified, wholesome philosophical paradigm of phenomenalism which is continuous with the traditional spirit and intentions of pre-Cartesian Natural Philosophy.

The hinge on which this Normal Realist paradigm of modern physics turns is, of course, the radical shift from thinking about light as something travelling in space to thinking of it as simply *what we see*, that is to say, the ultimate *phenomenon* from which, primarily, all the normal physical dimensions of distance, time, motion, size, shape and so on are projected. This defines the relativism of Mach rather than that of his follower, Einstein. In Chapter 3, we show how this paradigm-switch affects mainstream Special Relativity, in which it is axiomatic that 'light travels *in vacuo* at the constant speed c which is the same for all observers regardless of their state of motion or rest relative to one another'. First, however, in Chapter 2, we examine the standard orthodox Einsteinian conception of relative motion, comparing and contrasting it with our neo-Machian conception of motion as, first and foremost, a *phenomenon*, with c as a pure dimensional constant instead of a 'speed'.

Notes and References

[1] Moore, G. E.: 'The Refutation of Idealism', *Mind*, **XII** (1903). See *Philosophical Studies*, (Routledge & Kegan Paul, London 1960).

[2] As both a literary man and a scientist, Snow was particularly well equipped to write a book about science and literature. *The Two Cultures and the Scientific Revolution* (1959) and its sequel, *Second Look* (1964), constitute Snow's most widely known – and widely attacked – position. He argued that practitioners of the two disciplines know little, if anything, about each other and that this makes communication difficult, if not impossible, between them.

[3] It is well known that Einstein was a 'Realist' in this absolutist or 'God's-eye-view' sense.

[4] In every case, what we *see* comes first (*a priori*) and what we make of it (*i.e.*, how we interpret it) always second (*a posteriori*). Logically, as we shall see in the following chapters, not only is the customary interpretation of c as a 'speed' far from obligatory, it is also logically fallacious.

[5] An academic dissertation in the subject of 'Philosophy of Science' which led to the founding of Normal Realism was rejected by its examiners on the grounds that 'Philosophers should not presume to tell physicists what they should or shouldn't do'.

[6] For a full description, Internet users may key-in the phrase 'Normal Realism' on Google Search.

CHAPTER 2

Uniform Motion and the Constant *c*

2.1 Introduction

From what has been said in the previous chapter it is clear that the Normal Realist (NR) approach to physical science has to be radically different from that of current convention. For instance, in the NR approach there can be no 'absolute motion' with respect to any 'absolute space', as in classical physics. In NR, *all* motions are essentially the *relative* motions of objects whose defining properties and qualities are not those of absolute 'things in themselves' – far less of 'space in itself' – but those of *phenomena*. Needless to say, not only are these properties *etc.* of things *relative* to the observer, as in the separatist Relativity of Einstein, they are also *directly* related to observation, as in the relativist philosophy of Mach.

In this present chapter, we begin our alternative approach to relativity with a critical analysis of Special Relativity (SR), which is concerned, essentially, with uniform motion and the behaviour of light. In particular, we dispense with Einstein's interpretation of the constant *c* as a speed, and interpret this constant, instead, simply as a *conversion factor* for converting metres of optical distance into light-seconds. It will be seen that not only does our NR account of motion produce all the standard consequences of SR but also that it is much simpler, more conceptually economical and more philosophically coherent than Einstein's.

It is informative to note that Einstein's justification for his own 'relativistic' interpretation of mass, length and time was that it was based squarely on the phenomenalist philosophy of Ernst Mach. However, when Special Relativity first appeared, far from supporting it, Mach vigorously rejected it [1][2]. For Mach, Einstein's theory was not a consistent phenomenalism or relativism but a kind of barren hybrid, an eclectic compromise between antithetical ideas, which therefore made no logical or philosophical sense. At the heart of this inconsistency lies Einstein's absolutistic assumption of light travelling at the constant speed c invisibly *in vacuo*. The point of Mach's objection was that light 'travelling' *in vacuo* is impossible to observe, whereas observation is the very basis of relativity. This and other problems caused by the 'speed' interpretation of c are resolved by our alternative 'conversion factor' interpretation, which fits perfectly into Mach's phenomenalist approach to physics.

2.2 Uniform motion

Special Relativity was first proposed by Einstein in 1905 [3]. Primarily, this was in response to a crisis in classical physics that had developed during the latter half of the nineteenth century. Essentially, Einstein's basic postulates are that the laws of physics are the same in all frames of reference which move *uniformly* (*i.e.* have constant velocity) relatively to each other and that the 'speed of light' c, *in vacuo*, is the same relative to all such frames. Frames of reference in uniform relative motion are known as *inertial frames*. Einstein's first postulate is known as the *Principle of Relativity* and implies that there is no physical experiment that can detect the difference between two inertial frames. Note that constant velocity means constant speed in a fixed direction. Constant speed alone does not guarantee constant velocity.

Our common experience tells us that it does not make sense to talk about absolute motion, as though a body could be thought of as moving or stationary in itself, relatively to nothing. As Mach insisted, it makes sense only to talk about motion relative to a particular frame of reference. For example, when we drive a car, the speedometer tells us the speed of the car relative to the road. The road is stationary relative to the earth, but the earth is orbiting the Sun, which in turn, is orbiting the galactic centre … and so on. In short, no meaning can be ascribed to motion as such; only *relative* motion has any logical meaning [4]. The fact that mechanical laws must be the same in all inertial frames was initially recognised by Galileo (1564-1642). In his famous treatise [5], Galileo argued that a rock dropped from the top of the mast of a ship always lands at the foot of the mast regardless of whether the ship is stationary relative to some harbour or at sea sailing at a constant velocity. In this way, he argued, the fact that freely falling objects always travel vertically does not imply that the earth is stationary. In the same treatise, he implies that the results of any mechanical experiment performed in the cabin of a ship would be the same, whether that experiment was performed with the ship stationary relative to some harbour or with the ship moving at a constant velocity relative to that harbour.

This fact that the laws of mechanics must be the same in all inertial frames was also appreciated by Newton. He stated:

> The motions of bodies included in a given space are the same among themselves, whether that space is at rest, or moves uniformly forwards in a right (straight) line without any circular motion.

Notice that in this statement the condition that the motion is uniform is the important ingredient. Why is this? In contrast to uniform motion, non-uniform motion is very easy to detect. For example, let us imagine ourselves in a jet plane, which travels at a constant velocity relative to the ground. Suppose that the walls of our cabin are sound-proof and that shutters cover its windows. Any experiment we set up in the plane will not tell us whether the plane is in flight or standing stationary on the runway. It is only when we are able to look out of the window and are close enough to the ground that we can see we are travelling relatively to it. However, when the plane encounters turbulence or decelerates on landing, we can tell that we are no longer in a uniformly moving frame, due to the sensations that we feel with the jolting and/or severe braking on touchdown. In this case, any mechanical experiment would be able to detect the non-uniform motion.

Since all inertial frames are equivalent as far as the laws of mechanics are concerned, it seems logical that they should also be equivalent as far as all the laws of physics are concerned, since there is no reason to suppose that mechanics has a privileged position in physics. Hence our first NR postulate is the same as Einstein's first postulate for SR, namely:

Postulate 1: *The laws of physics are the same in all inertial frames.*

It is important to realise here that this postulate does not imply that the laws of physics are the same relative *only* to inertial frames. Indeed, it is incumbent upon any physical theory to ensure that, ultimately, its laws are the same for *all* observational frames. Einstein accomplished this when he formulated his General Relativity (GR), which builds upon SR and incorporates non-uniform motion. Like Einstein, in NR we begin with uniform motion and inertial frames, just as Galileo and Newton did before Einstein. This is for the reasons outlined above and because from a mathematical point of view it is the simplest motion to study. However, we shall argue in later chapters that, contrary to Newton's laws, since all motion is naturally orbital, uniform motion is in that sense, *unnatural*. For example, when we are in what seems to be uniform motion in a car travelling along a straight road we are actually orbiting the earth's centre, while the earth, in turn, is orbiting the sun, and so on.

The fact that all inertial frames are equivalent implies that even if a frame of reference at 'absolute rest' existed, it would be essentially undetectable. Einstein realised this when arguing for the complete equivalence of all inertial frames. Newton, on the other hand, maintained his belief in a frame of reference at absolute rest, *i.e.*, the space through which the stars and planets move [6]. Since such a frame of reference cannot be distinguished from any other inertial frame by experiment, Newton's view, from the outset, attracted scepticism from philosophers such as Leibniz and Berkeley.

Although this view of Newton's is clearly unsatisfactory, the trouble with insisting on the complete equivalence of all inertial frames is that it leaves us without a universal reference frame relative to which we can define all other inertial frames. Mach argued that since it is the various interactions between all matter in our 'universe' (over and above any 'gravitational' effects) which are the major source of inertial effects, and that the bulk of the matter resides in what he termed the 'fixed stars', then any inertial frame is a frame of reference in some privileged state of motion relative to the average motion of that stellar system. For Mach, it is this holistic system, through its masses, distributions and motions, which determines, both locally and non-locally, an inertial frame. This view is essentially *Mach's Principle*.

Newtonian mechanics is based on Newton's notion of 'force' which appeals to common experience. He gives the *force*, **f**, exerted on a body of constant mass *m* and acceleration, **a**, as

$$\mathbf{f} = m\mathbf{a} \qquad\qquad (2.1)$$

where **f** and **a** are vector functions of position and time. This is usually known as *Newton's Second Law*, but it is essentially a definition of **f**. It follows that if a body is not subjected to any external force, then **a** = **0** and so its velocity is constant. This immediately produces *Newton's First Law*:

> *A body, not subjected to any force, remains at rest or continues to move in a straight line with constant speed.*

This first law of Newton's enables us to define an inertial frame without reference to other such frames. The following definition is based on our experience of how, at least in theory, we can determine that we are in such a frame:

> An **inertial frame** is any frame of reference in which spatial relations, as determined by rigid scales at rest in the frame, are Euclidean and where there exists a universal time in terms of which free particles remain at rest or continue to move in straight lines at constant speed.

2.3 The constant *c*

In 1676 the Danish astronomer Olaus Römer, whilst studying the orbit of Io, the principal moon of Jupiter, at different times of the year, discovered that the time between successive eclipses of the satellite by its parent planet got shorter as Earth approached Jupiter, and longer as Earth moved farther away. Since the actual period of the satellite's orbit must remain constant, it was concluded that this extra time taken between its eclipses represented the time taken for the sunlight reflected off Io to 'travel' the extra distance across the diameter of Earth's orbit. Knowing the time taken over the distance, Römer was able to calculate what became known as the 'speed of light in space'. Unfortunately, the accepted value for the diameter of Earth's orbit at that time was incorrect, so that Römer's data produced too low a value for that 'speed'. Nevertheless, historically, Römer's observations have been heralded as the first successful determination of the constant 'speed of light c'.

The important point to realise here is that what Römer actually discovered was simply a constant relation between measures of observational distance and observational time in the constant ratio of units, c [7]. Logically, however, although c has the *dimensions* of speed, it need not necessarily have been interpreted as a speed – which would be like saying that because all bachelors are men, all men must be bachelors. The idea, then, that light 'travels' in any accepted sense is pure supposition. We never observe light leave an object and 'travel' towards us for us to see the object. Nor do we ever see light actually 'travelling' between one object and another in the pure vacuum of space.

Other astronomers, such as Bradley, in 1727, subsequently refined the value of the ratio c and this was further refined in terrestrial experiments first performed by Fizeau and Foucault in 1849. The most famous successful terrestrial measurements of the value of c were those performed by Michelson, starting in 1878 [8]. In particular, his 1926 experiments employed an apparatus consisting of a source of light, a rotating many-sided mirror, powered by an electric motor, and a distant plane mirror, about 35 kilometres away from the source. The speed of rotation of the many-sided mirror was adjusted so that light from the source, reflected by the distant mirror, could be recorded by a detector adjacent to the source. Knowing the speed of rotation of the many-sided mirror and the number of faces, Michelson was able to calculate the ratio of the optical distance to the time taken. Hence, the value of the constant c could be determined. Michelson obtained the result of $c \approx 3 \times 10^8$ metres per second [9]. Although many different experiments have been performed since 1926, this remains the accepted approximate value of the constant c.

It must be recalled that what Michelson actually found was that the so-called 'speed c' was measured relative to his apparatus here on earth. According to that same 'speed of light' assumption, c should be different for differently moving frames of reference. However, Einstein's second postulate for Special Relativity is that c has to be the same for *all* inertial observers. But this is intensely puzzling. It defies commonsense. According to our everyday experience, if we are travelling in a car at 80 kilometres per hour and another car passes us at 100 kilometres per hour, then its speed relative to us is 20 kilometres per hour. Even if this simple relationship ceases at much higher relative speeds, it makes no logical sense for one particular speed to be the same relative to all inertial frames, independently of their relative speeds! Yet Einstein's second postulate tells us, unequivocally, that if we were able to travel at, say, $0.9c$, a passing light signal would still have a 'speed' c relative to ourselves!

Since this is so obviously counter-intuitive, it is necessary to understand why Einstein postulated the universal constancy of the 'speed of light'. One of the main reasons comes from considerations involving electromagnetism.

2.4 Electromagnetism and Maxwell's equations

During the first half of the nineteenth century, the experiments of Oersted, Biot, Savart and Faraday demonstrated that electricity and magnetism are intimately connected, and so emerged the study of 'electromagnetism'. In 1856, the ratio of the unit of charge in electrostatic units to that in electromagnetic units was determined by Weber and Kohlrausch. They found that this ratio was remarkably close to the known value of the constant c and possessed the same dimensions, *i.e.*, the dimensions of a speed [10]. However, the intention of the Weber and Kohlrausch experiment had certainly not been aimed at determining the 'speed of light', although this ratio was later interpreted as such.

It was Maxwell who finally provided the explicit link between the new electromagnetism and optics. This was in a series of papers, published between 1862 and 1865, which culminated in *Maxwell's equations*. These equations (for free space) may be written in the form

$$\nabla.\mathbf{B} = 0, \tag{2.2a}$$

$$\nabla.\mathbf{E} = 4\pi\rho , \tag{2.2b}$$

$$\nabla \times \mathbf{E} = -\frac{1}{c}\frac{\partial \mathbf{B}}{\partial t} \quad , \qquad\qquad (2.2c)$$

$$\nabla \times \mathbf{B} = \frac{1}{c}\left(\frac{\partial \mathbf{E}}{\partial t} + 4\pi \mathbf{j}\right) . \qquad\qquad (2.2d)$$

In these equations, $\mathbf{E}$ is the *electric field intensity*, $\mathbf{B}$ is the *magnetic induction* and $\mathbf{j}$ is the *current density*. All are vector functions of position and time. The scalar variable ρ is also a function of position and time and signifies the *charge density*. In the present context, the only important fact to note is that the constant c in these equations is the ratio determined by Weber and Kohlrausch, which has the same dimensions and the same numerical value as the 'speed of light'. Hence, according to classical physics, Maxwell's equations are true in only one particular frame of reference and are different for different inertial observers. However, since the laws governing optics and electromagnetism cannot logically depend on the choice of observer, Maxwell's equations clearly indicate that there is something seriously wrong with classical physics. On the other hand, having adopted Postulate 1, namely, that Maxwell's equations must be the same for all inertial observers, the constant c must be the *same* constant relative to all inertial observers.

It can be deduced from Maxwell's equations that in the absence of charges and currents (so that $\rho = 0$ and $\mathbf{j} = \mathbf{0}$), $\mathbf{E}$ and $\mathbf{B}$ satisfy the three–dimensional wave equation. This seems to imply the existence of electromagnetic waves and so, if c in (2.2) is interpreted as the 'speed of light', then this supports the theory that 'light' (meaning the whole of the electromagnetic spectrum) is propagated in waves, in much the same manner as sound. In this sense, Maxwell's theory seems to support the *wave theory* of light, first proposed by Fresnel earlier in the nineteenth century [11]. Of course, there is no such implication of a 'wave theory' of light if c in equations (2.2) is interpreted merely as a constant.

In the nineteenth century, it was believed that electromagnetic waves require a medium in which to propagate, in the same way that water waves require water and sound waves require air. However, it was obvious that light reaches the earth from the sun and stars through the vacuum of space. Hence, a hypothetical carrier of electromagnetic waves, known as the '*luminiferous ether*', gained widespread acceptance.

In this way, it was assumed that light travels in 'waves', which were regarded as 'stresses propagated through the ether'. It seemed natural to identify this 'ether' frame with Newton's absolute space, so that electromagnetism became unified with Newtonian mechanics. The constant c in equations (2.2) then became interpreted as the 'speed of light' relative to the 'ether frame'. A most urgent problem of the time was therefore the detection of the earth's motion 'through the ether'. The famous Michelson and Morley experiment, first performed in 1881, set out to do just that [12]. This experiment set out to detect the ether by comparing the relative 'speeds of light' parallel and perpendicular to the 'ether wind' supposedly caused by the earth's motion through the ether. The results of this and other experiments, repeated over and over, were completely and consistently negative. The 'ether wind' remained undetected.

Reluctant though the classical physicists of the day were to accept this negative result, it appears that none of them thought of questioning the reliability of the experiment or its interpretation, such was the esteem in which Michelson was held. The simplest, most logical explanation for the null results of the Michelson-Morley experiment is that either there is no absolute reference frame of the 'ether' or that, even if the 'ether' does exist, its existence is undetectable.

Nevertheless, because the existence of the 'ether' was so firmly accepted by the physicists of that time, other ether-based explanations for the negative Michelson-Morley results were suggested. One was that the earth 'drags' nearby ether along with it, so that terrestrial experiments fail to detect it. This explanation is ruled out by experiments concerning the aberration of starlight. The apparent direction of a star changes over a six-month period, since the earth moves in its orbit with respect to 'incoming light' from the star. If the ether were moving with the earth, then the light from the star would be 'swept along' with it, and the star would appear always in the same direction. Another explanation, which received a lot of support, supposed that the null result of the Michelson-Morley experiment was due to the *Lorentz-Fitzgerald contraction effect*. This was the suggestion that all lengths shorten in the direction of the earth's motion through the ether by a particular amount but that they remain unaffected in other directions. Thus, the contraction effect could never be directly detected, since any measuring device would also shrink by the same amount. The conclusion, therefore, was that the 'ether' certainly exists but is not detectable by any observation or experiment! This hypothesis was later bolstered by Lorentz's electron theory of the composition of matter. However, other predictions of Lorentz's theory on the basis of that same 'ether' concept could not be experimentally verified.

The logical conclusion from all this, of course, especially from the NR point of view, is that any assumption as to the existence of an 'ether' is not only un-empirical but is also logically redundant. More importantly, if the constant c appearing in Maxwell's equations is interpreted simply as no more than just that, a dimensional *constant* of observation, then there is no implication of a 'wave theory' of light and its associated 'ether' – for what can possibly 'wave' in a *vacuum*? However, with c interpreted as simply a constant, the whole plethora of problems traditionally associated with the existence of that 'ether' disappears at a stroke.

2.5 The Normal Realist approach

Einstein's second postulate for Special Relativity follows logically by applying Postulate 1 to electromagnetic theory. Since, according to that first postulate, Maxwell's equations must be the same in any inertial frame, the constant c appearing in them must be the *same* relative to *all* inertial observers. Einstein went on to interpret this constant as the 'speed of light', as others had done before him, even though there is no logical reason why c needs to be interpreted in that fashion. Indeed, although Einstein claimed to have modelled SR on the phenomenalist philosophy of Mach, according to this Machian philosophy, the 'speed of light *in vacuo*' is not only unobservable but also the idea itself can make no logical sense, since it would represent an absolute motion with respect to the void itself – that is, literally, to nothing. Besides, interpreting c as the 'speed of light *in vacuo*' leads to other problems associated with the idea of 'light travelling'. For example, as soon as this idea is accepted, there is the problem of the wave/particle dualistic nature of light. With this 'travelling' idea in mind, the quantised character of the observed spectral energies (see Chapter 5, section 2) suggests that light 'travels as particles', whereas their period and resonant character suggests that light 'travels as waves'. This purely theoretical, dualistic behaviour of light leads to all sorts of conceptual problems, not least the problem of trying to imagine what sorts of 'particles' can possibly behave like waves in experimental situations.

Einstein's redundant additional interpretation of c as the 'speed of light' therefore, to say the least, appears rather odd, especially since one of the main achievements of SR was to make redundant the concept of the 'ether' as the hypothetical medium for the transport of 'light waves'. However, the essential ingredient for SR was that c is a *constant relative to all inertial observers, not* that it is the 'speed of light *in vacuo*' [13].

We would argue, then, that in view of all the difficulties attending the 'speed' interpretation of c it is much more conceptually efficacious, all round, to interpret c as a universal *conversion factor* for converting optical distances measured, say, in units of metres of distance into units of light-seconds. Of course, in astronomy, many distances are recorded by radar. As commonly conceived, an observer measures the distance of an object by sending out a 'light signal' which is reflected off the object and received back by the observer. This distance is then determined simply by halving the time-difference between emission and reception. It would be impractical and illogical to attempt, in this way, to measure vast distances in kilometres by means of that signal, when it is the signal itself on which we depend, basically, for providing the information about the distance. For instance, imagine how absurd it would be to measure the 'speed of light' across the distance of a light-year! Classically conditioned as we are into accepting scientific ideas as gospel, from a common sense point of view it certainly *seems* as though light is propagated through empty space with a constant speed – that is, until we try to construct in our minds any intuitive idea as to just how that motion takes place.

The idea of interpreting c as a conversion factor was proposed by Bondi as early as 1964 [14]. Pope had also proposed this same interpretation, independently, some years earlier, and afterwards corresponded with Bondi concerning their mutual idea [15]. But why, it may be asked, does the constant c have such a unique value, of $c \approx 2.99792458 \times 10^8$ metres to the second? The reason is simply the circumstantial choice of units for distance and time in our history of measurement. For instance, in Imperial units, c is 186,000 miles per second. In hindsight, we could have chosen the standard unit of distance to be the light-second, in which case, c would simply be unity and need never have appeared in any of the equations of physics to raise the plethora of problems that it has.

Aside from any practical, physical or philosophical objections, there are other logical and mathematical reasons against interpreting the constant c as a 'speed'. Some of these reasons will be explored in this and later chapters. For all these reasons, our Normal Realist replacement for Einstein's second SR postulate is

Postulate 2: *Observational distance and time have a constant ratio of units, c, for all inertial observers sharing that same conventional choice of units.*

In Einstein's original paper, his second postulate referred to the 'speed of light' alone but this was later amended to include a phrase to the effect that 'light travels rectilinearly'. Of course, in our approach, since light does not 'travel' in the usual sense, this additional assumption of its 'travelling in straight lines' makes no sense either.

Taken by themselves, our replacement Postulates 1 and 2 should not give too much cause for concern for practical physics. However, they imply the need for a fundamental philosophical change in our customary ideas about the nature of space and time. Some of the consequences of these Normal Realist postulates are discussed in the next chapter. In particular, we deduce from these new postulates that time as well as distance, is *relative* to the observer. This is in contrast to Newton's idea of an *absolute* 'God's-eye-view' time being the same for all observers [16].

2.6 Light as pure *information*

Our new approach to Special Relativity, which is based on interpreting the constant c simply as a conversion factor, first appeared in 1987 [2]. Bondi's reason for proposing that c can be interpreted purely as a conversion factor was simply that it was a useful teaching aid [17]. In contrast to Bondi, our different reason was, on that same basis, to develop a whole new philosophical approach to physics [15]. Our interpretation of c therefore lies right at the heart of our Normal Realist philosophy as described in Chapter 1 [18].

Since in any truly phenomenalistic account of physics, *phenomena* are fundamental to any scientific enquiry, there is no way to reconcile a phenomenalistic philosophy such as ours with Einstein's second postulate, whereby our observations of physical phenomena are mediated by light travelling at a constant speed *in vacuo*. This latter is known as the Einstein Separation between phenomena and their 'sources', which creates all sorts of logical problems. For example, how can the mass of a distant star or galaxy be said to be a property 'relative to the observer' when the observer can know nothing about it until the light from that object reaches him which, in the 'travelling' way of thinking, may be æons after it left the object? In this way, whilst Einstein's theory claims to be a relativistic theory it contains vestiges of the classical 'God's-eye-view' absolutism, as Mach complained, which is doubtless why it generates so many puzzles and paradoxes.

We maintain then, that our pure, theoretically unembroidered 'conversion factor' interpretation of c unblocks the route to a natural acceptance of the revolutionary relativism of Mach. But if we relinquish the traditional mechanistic 'streaming-substance' notions about light, then how may we conceive of light in this new context? The answer, we propose, is to think of it as *pure information,* *i.e.,* naïvely as 'what we see'. This, of course, includes phenomena which are detected and revealed by the use of instruments of any shape and kind at all levels of the spectral range. Now it is well known in modern physics that light is basically 'atomised' in ultimately discrete and irreducible energy-events called *quanta.* (This quantisation of light is explained in full in Chapter 5, section 2.) These quanta occur in our eyes and other instruments, like the pixels on a video screen out of informational patterns and sequences of which the viewer projects a video scenario. Those patterns and sequences of quantum 'blips' are the ultimate *information* from which, as observers, we project the distances of objects from ourselves and from one another in the three dimensional form we perceive as 'space'; and from the way those objects and their distances change, as measured by our clocks and other processes, we extrapolate the passage of 'time'. The masses of those objects can then be measured by the way in which, over time, they are seen to behave in relation to one another, in the same way that the masses of the sun and planets are measured without actually weighing them. Indeed, every physical property and quality that defines a physical object can be measured by these same optical methods. Hence, in this approach, light is not something that is just incidental to matter; it is basic to matter's very existence. This divergent approach to physics may be described as *digital* or *informational.* The light-in-space of the standard model becomes the *space-in-light* in this new informational model, which may be conceived as somewhat in the nature of a hologram [19].

Let us then emphasise and recapitulate this altogether vital point. In NR, the philosophy on which our lateral-thinking alternative approach to modern physics is based, light is not something that travels in space. It is just pure quantum information, the bare information from which the whole relativistic scenario of matter, space and time, hence, of travelling – even the assumed 'travelling' of light itself – is projected.

We recognise, of course, that light does *seem* to 'travel' in the accepted sense, since so many people will say that it can be 'observed doing so'. For example, in dusty atmospheres, interactions with dust-particles form 'rays' of illumination which seem to suggest that this illumination is 'travelling'. Also, some critics have pointed to the fact that, as they see it, the light from a galactic supernova can be 'seen' progressing through cosmic dust-clouds, and so on. However, in the last analysis, those 'rays' are no more than *phenomena* consisting of sequences of discrete atomic illuminations, giving the *impression* of motion, like the advertisement signs that are lit by on-off sequences of flashing light-bulbs. Where there is no dust or anything else present (that is, truly *in vacuo*) no such 'beams' can be detected.

In summary, then, in our alternative approach to physics the traditional model of the 'universe' as The Great Machine, whose ultimate parts are self-sufficient atoms separated by a self-sufficient vacuum and causally connected by an incidental travelling intermediary called 'light', is replaced by a very different, *informational* model, which has also been called the 'holographic' model. In this model, light, far from being some incidental travelling intermediary between atoms in space, is essentially and primarily *what is observed* in all its direct and instrumental manifestations. And in the same way that other observers and objects are informational projections from our received light-information, so we are informational projections from their received information, all in the informational matrix of to-ing and fro-ing we know at first hand as 'objective space'. This community of perspectives disposes of the Subjective Idealism of the early phenomenalists such as Berkeley, *et al.* (see previous chapter), and objectifies phenomenalism along the commonsense lines of Moore and Normal Realism [20].

2.7 Other arguments against the 'speed' interpretation of c

To reiterate what, in our opinion, is one convincing argument against interpreting the constant c as the 'speed of light', is that it is the same for all moving observers, whereas all common experience tells us that the speed of a moving object varies relatively to differently moving observers.

Another argument involves the particular case of electrical conduction, which is customarily said to travel at a 'speed' c [21]. A common belief is that 'electricity' is a 'flow of electrons' measured in amps, analogous to gallons of water flowing along a pipe [22]. However, in electrical conduction along a wire, no electrons actually 'flow' in that way. Rather, what is ineptly called the 'flow' can be described in terms of the general drift of localised shifts in the orbits of electrons around their atomic nuclei in the direction of the so-called 'current' [23]. What is alleged to 'travel' around the circuit at the 'speed' c, therefore, are not electrons as such but their *charge*, a disembodied energy measured in coulombs. The 'current', measured in amperes is then defined as this measure of coulombs per second [24].

Let us now return to the usual meaning of 'speed'. A commonplace example is as follows. In Fig. 2.1, below, is a road test circuit along which road vehicles, manufactured at A, travel from the exit at A around to the parking compound at B on the other side of the factory. At A there is a checkout counting the number of vehicles exiting the depot at short regular intervals. At the far end of the circuit is a swing-bridge which, when opened, allows canal barges to pass under, and when closed allows passage over the canal for the vehicles from A into the storage compound at B.

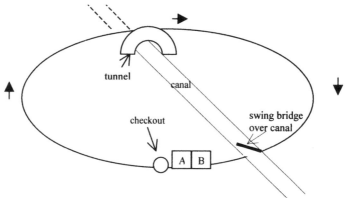

Fig. 2.1: A Road Test Circuit

Now an essential characteristic of any discrete object, such as a road vehicle, a bullet or an electron, that is said to be 'travelling' in the accepted sense, is that it can set out from a source and then travel freely as far as it may, regardless of what awaits it at the far end. In this example, if the bridge at the *B*-end is closed, then the vehicles from *A* pass over it and complete the circuit into the storage compound. If the bridge is open, then they cannot pass but get held up at that point. Meanwhile, regardless of whether the bridge at the far end is open or closed, at the checkout the count of vehicles exiting *A* at regular intervals into the circuit remains undiminished – for a while, that is. However, if the bridge remains open, then eventually, the steady stream of vehicles produced at *A* creates, at the open bridge *B*, a traffic hold-up which backs up to fill the road to its maximum capacity as far as the entry point *A*. Then everything is at a standstill and the count of vehicles passing the checkout at *A* is reduced to zero.

Now let us replace that road circuit with a simple electrical circuit, as in Fig. 2.2, below. This consists of a loop of electrical wire, a battery with a switch to one side of the battery and any kind of electrical detector on the other [25].

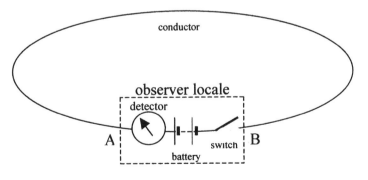

Fig. 2.2: A Simple Electric Circuit

It is to be noted that, as a matter of *fact*, when the switch at *B* is open (off) there is no detectable flow of anything analogous to that of the vehicles passing the checkout at *A* and entering the road in Fig. 2.1 [26]. With that switch open, *no current whatsoever is recorded by the instrument.* Nor is there anything analogous to the build-up of traffic and backing-up of vehicles behind those that are held up at that point. Despite the capacity of the circuit to accommodate the flow, even with the largest capacitor inserted into the circuit between *A* and *B*, with the switch open at *B* the detector at *A* reveals not even the smallest, most incipient surge of current passing into the circuit. The circuit remains completely empty of charge until the switch at *B* is closed. Then and only then will a current be detected. This will be after a time-interval which is the length of the circuit in metres divided by *c*.

In view of these facts, any suggestion that 'electricity travels at the speed *c*' is nonsense. For if we suppose that the conduction of electrons has such a 'speed' (as in the standard definition of an 'electric current'), then it must start, as in the road example, from the one pole of the battery, 'travel' through the detector into the conductor, like the vehicles into the road in Fig. 2.1, and then finish at either the opposite pole (*i.e.*, with the far-end switch closed) or at the switch if that switch remains open. This implies that some flow from *A* into the circuit should be detected at *A* *before* it reaches the switch at *B*, *regardless of whether that distant switch is open or closed*. This creates a mystery, because the detector reveals that the current does not even 'set out' from *A* when the far-end switch at *B* is in the 'off' position, no matter how great the length and capacitance of the conductor. So if we think of the current as 'travelling' we have to assume that it somehow 'knows', ahead of time, that the switch at the far end *B* is open or closed before 'setting out' from *A*. In that case, then the *effect*, detected at *A*, of the closing of the switch at *B* miraculously *precedes* that event by 3.3 nanoseconds for every metre length of the conductor, which is, of course, absurd. What else, then, can that 'current' be but a direct and instantaneous transfer from *A* to *B* of *pure disembodied energy*, which makes no sense in thinking of it any ordinary way as 'travelling'.

We argue that this direct and immediate transfer of pure disembodied energy in the case of electricity is the same as is measured in the form of light between points *A* and *B* in space. But, of course, light and electricity are very different. There is little similarity, for instance, between the way in which electricity is conducted in a circuit and the way in which light is conducted in space or, say, in an optic fibre, so the sort of experiment with electric circuitry so far described cannot be carried out in the same way with light. It is therefore theoretically possible that although the constant c is *not* a speed in the case of electricity, it may nevertheless be a speed in the case of light. However, there are arguments to prove, independently, that as in the case of electrical energy, regardless of the time that elapses between the cause and the effect (the switching at the source and the reading of the detector) the connection between the source and the detector, as a precondition for the transfer of energy is direct and therefore *instantaneous*. This is manifest in the well-known two-slit experiment of Thomas Young in which the discrete quantum interactions between the source and screen, like those between the switch and the detector in the electrical case, seem to take place with foreknowledge of the conditions for their reception at the far end.

These, of course, are technical, or experimental, evidences of the non-speed nature of c. However, this conclusion can be confirmed by pure commonsense logic, as may be seen in due course. In the next chapter we demonstrate that all the standard consequences of SR can be deduced without involving Einstein's unempirical second postulate that 'light has the constant speed c *in vacuo*'.

Notes and References

[1] Blackmore, J. T.: *Ernst Mach, His Life, Work and Influence* (Univ. of California Press, 1972).

[2] Pope, N. V. and Osborne, A. D.: 'A new approach to Special Relativity', *Int. J. Math. Educ. Sci. Technol.*, **18** (2) (1987), pp. 191-198.

[3] Einstein, A.: 'On the Electrodynamics of Moving Bodies', *Annalen der Physik*, **17** (1905), pp. 37-65.

[4] This view formed part of Ernst Mach's philosophy, first formulated in 1893. Mach's philosophy was based on ideas formulated much earlier by Leibniz and Bishop Berkeley. For Mach, any body situated in otherwise empty space cannot be said to travel, since there is no reference point relative to which the body can be said to be in motion. The same goes for the alleged 'motion of light'.

[5] Galileo, G.: *Dialogue Concerning the Two Chief World Systems – Ptolemaic and Copernican*, translated by S. Drake (University of California Press, 1953).

[6] Newton states in the *Scholium* in his *Principia* that 'Absolute space, in its own nature, without relation to anything external, remains always similar and immovable.'

[7] Pope, N. V.: *The Eye of the Beholder: The Role of the Observer in Modern Physics* (**phi** Philosophical Enterprises, Swansea, 2004) p. 3.

[8] Sanders, J. H.: *The Velocity of Light* (Pergamon Press, Oxford, 1965).

[9] Michelson began his experiments to determine c as early as 1878 but the most accurate ones began in 1926. Although the idea behind these experiments was a simple one, there were vast practical difficulties involved. Michelson performed many different experiments using rotating mirrors with differing numbers of sides.

[10] Assis, A. K. T.: *Weber's Electrodynamics* (Kluwer, Dordrecht, 1994).

[11] Rowlands, P.: *A Revolution Too Far* (PD publications, 1994) pp. 37-39.

[12] French, A. P.: *Special Relativity* (Chapman and Hall, New York, 1991) pp. 49-58.

[13] Regarding the absence of any explicit reference to the Michelson-Morley experiment in his first paper, Einstein stated 'The explanation is that I was, for general reasons, firmly convinced that there does not exist absolute motion and my problem was only how that could be reconciled with our knowledge of electrodynamics'.

[14] In 1964 Bondi wrote, 'Any attempt to measure the velocity of light is ... not an attempt at measuring the velocity of light but an attempt at ascertaining the length of the standard metre in Paris in terms of time-units.' See for example, H. Bondi, *Assumption and Myth in Physical Theory* (Cambridge University Press, 1965) p. 28.

[15] In correspondence with Pope in 1985, Bondi states, 'As regards your "New Approach to Special Relativity", I am in broad sympathy, both with your arguments and your conclusion.' As for the philosophical implications of that shift in thinking, Bondi told Pope that he would leave that to him (Pope) with his blessing. (See *Philosophical Glimpses*, Swansea County Hall, Archives Dept., ref. D/D NVP/1-17, **8,** pp. 2970, 2980-2981.)

[16] Again, in the *Scholium* to his *Principia*, Newton states that 'Absolute true and mathematical time, of itself, and from its own nature, flows equably without relation to anything external.'

[17] In correspondence with Pope, *op. cit.* reference 15.

[18] This philosophy is described in full on the POAMS website www.poams.org .

[19] See Pope, N. V.: 'From Light in Space to Space in Light: A Complete Relativistic Revolution', *Journal of Theoretics* (Internet), 6-1(2004).

[20] *Op. cit.* reference 7, pp. 5-8, 10-14.

[21] Not all physicists agree that the 'speed of electricity' is c. A minority view sets it at between 60 and 80 percent of c. The following argument will prove that whatever value we ascribe to the distance-time rate of conduction of an electric current, it cannot truly be a *speed*. In this book, we begin with the majority view that c, here, for electricity, is the same as for light.

[22] A measure of one amp (ampere) may be defined as a 'flow' of 6.25×10^{18} electrons per second.

[23] What is actually claimed to occur is a kinematic succession of incipient, limited local movements of electrons in which the electrons 'travel' at very small speeds over very short distances. See for example, *Enc. Brit.*, 1961, **8,** p. 295d.

[24] The 'driving force' for these disembodied charges is said to be an *electromotive force*. Measured in volts, this is defined as 'the characteristic of any energy source capable of driving electric charge around a circuit'. See for example, *Enc. Brit.*, 2001. CD Rom.

[25] Any electrical detector, even a voltmeter, records current flow. An ideal voltmeter would draw no current at all. In practice, however, a voltmeter must draw some current otherwise it wouldn't work. (See *Physics* by K. Dobson, D. Grace & D. Lovett, Harper-Collins, London 2002, p.217.) Any electrical detector, therefore, is analogous to the vehicle counter at the checkout in Fig. 2.1.

[26] As usually distinguished, the 'conventional flow' of the current is from positive to negative, whereas the so-called 'true flow' is from negative to positive. The effect illustrated is the same, however, no matter which way around the poles of the battery are connected.

CHAPTER 3

Time-Dilation and the Cone Model

3.1 Introduction

The two postulates on which Einstein based his Special Relativity are as follows:

Postulate 1: *(The Relativity Principle) The laws of physics are the same in all inertial frames.*

Postulate 2: *The speed of light* in vacuo *is the same for all observers in all uniformly moving frames of reference.*

In our Normal Realist paraphrase of that theory, this first postulate is the same, but the second postulate is different. Thus, the two postulates on which our alternative derivation of SR is based are:

Postulate 1: *(The Relativity Principle) The laws of physics are the same in all inertial frames.*

Postulate 2: *Observational distance and time have a constant ratio of units, c, for all observers sharing that same conventional choice of units.*

The difference, then, is that these latter postulates express a purely observational, or phenomenalist, approach to physics, of the kind adopted by Mach. The second postulate represents our phenomenalist alternative to Einstein's second postulate that the 'speed of light', c, is the same for all inertial observers. All that our second postulate states is that c acts as a conversion factor for interrelating observer-projected measures of distance and time. Hence, for example, if units of distance and time are chosen so that $c \approx 3 \times 10^8$ m s^{-1}, then our second postulate states that a distance of one metre may be recorded as $1/3 \times 10^{-8}$ seconds relative to all observers. Here, the 'second' is being used in two different senses; one in the usual sense of *duration* and the other in the sense of a distance equivalent. This idea should not appear the least bit strange to us. These days, measuring a journey by the time it takes is often more informative than the number of miles or kilometres it may be. But of course, different travellers can take different times to complete the same distance. What our Postulate 2 states is that the *observational* distance of one metre is *always* equivalent to an *observational* time of $1/3 \times 10^{-8}$ seconds.

In this chapter we demonstrate that these two postulates entail a fundamental change in our traditional concepts of space and time. We show how the phenomenon of time-dilation follows as a simple consequence of these postulates. In this respect, our approach puts time-dilation right 'at the heart' of relative uniform motion, rather than as a consequence of the special Lorentz transformation, as in Special Relativity. In addition, our derivation of the time-dilation formula enables us to construct a model of this phenomenon, known as the *cone model* [1].

3.2 Time-dilation in relative uniform motion

In classical representations of the motions of bodies, the distance of a body X relative to some fixed origin O is described by a curve plotted against two perpendicular axes, labelled s and t, say, which signify distance and time, respectively. If the motion of X relative to O is uniform and X passes O at time $t = 0$, then this curve is a straight line which passes through the origin with constant gradient $v = s/t$. The equation of this straight line is then $s = vt$, as shown in Fig. 3.1(a), below.

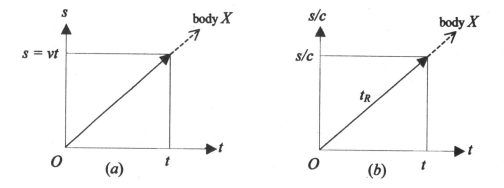

Fig. 3.1: Time-Dilation in uniform motion

Of course, *v*, here, is the constant speed of *X* relative to *O* and *s* is the distance travelled by *X* from *O* in the period *t*, relative to either *O* or *X*, since in classical physics, the passage of time is supposed to be the same for all observers.

However, let us now think of *t* as the passage of time recorded by a 'clock' moving with the body *X*. This is the natural choice for the duration of the motion since it is independent of the observer. Here, a 'clock' represents any device capable of recording a passage of time, which includes biological as well as mechanical devices. (The ultimate clocks are, of course, the periods of the atoms of which all physical objects are constituted.) Note that in Fig. 3.1(a), there is no special significance attached to the *length* of the line with equation $s = vt$ for a given value of *t* since in this kind of representation there is no fundamental interconnection between distance and time as such.

Taking account of our Postulate 2, this situation is drastically altered. If *c* is treated as a conversion factor, then a fixed geometrical relationship is established between the dimensions of *s* and *t*. Thus, on the grounds of plain commonsense, it is to be expected that with this overall connection, motion will affect time in some way. This is because motions are now geometro-dynamical combinations of time measures in different dimensions – analogous to the lengths of an ordinary area. Motion, that is to say, is now a composite space-time extension measured in units of approximately 3×10^8 metres/*c* or seconds, which are numerically and dimensionally the same. Remember here that the motion of the body *X* is the motion of *X* relative to the specified observer *O*, there being no single, universal 'God's-eye-view' of how motion separating *O* and *X* can be seen through the eyes of both observers at once.

To reiterate, *X* travels a distance *s* measured in metres, in a time *t*, recorded in seconds by *X*'s clock, relative to *O*. In keeping with Postulate 2, this distance travelled by *X* relative to *O* can be measured in seconds by the use of the conversion factor *c*. Then the distance-time diagram, Fig. 3.1(a), becomes the *two-dimensional time* diagram, Fig. 3.1(b). In the latter figure, the two axes (labelled *s*/*c* and *t*) are both measured in units of seconds. Bearing in mind that the line segment OX represents the path of X's clock relative to O, it follows that the length of OX in this second graph is the time t_R, as recorded by O, for X's clock to reach its position relative to O after time t. Then t_R will be simply the length of the hypotenuse of the triangle in Fig. 3.1(b), given by Pythagoras's theorem as

$$t_R^2 = t^2 + (s/c)^2 . \tag{3.1}$$

More precisely, since both axes in Fig. 3.1(b) are now measures of time, any measure of time is the magnitude of a vector in this two-dimensional system. Any such vector is generated by unit vectors **a** and **b** parallel to the t axis and s/c axis respectively. Hence t_R must be the magnitude of a vector $\alpha\mathbf{a} + \beta\mathbf{b}$ for some choice of α and β, so that

$$t_R^2 = \alpha^2 t^2 + \beta^2 (s/c)^2 .$$

If X always remains stationary with respect to O, then their clocks will record the same time, i.e. if $s = 0$, then $t_R = t$, giving $\alpha = 1$. With our interpretation of c as a conversion factor, if $t = 0$, then $t_R = s/c$, giving $\beta = 1$ [2].

Now the speed, v, of X relative to O (that is, *relative to O's clock*) is given by $v = s/t_R$, whence (3.1) becomes,

$$t_R^2 = t^2 + (vt_R/c)^2$$

so that

$$t^2 = (1 - v^2/c^2) t_R^2$$

and hence,

$$t_R = (1 - v^2/c^2)^{-\frac{1}{2}} t \tag{3.2a}$$

or

$$t = (1 - v^2/c^2)^{\frac{1}{2}} t_R . \tag{3.2b}$$

The positive square root is taken in (3.2) due to considerations of causality. Equation (3.2) is the standard formula for time-dilation which appears in Special Relativity [3]. Note that (3.2a) implies that O's time is dilated relative to X's time and (3.2b) indicates that a moving clock runs slower relative to an observer's clock. Note also that equation (3.2b) dictates that v cannot be greater than c, since otherwise t^2 would have to be negative! In this case, there is no sensible question of there being any 'superluminal speeds'. Equation (3.2b) also indicates, once again, that c cannot be treated as if it were a speed since otherwise for $v = c$, $t = 0$, independently of t_R. In this case, the 'travelling' clock would register no time difference, regardless of how great the distance 'travelled' might be.

This derivation shows that, observationally, there are two distinct measures of the speed of relative motion. One is the rate of change of observational distance relative to the time, t_R, as registered by the observer of the motion, known as the **observational time**, and the other is the rate of change of that same distance relative to the time, t, that the observer sees in his telescope/spectroscope registered by the moving body itself, known as the **proper time**. It also shows that time is a *relative* rather than an *absolute* concept. It is important to re-emphasise here, however, that any moving clock records the proper time, t, relative to its own rest frame, so that the proper time is *independent* of any observer and so serves as a *universal parameter*. In contrast, the observational time, t_R, is clearly observer dependent.

3.3 Experimental evidence for time-dilation

One of the most famous verifications of the time-dilation effect concerns 'elementary particles' known as *muons*. These are produced in appreciable numbers in the upper atmosphere by the primary cosmic radiation entering from outer space. Muons have a speed of about $0.9965c$ relative to an observer on the earth, so that according to classical physics, the mean distance they could cover before decaying is about 650 metres. In other words, classical physics predicts that the high altitude muons should decay long before they reached sea level. However, muons are, in fact, found in significant numbers at sea level, as first detected in experiments performed by Rossi and Hall in 1941 [4]. The explanation, of course, is that since the muons, with their speed $0.9965c$, have an intrinsic (proper) mean lifetime of $t = 2.2 \times 10^{-6}$ seconds, equation (3.2a) gives them a mean lifetime of $t_R \approx 2.64 \times 10^{-5}$ seconds, relative to the earth. Hence, the high altitude muons are able to travel a mean distance of about 7.9 kilometres, before decaying, and so can easily reach the earth's surface, as observed.

More recently, experiments performed by Hafele and Keating using atomic clocks in jet planes have also verified the time-dilation formula [5]. But perhaps by far the most convincing demonstration lies in the Stanford Linear Accelerator, which accelerates elementary particles up to speeds which are significant fractions of c. This accelerator is over three kilometres long and cost a hundred million dollars to build, whereas if classical physics were correct, it would have to be only about three centimetres long! (This, of course, is because, as in the case of muons, due to time-dilation the distance travelled by the high speed elementary particles before decay is much further than that predicted by classical physics.)

3.4 The cone model

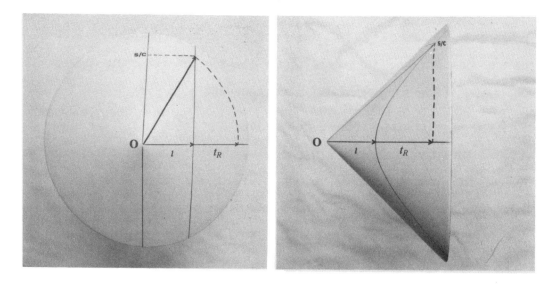

(a) **Front elevation:**
The Newtonian aspect of motion

(b) **Side elevation:**
The Einsteinian aspect of motion

Plate 3.1: The Cone Model

The idea of using a right-angled triangle to deduce the time-dilation effect has been used elsewhere [6][7]. However, our derivation of the time-dilation formula (3.2) provides a *model* for this phenomenon, which addresses the problem of

Machian action-at-a-distance (see the following section). Let t, s/c and t_R all be treated as variables in equation (3.1). Then (3.1) is the equation of a right-circular *cone* in three dimensions, relative to three mutually perpendicular time axes, t, s/c and t_R, which record proper time, observed distance-time and observational time respectively. As such, this conic surface represents a three-dimensional graph of time-dilation, as shown on the front cover of this book. The axis of the cone is the t_R axis and its apex is situated at $(0, 0, 0)$. The end and side elevations of such a graph for non-negative values of t, s/c and t_R, are shown in Plate 3.1. This model illustrates effectively the relationship between any given values of t, s/c and t_R and clearly indicates that $t < t_R$ for $v \neq 0$. The larger the value of s/c, the greater is the difference between t and t_R.

For any fixed value of t_R, (3.1) is the equation of a *circle* of radius t_R, centred at the origin. Such circles are obtained from the end elevation of the cone (a circle being a conic section cut in the direction perpendicular to the cone's axis), as indicated in Plate 3.1(a). On the other hand, if t is fixed and the time-measure s/c is plotted against the time-measure t_R, the result is a *rectangular hyperbola* with equation

$$t_R{}^2 - (s/c)^2 = t^2. \tag{3.3}$$

Such hyperbolæ are obtained from the side elevation of the cone (a rectangular hyperbola being a conic section cut in the direction parallel to the cone's axis), as indicated in Plate 3.1(b). Any such hyperbola is asymptotic to the lines with equations $s = \pm ct_R$. In mainstream SR, these lines form what is known as the (degenerate) *light cone* and represent 'paths of light signals' passing O at $t_R = 0$ [8]. Of course, there is no such physical interpretation of these lines in our NR approach.

3.5 The non-paradox of time-delayed instantaneity

Mach's contribution to physics provided not only the foundations for Special Relativity but also for the so-called 'Copenhagen' interpretation of Quantum Physics, established by Niels Bohr in the 1920s. In this interpretation, a particle and its observation form a single angular momentum system [9]. According to the principle of conservation of angular momentum, such angular momentum is conserved instantly between particles, regardless of distance, a condition called *non-locality*. This implies that some type of *instantaneous action-at-a-distance* takes place. In May 1935, a paper appeared by Einstein in collaboration with Boris Podolski and Nathan Rosen, which challenged Bohr and his followers [10]. This challenge was on the grounds of Einstein's assumption of *locality* or separateness (see Chapter 1, section 7), according to which it is nonsense to expect that measuring the state of a particle at one place is tantamount to determining, immediately, the state of another particle somewhere else, regardless of distance. Such an instantaneous action-at-a-distance was forbidden by SR, according to which 'nothing can travel faster than the speed of light'. Einstein, *et al.* argued that, at the very least, Bohr's theory of non-locality must be incomplete in some sense.

This clash between Bohr and Einstein continued unresolved for almost thirty years and became known as the 'Einstein-Podolski-Rosen (EPR) controversy'. Then in 1964, John Bell of CERN [11] suggested a way of deciding, on experimental grounds, whether or not Bohr's instantaneous action-at-a-distance existed [12]. Such experiments were performed in 1978 and 1982 [13], the results of which supported Bohr's contention against Einstein's. However, the controversy over what is now known as the 'EPR paradox' continues to rage. The 'paradox' is that both Bohr's and Einstein's positions seem to be confirmed experimentally. There is therefore an apparent contradiction within the context of any of the standard models, whereby on the one hand, Relativistic Physics implies that 'nothing can travel faster than light', while on the other, Quantum Physics implies that distant interactions can be instantaneous [14][15].

Instead of seeing this paradox as the natural *reductio ad absurdum* of the 'speed' interpretation of *c*, some theories [16] have taken this experimental evidence of instantaneous action-at-distance as having established the existence of some 'spooky', acausal, 'telepathic' influence passing between particles in advance of the 'speed of light'. Further, the fact that these theories do not define the sort of instantaneity they ascribe to these actions compounds the problem.

The relevance of our cone model to this action-at-a-distance debate is as follows. There are two distinct speeds associated with the uniform motion of a body X relative to an observer O. The first is what we can describe as the 'Newtonian' speed and is s/t, where s is the distance travelled by X in proper time t. The second is what can be described as the 'Einsteinian' speed and is s/t_R, where t_R is the time taken for X to travel the distance s relative to O's clock. Our conic representation of time-dilation clearly shows how the Newtonian speed-unlimited graph of physical motion (the end-elevation of the cone shown in Plate 3.1(a)) and the Einsteinian speed-limited aspect (the side-elevation of the cone shown in Plate 3.1(b)) can be *equally represented with no conflict whatsoever on the same conic surface*. Our model also shows that what is represented in the end-elevation as a theoretically unbounded Newtonian speed appears in the side elevation as the Einsteinian 'speed limit' c, the speed limit appearing as an asymptote to the graphs representing material particle motion. This clearly demonstrates that although the constant c is the least upper bound of all relative speeds, it is not a speed as such. To the question, then, of whether action-at-distance is instantaneous or time-delayed, the answer, as far as light is concerned, is plainly that it is *both*. This can also be seen from (3.1) and (3.2b). If $v = c$ in (3.2b), then $t = 0$, so that light-action is instantaneous in this sense, whereas $t = 0$ in (3.1) gives $t_R = s/c$ as the delayed time ascertained by observation and experiment. There is no contradiction here, since the instantaneity takes place in one observational dimension, whereas the time-delay takes place in a different observational dimension.

In Quantum Physics, as in Newtonian mechanics, there is, as can be seen from plate 3.1(a), no limit to the speed at which quantum influences may travel between fundamental particles, whereas for relativists, as can be seen in Plate 3.1(b), no physical influence whatsoever may be conveyed faster than the 'speed of light', c. The difference between the limits of these two aspects of motion, matching the photographs in Plate 3.1, is schematically portrayed in Fig. 3.2, below, which depicts a sequence of increasing speeds.

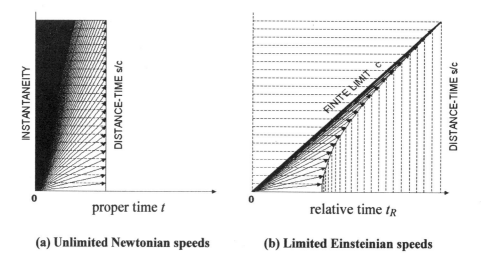

(a) Unlimited Newtonian speeds   **(b) Limited Einsteinian speeds**

Fig. 3.2 : The Double Aspect of Speed

The time-dilation formula, (3.2b), tells us, in effect, that in the case of light interaction, every quantum of the energy that 'starts out' from a source A 'arrives' *instantly* at a recipient B; that is, in its own, intrinsic, proper time $t = 0$. In that case, the relative or observationally delayed time $t_R = s/c$, whence $s/t_R = c$ for any disembodied energy such as electricity or light. However, it needs to be stressed that despite this making the signal *appear* to have this 'speed', the time-delay, over the distance s is not really a speed but a pure ratio of conventional units of metres to seconds in the measuring of distance. This is why the quanta that are 'poised', as it were, to leave the higher-energy source, at A, in our electricity example in section 2.7 seem to 'know ahead of time', whether or not they can be received at B. It is because with their 'transit-time' being instantaneous they are, in a definite sense, in *both places at once*. This was described by Gilbert Lewis in 1926 as a proper time instantaneous 'quantum touching' [17]. In this way, the instantaneous light-action can be considered to be a single quantum event common to both source and observer [18]. Indeed, logic tells us that the transportation of energy between atoms *has* to be *instantaneous* regardless of distance; otherwise there is a time-lapse between a quantum of energy 'leaving' a source-atom and being consummated at the distant atom, which the law of conservation of energy cannot allow.

At first sight, this double aspect of light-action appears puzzling. What we are really saying here is that an action may have both time-delayed and instantaneous *components*, without there being any logical contradiction [19]. The action in a movie testifies to this. In a movie, the instantaneous connection between objects in the 'stills' (still frames) is analogous to the 'instantaneous' (or quantum) component of atomic interaction, t, and the analogy of the observationally time-delayed component t_R, is the sequencing of those stills in the running of the film. Just this one homely factual example is a logically sufficient refutation of any idea that quantum instantaneity and relativistic time-delay are contradictory.

3.6 The Doppler effect

The (optical) Doppler effect is a well-known observed fact. When a light source is receding from an observer, its light-spectrum is shifted towards the red, whereas when it is approaching the observer, its spectrum is shifted towards the blue [20]. We shall demonstrate in this section how this effect is a direct consequence of the time-dilation formula, (3.2).

Consider a light source X, travelling at speed v in a fixed direction, relative to an observer O. Initially, we shall assume that X is moving *away* from O. Let the very small period of time between successive 'pulses' be δt, as recorded by a clock moving with the source X. This time will be recorded by O's clock as δt_R, where by (3.2a),

$$\delta t_R = (1 - v^2/c^2)^{-\frac{1}{2}} \, \delta t. \tag{3.4}$$

However, in that time, the light source has increased its distance from O by $v\delta t_R$, relative to O. Hence, according to O, the next 'pulse' arrives at O at time

$$\delta t_R^* = \delta t_R + v\delta t_R/c. \tag{3.5}$$

The times δt and $\delta t_R{}^*$ are, respectively, inversely proportional to the *proper frequency*, v_0, of the source, as recorded at the source, and the *frequency*, v, of the source, as recorded by O. It then follows by (3.4) and (3.5) that

$$\frac{v}{v_0} = \frac{\delta t}{\delta t_R{}^*} = \frac{\delta t}{\left(1+v/c\right)\left(1-v^2/c^2\right)^{-1/2}\delta t} = \frac{1}{\left(1+v/c\right)\left(1+v/c\right)^{-1/2}\left(1-v/c\right)^{-1/2}}$$

and hence,

$$v = \frac{\left(1-v/c\right)^{1/2}}{\left(1+v/c\right)^{1/2}} v_0. \tag{3.6}$$

Since the light source X is receding from the observer O, the speed v is positive and so it follows from (3.6) that $v < v_0$. It then follows that the light is red-shifted by the relative motion of its source. If, on the other hand, X is approaching O, so that the speed is negative, it follows from (3.6) that $v > v_0$. In this case, the light is blue-shifted by the relative motion of its source.

The simple scenario presented here can be generalised to more complicated situations [21], but this argument, so far, should be sufficient to indicate the versatility of the time-dilation formula.

3.7 The 'twins paradox' [22] [23]

A famous controversy which has surrounded the time-dilation formula, (3.2), from soon after its first appearance, is the so-called 'twins paradox'. Consider twin brothers each of whom carries some type of clock. Initially, they are together on earth and synchronise their clocks. One twin, O, remains on earth, while the other, X, sets off in a space-craft, which after leaving earth, travels at high constant speed to a distant planet. The space-traveller, X, then returns to earth at the same high constant speed, relative to his stay-at-home brother O, and meets up again with him. Ignoring the accelerations and decelerations on take-off and touch-down, it follows by (3.2b) that X's clock will have recorded a shorter passage of time than O's clock does relative to O. Hence, if the twins have the same age before the space-traveller's journey, then when they meet up again, the traveller will be relatively younger than the other, since each observer ages at the same rate relative to his own clock.

The alleged 'paradox' is this. On the face of it, it seems that X could claim with equal right that it was he who remained where he was, while it was O who went on the round trip, with the consequence that O should be the younger when they meet again. However, there is no such paradox, because it must be remembered that equation (3.2b) applies only to relatively *uniform* motion. In order to make his trip, the traveller, X, must undergo an initial period of acceleration and when he reverses direction to return this necessarily involves a period of deceleration and acceleration, which has definitely observable and measurable physical (for example, visceral) effects. Hence, X is not in an inertial frame for the whole journey, as is O, and so O's and X's observational frames are not physically or mathematically interchangeable. This is essentially the argument provided by Einstein in correspondence with Pope in 1954 [24]. Although (3.2b) applies for most of the journey of X relative to O, the periods of acceleration and deceleration of X, no matter how short compared to the length of the whole journey, destroy the otherwise symmetrical situation between O and X. For these short periods, X will be aware of the physical effects on his body produced by the non-uniform motion, whereas O will detect no such effects. A good analogy for the fact that very short periods of non-uniform motion have a huge impact on the whole journey has been provided by Bondi. Imagine travelling in a car at constant speed along a straight road. Suppose at some point, the car turns right and continues to travel at constant speed along another straight road. The negligible period of non-uniform motion, when the car turns right, has a very large effect on the car's destination!

Let us examine this asymmetry between the twins O and X in more detail. In order to remove as many effects due to non-uniform motion as possible, imagine O and X being two astronauts somewhere in deep space, far away from any possible gravitational effects. As before, X moves away from O at uniform speed, then reverses direction and returns to O at the same uniform speed. Note that any precept that there is some underlying 'God's-eye' overview that can be taken of the recordings of O and X together must be abandoned [25]. In that case, the only way in which the twins can compare their time-readings is for each of them, by means of a telescope, say, reading the other's clock and comparing those readings with the readings of his own clock all through the out-and-back motion. Of course, as already stated, the 'clock' in this case, need not be a mechanical clock; it may be any regular physical or biological process. To take the most exacting case, the 'clock' could be of the sort used in the Mössbauer method of counting the periods of gamma-ray quanta by means of spectroscopes [26].

As O and X move apart in space, the ticks of the atomic clock that each twin observes of the other in his telescope are slowed relatively to his own due to the extra time s/c incurred by the increasing distance between them. This is the observed Doppler effect discussed in the last section. When a body is receding from an observer, its light-spectrum is shifted towards the red, so that the 'ticks' of its atomic clocks appear slowed, whereas when it is approaching the observer, its spectrum is shifted towards the blue so that its 'atomic ticks' appear quickened. Suppose that O and X move steadily apart at such a speed that the ticks of each one's clock, as viewed by the other, are twice as long as his own. Suppose also that X reverses direction after one year, as measured by his (X's) atomic clock. We know that due to the Doppler lengthening of the ticks of X's atomic clock in O's view of X, O will record that reversing action of X's after *two* years of his (O's) own time, as shown in Fig. 3.3 below.

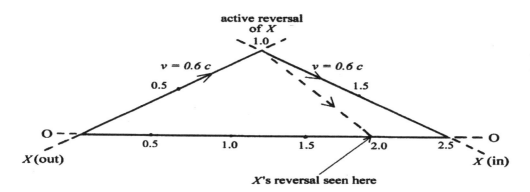

Fig. 3.3: The Differential Aging of Twins in Relative Motion

Neglecting the time taken for his turnaround, X meets up with O after a further time of one year, as measured by his (X's) own atomic clock. Meanwhile, during the return journey of X, after the two years already elapsed in O's time, O will observe the ticks of X's atomic clock from then on at the faster (blued) rate of half their standard length, which means that in the one year that X's atomic clock will have registered in returning to O, O's atomic clock will have registered a *half* of that time, that is, six months. It follows, then, that while the total time registered by X's clock between their leaving and meeting up again is just *two years*, for O it is *two and a half years*. And what is the case for clocks must obviously be the same for all other processes, such as heartbeats, aging-rates and so on. So when they get back together, the result of the relative motion is that twin O will have aged six months more than twin X.

The situation for O and X is therefore plainly *asymmetrical*, because O counts slower ticks from X for a longer period than X does from O and counts faster ticks from then on for a correspondingly shorter period. This asymmetry is graphically portrayed in Fig. 3.3. Notice that the time-dilation factor from O's time to X's time for the whole journey is 1.25, which, by (3.2b), gives a speed of $v = 0.6c$ for X relative to O, on both the outward and return journeys.

In summary, this analysis reveals that whichever of the twins undertakes a reversing action to bring the two back together switches immediately at that point from counting red-shifted to blue-shifted periods in his spectroscopic readings of the other's clocks. Meanwhile, for the other, that reversing action will not be observed immediately but only after an interval which is the distance-time s/c of that distant motion-reversal (see Fig. 3.3). This asymmetry in the period-counting, between the observers, disposes of the so-called paradox. Of course, any proper treatment of the 'twins paradox' should take the effects of any non-uniform motion into proper account, and we shall return to this later in this book.

3.8 Minkowski space-time

It follows from the time-dilation formula (3.2), that times as well as positions in space, as recorded by an observer, are *relative*. We shall now adopt the standard notation and denote the time as recorded by an observer's clock as t, rather than t_R, as in previous sections. Using standard Cartesian coordinates, any point in space has position (x, y and z) relative to an observer O, situated at the origin of that coordinate system. In view of the time-dilation formula, different observers' clocks run at relatively different rates. Hence, it is clearly not adequate to talk about a particular observation of O's occurring at a particular point in space relative to O; rather, the particular observation must be specified not only by its position, but also by the time t at which it happens relative to O.

An observation occurring at a point in space with Cartesian coordinates (x, y, z) and at a time t relative to an observer O, is called the **event** with coordinates (t, x, y, z). The set of all events is known as **space-time**. Note here that we follow the convention that the time coordinate comes first in the coordinates of an event. However, other authors may use a different convention. The hyphen in 'space-time' conveys the fact that space and time are intimately connected, in the way we have already described. Hence, when we talk of observations, we are really talking about events. For an obvious reason, the time t relative to observer O is usually known as **coordinate time**.

At first sight, it appears that all measures are relative to a particular observer. However, as explained in section 3.2, any moving clock records the proper time relative to its own rest frame, so that the proper time is independent of any observer and so serves as an absolute, rather than a relative parameter. From now on, we shall use the more standard notation of τ for proper time.

Consider any clock X moving with uniform velocity relative to an observer O, as in section 3.2. Then relative to O's spatial Cartesian coordinates x, y and z, after a passage of time t relative to O, X travels a radial distance r, where

$$r^2 = x^2 + y^2 + z^2.$$

Also, it follows by (3.1) that the proper time, τ, recorded by clock X is given by

$$t^2 = \tau^2 + (r/c)^2,$$

that is,

$$-c^2\tau^2 = -c^2t^2 + r^2$$

and so

$$-c^2\tau^2 = -c^2t^2 + x^2 + y^2 + z^2. \tag{3.7}$$

Since the proper time, τ, is a physical parameter which is invariant with respect to all observers and c is also invariant, it follows that the right-hand-side of (3.7) immediately provides an invariant quantity for all inertial observers. This is known, in this context, as the **separation** or **interval** between two events. The set of all events, together with this invariant quantity, provides a mathematical model for studying uniform motion, known as **Minkowski space-time** [27].

More generally, suppose that the clock X moves with *non*-constant velocity, $\mathbf{v}(t)$, relative to observer O. It follows by (3.2b) and the definition of the Riemann integral that in this case, the relatively moving clock X records proper time τ given by

$$\tau = \int (1 - v^2(t)/c^2)^{1/2} \, dt,$$

that is,

$$\frac{d\tau}{dt} = (1 - v^2(t)/c^2)^{1/2}, \tag{3.8}$$

where $v(t) = \|\mathbf{v}(t)\|$ is the speed of X relative to O. In this case, relative to O's spatial Cartesian coordinates, x, y and z,

$$\mathbf{v}(t) = \left(\frac{dx}{dt}, \frac{dy}{dt}, \frac{dz}{dt}\right),$$

so that (3.8) gives

$$c^2\left(\frac{d\tau}{dt}\right)^2 = c^2 - v^2(t) = c^2 - \left(\frac{dx}{dt}\right)^2 - \left(\frac{dy}{dt}\right)^2 - \left(\frac{dz}{dt}\right)^2$$

and hence

$$-c^2 d\tau^2 = -c^2 dt^2 + dx^2 + dy^2 + dz^2. \tag{3.9}$$

Once again, it follows that since the proper time is a physical invariant, the right-hand-side of (3.9) is invariant with respect to all inertial observers. This quantity is the infinitesimal version of the right-hand-side of (3.7) and is known as the **elementary separation** between two events. The expression (3.9) provides the **metric** for Minkowski space-time, which forms the basis of study of relativistic kinematics and dynamics. This will be discussed again in the next chapter.

It should be noted here that our approach has a big advantage over standard SR in the sense that we are able to construct Minkowski space-time directly from the time-dilation formula in a simple way. Moreover, in this approach, Minkowski space-time is not simply a convenient mathematical model for studying relative uniform motion but, rather, a direct expression of the fundamental physical phenomenon of time-dilation. By contrast, in standard Special Relativity, Minkowski space-time is presented as a consequence of the fact that the separation of events is invariant with respect to the special Lorentz transformation. In addition, the invariance of the separation of events is not, usually, initially related to the invariance of proper time [28].

Now an objective characteristic of physical phenomena is, as A.J. Ayer remarked [29],

> Places are places in a visual field and the times those that furnish the temporal order of experience ... In this way the framework is set for the description of visual appearances ... We can identify a sense field by reference not only to its own character but also that of its neighbours, and if necessary to that of their neighbours and so on.

However, Normal Realism takes full account of the empirical fact that there is no direct or instrumental way in which the world can be described from two or more separate places at once. The nearest we get, in physics, to that objective, decentralised view of the world is *via* the Lorentz transformation. This is why, in standard relativistic physics much use is made of that transformation procedure, which enables one, in theory, to project one's own observational perspective to those of other observers in the way Ayer describes.

In the next chapter we demonstrate how that transformation may be derived in Normal Realist terms.

Notes and References

[1] Pope, N. V. and Osborne, A. D.: 'A new approach to Special Relativity', *Int. J. Math. Educ. Sci. Technol.,* **18** (1987) pp.191-198.

[2] Pope, N. V. and Osborne, A. D.: 'Instantaneous Relativistic Action-at-a-Distance', *Physics Essays,* **5** (1992) pp. 409-421.

[3] See for example, Rindler, W.: *Relativity: Special, General and Cosmological* (Oxford University Press, 2001) p. 64.

[4] French, A. P: *Special Relativity* (Chapman & Hall, New York, 1991), pp. 101-105.

[5] Hafele, J. C. H. and Keating, R.: *Science* **177** (1972) p.166.

[6] Bondi, H.: *Assumption and Myth in Physical Theory* (Cambridge University Press, 1967), p. 28.

[7] Epstein, L.: *New Scientist,* **8** (1983) p. 690.

[8] See, for example, Muirhead, H.: *The Special Theory of Relativity* (Macmillan, London, 1973) pp. 21-22.

[9] Polkinghorne, J. C.: *The Quantum World* (Pelican, London, 1986) pp. 63-64, 70-77.

[10] Einstein, A., Podolski, B. and Rosen, N.: 'Can Quantum-Mechanical Description of Physical Reality Be Considered Complete?' *Physical Review,* **47** (1935) pp. 777-780.

[11] The European Centre for Research, Geneva.

[12] D'Espagnat, B.: *Conceptual Foundations of Quantum Mechanics* (Benjamin, 1971).

[13] These experiments were carried out in 1978 at Berkley, USA, by John Clauser and his team, and also in 1982 by Alain Aspect and his group. See, for example, Aspect, A., Dalibard, J. and Roger, G.: 'Experimental Tests of Bell's Inequalities Using Time-Varying Analysers', *Phys. Rev. Letters,* **49** (1982) pp. 1804-7.

[14] Pope, V.: *The Eye of the Beholder: the Role of the Observer in Modern Physics* (phi Philosophical Enterprises, Swansea, 2004) pp. 46-48.

[15] Davies, P.: *Other Worlds* (Pelican, London, 1988) Chapter 6.

[16] For example, Bohm, D.: *Wholeness and the Implicate Order* (Routledge, London, 1980)

[17] Gilbert Lewis saw it as a consequence of Relativity that the quantum ('photon') interaction between two atoms is a simultaneous and reciprocal action-reaction event in accordance with Newton's Third Law of Motion. See Lewis, G. N.: 'Light Waves and Corpuscles', *Nature* **117** (1926) p. 256.

[18] The Wheeler-Feynman action-at-a-distance theory (J.A. Wheeler and R.P. Feynman, *Rev. Mod. Phys,* **21**, (1949) 425) discusses direct particle interaction, but there is still an *a priori* space-time substructure assumed. We suggest that there is no such *a priori* substructure and that therefore the principles of 'advanced' Newtonian and 'retarded' light propagational spatiotemporal interaction are not competing principles as these writers assume.

[19] *Op. cit.* reference 14, pp. 10-14.

[20] See, for example, Lawden, D. F.: *Elements of Special Relativity* (Wiley, 1985) pp. 32-34.

[21] Rindler, W.: *Relativity: Special, General and Cosmological* (Oxford University Press, 2001) pp. 78-81.

[22] See for example, Marder, L.: *Time and the Space-Traveller* (Allen and Unwin, 1971).

[23] The idea of the so-called 'clock paradox' was first introduced by Einstein, although he did not believe the result to be a paradox at all. The line of argument was later refined and extended by Langevin in 1911, when it became known as the 'twins paradox'.

[24] Letter from Einstein to N. V. Pope in March 1954. County Hall, Swansea, Archives ref. D/D NVP/1-17 Volume 1, pp. 4-5; website http://www.swansea.gov.uk.

[25] If such a 'God's-eye' overview is stuck to throughout, then this merely defeats the argument by adhering dogmatically to what that argument seeks to refute.

[26] Pope, N. V., Osborne, A. D. and Winfield, A. F. T. (eds.): *Immediate Distant Action and Correlation in Modern Physics: The Balanced Universe* (Edwin Mellen Press, New York, (2005) p. 272.

[27] Minkowski first presented his space-time in a lecture given in Gottingen in 1907, about 18 months after the publication of Special Relativity. He presented a less technical account at the eighteenth Congress of German Scientists and Physicians in Cologne, in September 1908.

[28] D'Inverno, R.: *Introducing Einstein's Relativity* (Clarendon, Oxford, 1992) pp. 26-27.

[29] Ayer, A. J.: *The Central Questions of Philosophy* (London, 1973) pp. 91 and 93.

CHAPTER 4

Relativistic Kinematics and Dynamics

This chapter is concerned with kinematics and dynamics relative to inertial observers, that is, with observers in uniform relative motion. Our two fundamental postulates for uniform motion are as laid out at the start of the previous chapter. We begin, here, by deriving the *special Lorentz transformation*, which relates spatial positions and times recorded by different inertial observers. We shall derive this transformation directly from the time-dilation formula, (3.2), without any of the 'electrodynamical' rationale of the standard derivation in Special Relativity and, in particular, without Einstein's counter-intuitive Second Postulate that light travels *in vacuo* at a velocity which is constant relative to all differently moving observers [1]. Once we have the Lorentz transformation, some of the standard applications and consequences of SR directly follow [2]. However, a no less important consequence of the time-dilation formula, (3.2), is the Minkowski space-time structure, as derived in section 3.8. This provides a mathematical model for studying relativistic kinematics and dynamics and leads to further famous consequences of SR [3], which are studied later in this chapter.

4.1 The special Lorentz transformation

Consider two observers O and O', each situated at the origin of a set of Cartesian axes labelled x, y, z, and x', y', z' respectively. We suppose that O' moves along the x-axis in the positive direction with constant speed v relative to O such that the x', y' and z' axes remain parallel to the x, y and z axes respectively. Let t be some passage of time as recorded by a clock in O's observational frame and let t' be the corresponding passage of time as recorded by a clock in O''s observational frame. We suppose that the observers O and O' synchronise their clocks when they coincide at $t = 0$, so that when $t = 0$ at $(0, 0, 0)$ relative to O, we have $t' = 0$ at $(0, 0, 0)$ relative to O'. This situation is indicated in Fig. 4.1, below, in which the z dimension is suppressed. We shall call this the *standard situation* involving inertial observers O and O'.

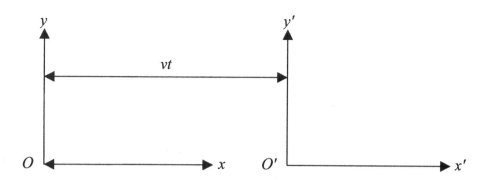

Fig. 4.1: Relative Uniform Motion

The figure shows the position of O''s frame relative to O's, after time t, as recorded by O. According to classical physics, after time t relative to O has elapsed,

$$x' = x - vt, \qquad (4.1a)$$

as can be seen from the figure, and

$$y' = y, z' = z, t' = t. \qquad (4.1b)$$

Equations (4.1) together form the *Galilean transformation*. However, since time is not an absolute quantity, as clearly demonstrated in the last chapter, the Galilean transformation cannot give the correct relationship between events in two inertial frames.

In general, since, by hypothesis, O' moves with constant velocity relative to O, objects which move with constant velocity relative to O must move with constant velocity relative to O'. It then follows from our initial condition concerning the times t and t' that the most general transformation which maps (x, t) to (x', t') under these conditions must be linear. By hypothesis, after time t relative to O, O' has moved a distance $x = vt$, as indicated in Fig. 4.1 so that we obtain

$$x' = \gamma (x - vt), \qquad (4.2)..$$

for some *constant* γ to be determined. It follows from (4.2) and Postulate 1 that since O travels at speed v in the negative x' direction relative to O', then

$$x = \gamma \, (x' + vt') \,. \tag{4.3}$$

From (4.2) and (4.3) we have

$$x = \gamma \, (\gamma x - \gamma vt + vt') \,,$$

so that

$$t' = \gamma \, (t - (1 - 1/\gamma^2)x/v) \,. \tag{4.4}$$

These are the same equations which appear in Special Relativity. However, whereas SR resorts to the concept of 'travelling light signals' in order to deduce the value of γ in (4.2), in our approach this value is obtained directly by using (4.4) and the time-dilation formula, (3.2). Note that (4.2) and (4.4) include the Galilean transformation as a special case, with $\gamma = 1$. It is clear from (4.4) that only in this case of $\gamma = 1$ does $t' = t$.

To reiterate, after time t relative to O, O' has moved a distance $x = vt$. The same passage of time, t', as recorded by O''s clock relative to O is then given by (4.4) with $x = vt$, so that

$$t' = \gamma \, (t - (1 - 1/\gamma^2) \, t) = t/\gamma \,. \tag{4.5}$$

But here, $t' = \tau$, the *proper time* recorded by O''s clock, so that (4.5) is the *same* equation as (3.2b), *i.e.*,

$$\tau = (1 - v^2/c^2)^{1/2} \, t.$$

This immediately produces

$$\gamma = (1 - v^2/c^2)^{-1/2}, \tag{4.6}$$

as in SR, where it is known as the *Lorentz factor*.

With this value of γ, we have

$$1 - 1/\gamma^2 = v^2/c^2,$$

and so (4.5) reads

$$t' = \gamma \, (t - vx/c^2) \,. \tag{4.7}$$

Since, in the case that the observers O and O' describe, positions in the y and z directions are not affected by relative motion in the x-direction, it follows that

$$y' = y, z' = z. \tag{4.8}$$

The equations (4.2), (4.6), (4.7) and (4.8) constitute the **special Lorentz transformation (SLT)** for speed v. We claim that our derivation of this transformation is simpler than any of the standard derivations in Special Relativity [4]. Of course, all the standard consequences of SR which derive directly from the special Lorentz transformation must also hold in our approach. We examine some of these consequences in the next section. However, it is not the aim of this chapter to reproduce all the standard results, which can be found elsewhere [2]. But careful consideration has to be given to the *physical* interpretation of some of these results. We must emphasise again here that, in our approach, light does not *travel* in the usual sense of the word.

The situation between the two inertial observers O and O' described above may be generalised to the case where O' travels with constant velocity in any direction relative to O [5]. It can also be generalised still further to the case where the axes of each inertial frame rotate and so on [6][7]. However, in practice, given two inertial observers, we may always choose Cartesian axes in each observer's frame so that the *standard situation* described above holds.

4.2 Some consequences of the special Lorentz transformation

The special Lorentz transformation [8] for speed v is best summarised as follows. In the *standard situation* involving inertial observers O and O' as given in the previous section, if (t, x, y, z) is an *event* as recorded by O and (t', x', y', z') is the same event relative to O', then

$$x' = \gamma(x - vt), \ t' = \gamma(t - vx/c^2), \ y' = y, \ z' = z, \ \gamma = (1 - v^2/c^2)^{-1/2}. \tag{SLT}$$

Note that the constant γ is not defined when $v = c$ and that it is not a real constant for $v > c$. These considerations again add weight to our view that c cannot be treated as a speed in the normal sense and that 'superluminal speeds' are not physically possible. Note also that when v is a small fraction of c, the SLT reduces to the Galilean transformation (4.1). Hence, classical (Newtonian) physics is perfectly adequate for studying uniform motion when the speeds involved are small fractions of c. For example, jet planes travel at speeds in the order of $10^{-6}c$.

In the *standard situation* involving inertial observers O and O', O moves in the *negative x'-direction* with speed v relative to O' and so it follows directly from the SLT that

$$x = \gamma(x' + vt'), \quad t = \gamma(t' + vx'/c^2), \quad y = y', \quad z = z', \quad \gamma = (1 - v^2/c^2)^{-1/2}.$$

This can also be checked by solving (SLT) for x and t.

EXAMPLE 4.1: Length contraction

Let a measuring rod of length L' relative to O' be positioned along the x'-axis, with one end at the origin in O''s inertial frame. Let the length of the rod be recorded as L by O when O' passes O at time $t = 0$. It then follows by the SLT with $x' = L'$ with $x = L$ and when $t = 0$, that

$$x' = L' = \gamma(x - vt) = \gamma(L - v \times 0).$$

Therefore:

$$L = L'/\gamma = (1 - v^2/c^2)^{1/2}L'. \tag{4.9}$$

Since $v < c$, it follows by (4.9) that $L < L'$ for $v > 0$. Hence the length of the rod appears shorter relative to O. Notice that if, instead, the rod is stationary in O's frame, then its length relative to O', recorded when O passes O' at time $t' = 0$, is given by

$$L' = (1 - (-v)^2/c^2)^{-1/2}L = (1 - v^2/c^2)^{1/2}L.$$

This result does not contradict (4.9) since it refers to a different physical situation. Remember that the length contraction is only a relative effect and not an absolute one [9]. It must be noted that no observer *sees* a shortening of the rod in relative motion. In order to investigate what is seen, the effect of the relative motion on the visual appearance of the moving rod has to be taken into account [10].

Due to the present state of our technology, no experimental verification of the length contraction prediction has been performed, since any such experiment would have to involve accelerating a macroscopic body of an appreciable length to a significant fraction of c.

EXAMPLE 4.2: Relativistic speeds

Consider, once again, the *standard situation* involving inertial observers O and O'. Suppose that O and O' observe a moving material particle, P, travelling at (not necessarily) a constant speed $u(t)$ along the x-axis, relative to O. Then P travels along the x-axis at speed $u'(t')$, say, relative to O'. According to classical physics, the Galilean transformation (4.1) then gives

$$u' = \frac{dx'}{dt'} = \frac{dx'}{dt} = \frac{dx}{dt} - v = u - v.\qquad(4.10)$$

This result supports our everyday experience of relative speeds. For example, if we are travelling down the motorway at 50 kilometres per hour and a car passes us at 80 kilometres per hour (relative to the ground), then relative to us, the car passes us at $80 - 50 = 30$ kilometres per hour. For much higher speeds, however, the special Lorentz transformation (SLT) dictates that this result cannot be correct. But, of course, our everyday experience does not encompass such speeds.

It follows by the SLT that

$$\frac{dx'}{dt} = \gamma\left(\frac{dx}{dt} - v\right) = \gamma(u - v),$$

and that

$$\frac{dt'}{dt} = \gamma\left(1 - \frac{v}{c^2}\frac{dx}{dt}\right) = \gamma\left(1 - \frac{uv}{c^2}\right).$$

It then follows by the chain rule for differentiation that

$$u'(t') = \frac{dx'}{dt'} = \frac{dx'}{dt}\frac{dt}{dt'} = \frac{dx'}{dt}\left(\frac{dt'}{dt}\right)^{-1} = \frac{\gamma(u-v)}{\gamma(1-uv/c^2)},$$

so that

$$u'(t') = \frac{u - v}{1 - uv/c^2}.\qquad(4.11)$$

Equation (4.11) is the formula for relativistic subtraction of speeds. When v is very much less than c, this result reduces to the classical formula, (4.10). But when v is an appreciable fraction of c, relativistic effects become important and we no longer have the simple relationship (4.10).

Since observer O moves in the negative x' direction with speed v relative to O', it follows immediately by (4.11) that

$$u(t) = \frac{u' + v}{1 + u'v/c^2} . \qquad (4.12)$$

This is the formula for relativistic addition of speeds. It follows from (4.12) that if $0 \le u' < c$ and $0 \le v < c$, then $u < c$. Hence, two observational (Einsteinian) speeds cannot be combined to give a 'speed' of greater or equal to c. This tells us that c acts as a universal 'speed limit' for all material particles, being the least upper bound of all possible speeds, but not a speed itself. Note that if both u' and v take the value c in (4.12), then $u = c$. This is in agreement with our Postulate 2, that c is the same 'conversion factor' for *all* inertial observers.

EXAMPLE 4.3: Relativistic velocities

Let O be an inertial observer and let P be a moving object which traverses a path C relative to O. At any instant of time, t, relative to O, the **position vector** of P is defined by

$$\mathbf{r}(t) = (x(t), y(t), z(t)), \qquad (4.13)$$

where x, y, z are Cartesian coordinates for O's frame. This position vector gives the position of P in relation to O at any time and as t varies, $\mathbf{r}(t)$ varies and traces out the path of P. Hence, $\mathbf{r} = \mathbf{r}(t)$ is the equation for P's path C, relative to O. The **velocity, $\mathbf{v}(t)$,** of P relative to O is the rate of change of P's position, so that

$$\mathbf{v}(t) = \frac{d\mathbf{r}}{dt} = \left(\frac{dx}{dt}, \frac{dy}{dt}, \frac{dz}{dt} \right), \qquad (4.14)$$

(see section 3.8). The **speed** of P is then $v(t) = \|\mathbf{v}(t)\|$, the magnitude of P's velocity, and the **acceleration, $\mathbf{a}(t)$,** of P relative to O is the rate of change of P's velocity, whence

$$\mathbf{a}(t) = \frac{d\mathbf{v}}{dt} = \frac{d^2\mathbf{r}}{dt^2}. \tag{4.15}$$

As stated earlier, an object with *constant* velocity, *i.e.* in *uniform* motion, travels in a straight line.

Let us consider, once again, the *standard situation* involving inertial observers O and O'. Suppose that O observes a particle P moving with velocity

$$\mathbf{u}(t) = (u_1(t), u_2(t), u_3(t)).$$

The velocity of that particle relative to O' is, say,

$$\mathbf{u}'(t') = (u_1'(t'), u_2'(t'), u_3'(t')).$$

It follows by the SLT, exactly as in Example 4.2, that

$$u_1'(t') = \frac{dx'}{dt'} = \frac{u_1 - v}{1 - u_1 v / c^2}.$$

Also by the SLT, using the results of Example 4.2,

$$u_2'(t')\frac{dy'}{dt'} = \frac{dy}{dt'} = \frac{dy}{dt}\frac{dt}{dt'} = \frac{dy}{dt}\left(\frac{dt'}{dt}\right)^{-1} = \frac{u_2}{\gamma}\left(1 - u_1 v / c^2\right)^{-1},$$

and similarly for $u_3'(t')$. Hence, altogether it follows that

$$\mathbf{u}'(t') = \left(1 - u_1 v / c^2\right)^{-1}\left(u_1 - v, u_2/\gamma, u_3/\gamma\right),$$

so there is no simple relationship between $\mathbf{u}'(t')$ and $\mathbf{u}(t)$. This result makes it possible to find the relationship between the accelerations of P relative to O and O' by differentiating and using the SLT again.

As already mentioned, there are many other consequences of the special Lorentz transformation. However, some results which, traditionally, are a consequence of the SLT are really a direct consequence of the time-dilation formula alone, such as the radial Doppler effect discussed in the previous chapter.

4.3 Minkowski space-time again

Minkowski space-time, first introduced in section 3.8, conventionally provides a mathematical model for studying uniform motion. Recall that it is the set of all *events* (t, x, y, z) relative to any inertial observer, together with the *separation* $-c^2t^2 + x^2 + y^2 + z^2$. Since

$$-c^2\tau^2 = -c^2t^2 + x^2 + y^2 + z^2, \tag{4.16}$$

where τ denotes the proper time, an invariant parameter, it follows that the separation is invariant with respect to all inertial observers. This dictates that the separation must be invariant under any special Lorentz transformation, which is easily checked, as follows. Using the SLT gives

$$
\begin{aligned}
-c^2t'^2 + x'^2 + y'^2 + z'^2 &= -c^2t'^2 + x'^2 + y^2 + z^2 \\
&= -c^2\gamma^2(t - vx/c^2)^2 + \gamma^2(x - vt)^2 + y^2 + z^2 \\
&= -c^2\gamma^2(t^2 - 2vxt/c^2 + v^2x^2/c^4) + \gamma^2(x^2 - 2vxt + v^2t^2) + y^2 + z^2 \\
&= -c^2\gamma^2t^2(1 - v^2/c^2) + x^2\gamma^2(1 - v^2/c^2) + y^2 + z^2 \\
&= -c^2t^2 + x^2 + y^2 + z^2,
\end{aligned}
$$

so that the separation is invariant under the SLT, as required. More generally, the separation must be invariant under any transformation connecting events relative to different inertial frames [11].

Paths of material particles (relative to some inertial observer) can be represented by means of a *space-time diagram* [12]. Any point in such a diagram represents an event relative to the chosen observer. Such paths in Minkowski space-time are known as *world-lines*. The *metric* for Minkowski space-time is given by

$$-c^2d\tau^2 = -c^2dt^2 + dx^2 + dy^2 + dz^2, \tag{4.17}$$

where the right-hand-side of (4.17) is the *elementary separation*; see eqn. (3.9). Remember that in our approach, this is simply another way of expressing the time-dilation formula for general motion, (3.8).

4.4 Velocity and acceleration in Minkowski space-time

In classical physics, if a material particle follows a path in space with position vector $\mathbf{r}(t)$, given by (4.13), then its *velocity* and *acceleration* are defined by (4.14) and (4.15) respectively. It should be clear that these definitions are not satisfactory since they are observer-dependent; in particular, they rely on Newton's absolute time, t. Instead, we may formulate analogous definitions in Minkowski space-time that are not observer-dependent.

Let C denote the world-line of a material particle in Minkowski space-time and let the **position vector**, $\mathbf{R}(\tau)$, of any event on C, at any instant of proper time be defined by

$$\mathbf{R}(\tau) = (t(\tau), x(\tau), y(\tau), z(\tau)). \tag{4.18}$$

Then the **four-velocity**, $\mathbf{U}(\tau)$, and **four-acceleration**, $\mathbf{A}(\tau)$, of the material particle at any instant of proper time are defined respectively by

$$\mathbf{U}(\tau) = \frac{\mathrm{d}\mathbf{R}}{\mathrm{d}\tau} = \left(\frac{\mathrm{d}t}{\mathrm{d}\tau}, \frac{\mathrm{d}x}{\mathrm{d}\tau}, \frac{\mathrm{d}y}{\mathrm{d}\tau}, \frac{\mathrm{d}z}{\mathrm{d}\tau} \right) \tag{4.19}$$

and

$$\mathbf{A}(\tau) = \frac{\mathrm{d}\mathbf{U}}{\mathrm{d}\tau} = \frac{\mathrm{d}^2\mathbf{R}}{\mathrm{d}\tau^2}. \tag{4.20}$$

Compare the definitions (4.18), (4.19) and (4.20) with the classical definitions (4.13), (4.14) and (4.15). The four-velocity records the rate of change of *events* relative to proper time, as compared to the classical (three-)velocity, which records the rate of change of *position* relative to Newton's absolute time, and similarly for the four-acceleration. These new definitions are clearly independent of the observer, since they are formulated in terms of the proper time parameter.

Consider a material particle travelling at a (not necessarily constant) velocity $\mathbf{v}(t)$, relative to some observer. It follows by the time-dilation formula, and in particular (3.8), that

$$\frac{\mathrm{d}t}{\mathrm{d}\tau} = (1 - v^2(t)/c^2)^{-1/2} = \gamma(t), \tag{4.21}$$

say, where $v(t) = \|\mathbf{v}(t)\|$ is the speed of the particle. This also follows from the metric, (4.17), for Minkowski space-time and the definition of $\mathbf{v}(t)$. Then using the definition of four-velocity, (4.19), definitions (4.13) and (4.14), plus (4.21),

$$\mathbf{U}(\tau) = \left(\frac{dt}{d\tau}, \frac{d\mathbf{r}}{d\tau}\right) = \frac{dt}{d\tau}\left(1, \frac{d\mathbf{r}}{dt}\right) = \frac{dt}{d\tau}(1, \mathbf{v}) = \gamma(t)(1, \mathbf{v}), \qquad (4.22)$$

where $\gamma(t)$ is given by (4.21). Equation (4.22) provides the fundamental connection between the relativistic four-velocity, $\mathbf{U}(\tau)$, and the classical velocity, $\mathbf{v}(t)$. It is possible to obtain an expression for the four-acceleration, $\mathbf{A}(\tau)$, in terms of the classical velocity $\mathbf{v}(t)$ and acceleration $\mathbf{a}(t)$, by differentiating (4.22) with respect to τ and using (4.21) again. However, there is no simple relationship between $\mathbf{A}(\tau)$ and $\mathbf{a}(t)$ [13].

4.5 Some relativistic dynamics

In classical dynamics, the (linear) **momentum** of a particle of mass m, moving at velocity $\mathbf{v}(t)$ is denoted and defined by

$$\mathbf{p} = m\mathbf{v}. \qquad (4.23)$$

The **force** exerted on the particle at any instant of time is then denoted and defined by

$$\mathbf{f} = \frac{d\mathbf{p}}{dt}, \qquad (4.24a)$$

that is, the force is the rate of change of momentum. Note that both $\mathbf{f}$ and $\mathbf{p}$ are vector quantities, with $\mathbf{p}$ parallel to $\mathbf{v}$. Definition (4.24a) is usually known as *Newton's Second Law* (see Chapter 2). If the mass m is constant, then it follows by (4.24a) and (4.23) that

$$\mathbf{f} = \frac{d(m\mathbf{v})}{dt} = m\frac{d\mathbf{v}}{dt} = m\mathbf{a}, \qquad (4.24b)$$

where $\mathbf{a}(t)$ is the particle's acceleration. In this case, if no force is exerted on the particle, then $\mathbf{a}(t) = \mathbf{0}$, so that $\mathbf{v}(t)$ is constant and the particle moves in a straight line. This is essentially *Newton's First Law*.

Newton's Third Law, or the law of *action and reaction*, states that if two particles act on each other, then the force exerted by the first on the second is equal in magnitude and opposite in direction to the force exerted by the second on the first. This law leads directly to the following conservation principle [14].

Conservation of (linear) momentum: *In any system of particles not subjected to external forces, the total (linear) momentum is constant.*

Once again, it should be noted that the classical definitions of momentum and force are not satisfactory since they are observer-dependent. However, noting the definitions of four-velocity and four-acceleration, together with these Newtonian definitions, it should be clear that the following relativistic definitions are the natural ones to make. Moreover, these definitions are independent of the observer.

Let a material particle have **rest mass** m_0, defined as the mass of the particle as recorded by any observer travelling with the particle, and four-velocity $U(\tau)$ in Minkowski space-time. Then the **four-momentum** of the particle is denoted and defined by

$$P(\tau) = m_0 U \tag{4.25}$$

and the **four-force** exerted on the particle is denoted and defined by

$$F(\tau) = \frac{dP}{d\tau} \tag{4.26}$$

Note that the rest mass is independent of the observer.

It follows directly from definition (4.25) and (4.22) that

$$P(\tau) = \gamma(t)m_0(1, v) \tag{4.27}$$

where $v(t)$ is the classical (observer-dependent) velocity and $\gamma(t)$ is given by (4.21). Relative to an observer for whom a particle has speed $v(t)$, the **relativistic mass** of the particle is denoted and defined by

$$m(t) = \gamma(t)m_0 = (1 - v^2/c^2)^{-1/2}m_0, \tag{4.28}$$

where m_0 is the rest mass of the particle. Equation (4.27) then reads

$$\mathbf{P} = (m, m\mathbf{v}). \tag{4.29}$$

Since momentum is conserved in Newtonian dynamics, it seems reasonable to argue that in Minkowski space-time, there exists an analogous conservation law. Hence, it is assumed that the following conservation principle holds.

Conservation of four-momentum: *The total four-momentum of any system of particles, not subjected to external four-forces, remains constant.*

It is important to realise here that this conservation principle cannot be established using only Postulates 1 and 2; whatever approach is taken, additional assumptions are required. Hence the conservation principle may be regarded as an additional postulate. However, any consequences of this law have been experimentally verified beyond reasonable doubt.

Because of conservation of four-momentum, it follows by (4.29) that both the relativistic mass, m, and the **relativistic momentum**, $m\mathbf{v}$, are conserved. This implies that a particle travelling at speed $v(t)$ relative to an observer O, has an effective mass $m(t)$, given by (4.28), relative to O. Note here that $m(t) > m_0$ as long as $v \neq 0$, so that the *faster* the particle travels relative to O, the *heavier* it appears to be relative to O. This is the *mass-increase-with-speed* effect, which has also been experimentally verified beyond reasonable doubt.

The fact that mass increases with speed was first detected by Kaufmann and Bucherer in the early 1900's. Whilst investigating beta ray radiation, they found that the speeds with which elementary particles were ejected from different radioactive substances were appreciable fractions of c and that the greater the speed, the greater the effective mass of the particle. Using (4.28), they found that the rest mass of each particle was the same and equal to the recorded rest mass of an electron. They also discovered that each particle had the same electric charge as an electron and so concluded that beta ray radiation was caused by electrons being ejected at high speeds from radioactive materials [15].

A number of different problems involving interacting particles can be solved by applying conservation of four-momentum. These include coalescence, elastic collision and disintegration problems. Since most textbooks on Special Relativity consider these types of problems [16], we shall not go into any great detail here, but simply provide one particular example. The central technique is to equate the total relativistic mass before and after interaction, and the total relativistic momentum before and after interaction.

EXAMPLE 4.4

Suppose that a particle P_1 of rest mass m_0 travels at speed $3c/5$ in a fixed direction relative to an observer O. This particle collides and coalesces with a particle P_2 of rest mass $2m_0$ travelling in the opposite direction with speed $5c/13$. The result is a particle P_3 of rest mass M_0 travelling at, say, speed u. We may find the values of u and M_0 by applying conservation of four-momentum. Of course, according to classical physics, $M_0 = m_0 + 2m_0 = 3m_0$, but this is not the case, as we shall demonstrate, since it is the total *relativistic* mass and not the total rest mass which is conserved.

For simplicity, we may choose coordinates so that P_1 travels in the positive x-direction relative to O. Then by conservation of momentum, P_3 also travels in the x-direction relative to O. Using (4.28), the relativistic mass of P_1 is

$$(1 - (3c/5)^2/c^2)^{-1/2}m_0 = (1 - 9/25)^{-1/2}m_0 = (16/25)^{-1/2}m_0 = 5m_0/4,$$

and the relativistic mass of P_2 is

$$(1 - (5c/13)^2/c^2)^{-1/2}2m_0 = 2(1 - 25/169)^{-1/2}m_0 = 2(144/169)^{-1/2}m_0 = 13m_0/6.$$

Equating relativistic mass then gives

$$5m_0/4 + 13m_0/6 = \gamma(u)M_0 = (1 - u^2/c^2)^{-1/2}M_0,$$

that is,

$$41m_0 = 12\gamma(u)M_0. \tag{4.30}$$

Also, equating relativistic momentum in the x-direction gives

$$(5m_0/4)(3c/5) - (13m_0/6)(5c/13) = \gamma(u)M_0\,u,$$

that is,

$$-m_0c = 12\gamma(u)M_0u. \tag{4.31}$$

Dividing (4.31) by (4.30) gives $u = -c/41$, so that the speed of P_3 is $c/41$ and P_3 travels in the same direction as P_2. Then from (4.30),

$$M_0 = 41m_0/12\gamma(u) = 41(1 - u^2/c^2)^{1/2}m_0/12 = 41(1680/41^2)^{1/2}m_0/12 = \sqrt{105}m_0/3.$$

Note, here, that $M_0 > 3m_0$, the difference between M_0 and $3m_0$ representing the extra rest mass gained in the collision.

4.6 Relativistic mass and energy

In classical dynamics, naïvely, *potential energy* is the capacity to do *work*. For example, energy is required to move a body through a distance, and work is done by the force required to move the body through that distance. In general, the **work**, W, done by a force $\mathbf{f}(x, y, z)$ in displacing a particle along a curve C in three-dimensional space, from an initial point A to a final point B is defined by the line integral

$$W = \int_C \mathbf{f}.d\mathbf{r}, \tag{4.32}$$

where $d\mathbf{r} = (dx,\ dy,\ dz)$. Suppose that the force $\mathbf{f}$ is *conservative*, i.e., W is independent of the curve C joining A to B. Then $\mathbf{f}$ takes the form

$$\mathbf{f}\,(x, y, z) = -\left(\frac{\partial V}{\partial x},\ \frac{\partial V}{\partial y},\ \frac{\partial V}{\partial z}\right)$$

for some function $V(x, y, z)$ [17]. It then follows from (4.32) that

$$W = -\int_A^B \frac{\partial V}{\partial x}\,dx + \frac{\partial V}{\partial y}\,dy + \frac{\partial V}{\partial z}\,dz = -\int_A^B dV = V(A) - V(B), \tag{4.33}$$

independently of the curve joining A to B. The function $V(x, y, z)$ defines the **potential energy** at any particular point. Equation (4.33) expresses the fact that the work done equates to the loss of potential energy when the force $\mathbf{f}$ moves from A to B.

Now suppose the mass, m, of the body is constant. It then follows by (4.32) and (4.24b) that

$$W = \int_C \mathbf{f}.d\mathbf{r} = m \int_C \mathbf{a}.d\mathbf{r} = m \int_C \mathbf{v}.\mathbf{a}dt \qquad (4.34)$$

where $\mathbf{v}$ is the velocity of the body. Note that if $v = \|\mathbf{v}\|$ is the body's speed, then

$$\frac{d}{dt}(v^2) = 2v\frac{dv}{dt} = \frac{d}{dt}(\mathbf{v}.\mathbf{v}) = 2\mathbf{v}.\frac{d\mathbf{v}}{dt} = 2\mathbf{v}.\mathbf{a} . \qquad (4.35)$$

Hence, from (4.34),

$$W = \frac{m}{2} \int_A^B \frac{d}{dt}(v^2)dt = \frac{m}{2}\left(v^2(B) - v^2(A)\right), \qquad (4.36)$$

independently of the curve C joining A to B.

The **kinetic energy** of a moving particle with mass m and speed $v(t)$ at any point is denoted and defined by

$$K = \frac{1}{2}mv^2. \qquad (4.37)$$

Equation (4.36) expresses the fact that when work is done by moving the force $\mathbf{f}$ from A to B, there is a gain in kinetic energy. In other words, as a consequence of doing work, some potential energy is converted into kinetic energy. The **total energy**, E, is defined by

$$E = K + V. \qquad (4.38)$$

It follows by (4.33) and (4.36) that, in this case, the total energy is constant. This is the *law of conservation of energy*.

Once again, this classical treatment of energy requires modification in relativity. We now show how Einstein's famous formula, which relates relativistic mass and energy, essentially follows from the 'gamma factor' of the time-dilation formula, given by (4.21). It follows by (4.21) that for any particle moving with relative speed $v(t)$,

$$\gamma(t) = (1 - v(t)^2/c^2)^{-1/2},$$

so that using (4.35),

$$\frac{d\gamma}{dt} = -\frac{1}{2}\left(-\frac{2v}{c^2}\frac{dv}{dt}\right)\left(1-\frac{v^2}{c^2}\right)^{-3/2} = \frac{\gamma^3 v}{c^2}\frac{dv}{dt} = \frac{\gamma^3}{c^2}(\mathbf{v.a}). \qquad (4.39)$$

Using (4.39), together with the definition of $\gamma(t)$ then gives,

$$\mathbf{v}.\frac{d}{dt}(\gamma \mathbf{v}) = \gamma(\mathbf{v.a}) + v^2\frac{d\gamma}{dt} = c^2\frac{d\gamma}{dt}\left(\frac{1}{\gamma^2} + \frac{v^2}{c^2}\right) = c^2\frac{d\gamma}{dt} .$$

It follows that if a particle of constant rest mass m_0 is initially at rest at time t_0 and finally attains velocity **v** at time t relative to some observer, then

$$c^2\frac{d}{dt}(\gamma m_0) = \mathbf{v}.\frac{d}{dt}(\gamma m_0\mathbf{v}) \quad \Rightarrow \quad c^2\frac{dm}{dt} = \mathbf{v}.\frac{d}{dt}(m\mathbf{v}),$$

where m is the relativistic mass of the particle, so that

$$c^2\int_{t_0}^{t}\frac{dm}{dt}dt = \int_{t_0}^{t}\mathbf{v}.\frac{d}{dt}(m\mathbf{v})dt = \int_{t_0}^{t}\mathbf{v}.\frac{d\mathbf{p}}{dt}dt = \int_{t_0}^{t}\frac{d\mathbf{r}}{dt}.\mathbf{f}dt = \int_{t_0}^{t}\mathbf{f}.d\mathbf{r} .$$

Here, **p** is the relativistic momentum of the particle and **f** is the force exerted on the particle. Then finally we get

$$(m(t) - m_0)c^2 = \int_{t_0}^{t}\mathbf{f}.d\mathbf{r} . \qquad (4.40)$$

It follows by (4.32) that the right-hand side of (4.4) represents the work done in accelerating the particle from rest and so by (4.36), the gain in the *relativistic kinetic energy* of the particle must be $(m - m_0)c^2$. This fact is supported by calculating this quantity by using (4.21) as follows.

$$(m(t) - m_0)c^2 = (\gamma(t) - 1)m_0c^2 = m_0c^2((1 - v^2/c^2)^{-1/2} - 1),$$

where $v(t)$ is the speed of the particle. Since $v^2/c^2 < 1$, we may expand $\gamma(t)$ in a convergent binomial series to obtain,

$$(m(t) - m_0)c^2 = m_0 c^2 \left(1 - \frac{1}{2}\left(-\frac{v^2}{c^2}\right) + \frac{1}{2!}\left(-\frac{1}{2}\right)\left(-\frac{3}{2}\right)\left(-\frac{v^2}{c^2}\right)^2 + \dots - 1 \right)$$

$$\approx m_0 c^2 \left(\frac{v^2}{2c^2} + \frac{3v^4}{8c^4} \right) = \frac{1}{2} m_0 v^2 + \frac{3}{8} m_0 \frac{v^4}{c^2}. \tag{4.41}$$

If v is much smaller than c, then (4.41) shows that $(m - m_0)c^2$ is approximately equal to the Newtonian kinetic energy of the particle, given by (4.37). The other terms in the series for $(m - m_0)c^2$, of which $3m_0 v^4/8c^2$ is the dominant term, represent the relativistic correction.

Let a particle, P, have rest mass m_0, and relativistic mass $m(t)$ relative to some observer. From the arguments just presented, we may define the **relativistic kinetic energy** of P at any time t as $(m - m_0)c^2$. Then bearing in mind the classical definitions of potential and total energy given previously, we define the **internal energy**, E_0, of P by

$$E_0 = m_0 c^2 \tag{4.42}$$

and the **total energy**, E, of P at any time t relative to the observer by

$$E = mc^2. \tag{4.43}$$

The relativistic kinetic energy of P at any time t relative to the observer is then $E - E_0$. Note that the internal energy is independent of the observer. Comparing these definitions with their Newtonian counterparts, it is easily seen that the internal energy is the relativistic analogue of potential energy. Since c^2 is such a large factor, any particle contains an enormous amount of energy in relation to its rest mass.

It follows from (4.43) that

$$E = (1 - v^2/c^2)^{-1/2} m_0 c^2$$

where v is the speed of the particle P. This provides another argument against the interpretation of c as a speed. For if c was a speed, then it would take an infinite amount of energy to accelerate a particle from a speed less than c to 'speed' c, so that such an acceleration is not physically possible. Rather, definitions (4.42) and (4.43) show that c^2 acts as a *conversion factor* for converting mass into energy, in the same way that c acts as a conversion factor for converting observational time into observational distance. In this sense, when we talk about mass, what we are really talking about is energy [18].

It is now well known that energy is released upon the break-up of the nucleus of any chemical element with an atomic weight greater than 108, in a process known as *nuclear fission*. Experiments in nuclear fission were first performed by Cockcroft and Walton in Cambridge, in 1932. It was found that the amount of energy released upon the break-up of lithium nuclei was as predicted by the formula (4.42). Following Cockcroft and Walton's pioneering work, experiments concerning uranium fission were performed by Hahn and Strassmann in Berlin, in 1938. The fact that uranium fission is self-sustaining, thereby producing a nuclear chain reaction, was discovered by Fermi, an Italian who fled to the US before the start of the Second World War. It was advice from Einstein, Fermi and his co-worker Szilard to President Roosevelt concerning the potential destructive power of uranium fission which led to the *Manhattan Project* for the development of the atomic bomb. Einstein, a dedicated pacifist, was extremely reluctant to encourage the development of the atomic bomb. In 1945, he was devastated to learn that such a bomb had been dropped on Hiroshima.

Energy is released when two or more nuclei of elements with an atomic weight of less than 108 are fused together in a process called *nuclear fusion*. Hydrogen fusion takes place in the Sun and all other stars. This fact was first discovered independently by Bethe and Weiszsäcker in 1939. Their discovery solved the problem of the source of solar energy. A hydrogen bomb works on the basis of hydrogen fusion. The first such bomb, one thousand times more powerful than the first atomic bomb, was detonated in the Marshall Islands in 1952.

In this and the previous chapter we have demonstrated that all the standard practical consequences of Special Relativity can be deduced in a straightforward way without Einstein's eminently counter-intuitive postulate that light travels in the vacuum at a *velocity* which is *the same for all relatively moving observers*. So far we have dealt specifically with the time-dilational effects on bodies moving uniformly relative to one another. In Chapter 8, we return to time-dilational effects , not in relation to ideal uniform rectilinear motion but in relation to natural *orbital* motion.

Notes and References

[1] Osborne, A. D. and Pope, N. V.: 'A Neo-Phenomenalist Alternative to Special Relativity Theory', *Galilean Electrodynamics*, (to appear).

[2] See, for example, Rindler, W.: *Relativity: Special, General and Cosmological* (Oxford University Press, 2001) Chapters 3 and 4.

[3] Rindler, W., *ibid*, Chapters 5 and 6.

[4] See, *e.g.*, Muirhead, H.: *The Special Theory of Relativity* (Macmillan, London, 1973) pp. 16-20.

[5] Aharoni, J.: *The Special Theory of Relativity* (Clarendon, Oxford, 1959) pp. 48-50.

[6] Taylor, J. G.: *Special Relativity* (Clarendon, Oxford, 1975) pp. 59-61, 72-80.

[7] Kay, D. C.: *Tensor Calculus* (McGraw-Hill, New York, 1988) p. 167.

[8] The special Lorentz transformation is so-called since Lorentz was the first to introduce it in 1904, as a basis for a modification of electromagnetic theory in order to explain the null result of the Michelson-Morley experiment.

[9] In 1911, Einstein had to explain that, '...the contraction ...does not "really" exist in so far as it does not exist for an observer who moves with the rod; it "really" exists, however, in the sense that it can, as a matter of principle, be demonstrated by a resting observer.'

[10] *Op. cit.* reference 2, pp. 82-85.

[11] *Op. cit.* reference 6, Chapter 6.

[12] *Op. cit.* reference 2, pp. 90-94.

[13] *Op. cit.* reference 2, p. 99.

[14] McCuskey, S. W: *An Introduction to Advanced Dynamics* (Addison-Wesley, 1959), pp. 22-23.

[15] See, for example, Shankland, R. S.: *Atomic and Nuclear Physics* (Macmillan, 1961).

[16] *Op. cit.* reference 2, Chapter 6.

[17] *Op. cit.* reference 14, pp. 12-13.

[18] Pope, N. V., Osborne, A. D. and Winfield A. F. T. (eds.): *Immediate Distant Action and Correlation in Modern Physics: The Balanced Universe* (Edwin Mellen, New York, 2005) p. 40.

CHAPTER 5

The Ultimately Discrete Nature of Physical Phenomena

5.1 The quantisation of physical measures

One of the most basic definitions of science must be that it is the rational interpretation of observational and instrumental *information*. Hence, science is naturally *relativistic*, which is to say that whatever it describes as existing in nature is described and measured relatively to *observation*. From the standpoint of Normal Realism, all fundamental physical quantities must ultimately be based on observation. Observations provide *information* and for information to be information, its ultimate elements, or informational *bits*, must be discrete and unconnected, that is to say, *quantised* [1].

Now a flow of real information that does not involve energy is inconceivable. Indeed, since the work of Shannon and Weaver it is known that both information and energy are governed by virtually the same law, namely, the statistical Second Law of Thermodynamics, or Entropy [2]. A quantum of observational information is therefore also a quantum of energy, and a quantity of energy is the product of energy and time, or *action*. So any natural limit to the reduction of observational *information* – *i.e.*, ultimately, light – implies a corresponding limit of reduction in the amount of energy (action). In that case, if there is an empirical limit of reduction of action /information, then any increase in that quantity has to be in integer multiples of that fundamental unit. In that absolute limit, any further reduction of the action-components, energy and time, can take place only reciprocally. That is to say, any reduction in the energy can be achieved only at the cost of increasing the time, and *vice-versa*, so that the action unit overall remains the same. In this chapter it may be seen that there is, in fact, such a natural limit of reduction, of just the sort that is to be expected on the grounds of Normal Realism.

Given, then, that action can increase and decrease only in integer multiples of whatever might turn out, empirically, to be the ultimate measure of that quantum, we may suppose that the units of its component measures (energy and time) are also quantised. In the following sections we shall see that this supposition is confirmed. This means that all equations involving these fundamental physical measures are *Diophantine equations, i.e.* equations in integers. Starting with things at the empirical level of reality, that is, with things we actually observe, we may say that these ultimate parts of observational elements into which those things may be sensibly and/or instrumentally analysed, have no qualities or characteristics other than in the contexts of those observational wholes of which they are the analysed parts [3].

This discrete nature of physical measures is also manifest on the macro-scale, albeit in a different way. For instance, although mathematically speaking, the irrational numbers provide the completion of the set of rational numbers to the set of real numbers, thus providing a *continuum* on which to build calculus, such irrational numbers are not recordable in any sense of practical measurement. This is because the ultimate accuracy of the recording will always depend on that of the chosen measuring device which can never be one-hundred percent accurate. In other words, only *rational approximations* of irrational numbers are ever recordable. All recordable physical measures are therefore, *de facto*, ultimately discrete.

This fundamental quantisation of physical phenomena was first suggested by the studies of Max Planck, who proposed that electromagnetic energy is ultimately discrete. It led to the beginnings of quantum physics, as described in the next section. Although all physical measures are ultimately discrete on a small enough scale, the fact that they are so small makes them appear, for all practical purposes, to be continuous on the macro-scale. This is known as the *correspondence principle* in quantum physics. Indeed, in order to construct a *mathematical model* of some physical phenomenon on the macro-scale (as opposed to the phenomenon itself), we must necessarily use continuous variables.

The fact that physical measures are ultimately quantised leads us to consider the fundamental difference, if any, between physical phenomena on the macro- and micro-levels. This consideration leads to two fundamentally different approaches to physics [4]. Classical physics is what might be described as an *analog* approach, in which the explanations of physical phenomena are couched in terms of conceptions of mechanical processes of essentially the same kind as those we observe on levels of ordinary sensation and perception. In that way of thinking, the ultimate elements of things are microphysical bits of matter moving about in essentially the same space as that in which things move about on ordinary macrophysical levels. By contrast, what we may call a *digital* approach to physics is one which seeks to explain all physical phenomena in terms of mathematical systems of elements, which, in themselves, have none of the usual physical features of motion, duration *etc.*, being the ultimately irreducible informational bits into which all those phenomena are analysed.

However, there are two kinds of these digital approaches which need logically to be distinguished. The aim of the one is to produce explanations in terms of elements such as pure numbers (for example, digital matrices of abstract and intrinsically featureless ones and noughts), whereas the aim of the other is to explain things in terms of systems of actual sensory/instrumental *information* (what Mach termed 'sense-data'). In the first of these approaches, which we may call the *numerical approach*, the 'geometry' of the things we see in the world is an automatic construct out of relations between pure numbers (or points), in the manner conceived originally by the Pythagoreans [5]. Our Normal Realist philosophy, however, dictates that we follow the second digital approach, in which geometry is essentially a natural *a priori* feature of *phenomena*, the ultimate elements of which are the end-result of a reductive process of analysis of phenomena, terminating, empirically, in further-irreducible quantum measures of physical *information*. We call this approach the *sense-datum approach* [6].

5.2 The origins of quantum physics

In Physics, the quantisation of energy was first proposed by Max Planck to explain the apparently paradoxical results of the Rayleigh and Jeans study of *black body* radiation. A *black body* is an object which absorbs and then re-emits all electromagnetic radiation that falls onto it. In 1900 Rayleigh and Jeans studied the problem of the radiant energy confined to a container whose walls are *black* in this sense. Using classical physics, they derived a formula for the energy per unit volume of radiated electromagnetic waves of a certain frequency. This depended only on the frequency and the temperature of the enclosure. Their formula not only firmly contradicted results of experiments for high frequencies but also predicted that the total energy of radiation per unit volume of the container would be infinite! This result became known as the *ultraviolet catastrophe.*

Planck provided an answer to this dilemma about a year later. Rayleigh and Jeans had supposed that the radiant energy was absorbed and re-emitted by the black body in a *continuous* way. Planck, on the other hand, proposed that this radiant energy could be emitted and absorbed only in the form of discrete 'packets', which he called *quanta.* According to Planck, electromagnetic radiation with *frequency* v (*i.e.* oscillating at v times per second) is made up of a *whole number* of quanta of energy, E, proportional to v, so that,

$$E = hv \tag{5.1}$$

where h is a constant known as *Planck's constant.* In other words, electromagnetic radiation is ultimately discrete, in the same way that a bowl of sugar consists of individual grains. Using this postulate, he replaced the Rayleigh-Jeans formula with a new one known as Planck's law [7]. Not only did his new formula agree entirely with the results of experiments and with the Rayleigh-Jeans formula for low frequencies, it also avoided the ultraviolet catastrophe. He was able to deduce the value of h using the known values of observed frequencies, temperatures and total energies and obtained $h \approx 6.626 \times 10^{-34}$ joule seconds. Of course, this value of h is tiny, so that on the macro-scale, the discrete energy levels come so close that the radiant energy appears to be continuous. This is an example of the correspondence principle mentioned earlier.

Following Planck's pioneering work, it was soon discovered that a discrete structure was persistent throughout all physical phenomena. In 1905, Einstein called upon Planck's ideas to explain the *photoelectric effect*, which concerned the way in which electrons are ejected from metals by incident light [8]. According to the firmly accepted wave theory of light, discussed in section 2.4, the number of electrons ejected could not depend on the frequency of the light. But experiment showed that they did. Such experiments demonstrated that below a certain critical frequency no electrons were ejected, regardless of the intensity of the radiation. Einstein suggested that not only is energy exchanged between matter and radiation in discrete packets, but also that electromagnetic radiation itself actually consists of action quanta, h, which he called *photons*, each of energy given by (5.1). Below the critical frequency, the energy of a photon would be too weak to displace an electron. This seemed to be confirmation, by modern physics, of Newton's once prestigious 'corpuscular', or *particle theory* of light.

However, in explaining the photoelectric effect, Einstein created an apparent paradox. How could light have both wave-like characteristics and particle characteristics? The answer to this dilemma, first proposed by Einstein and Louis De Broglie, was purely *ad hoc*, namely, that light has wave characteristics as well as particle characteristics. And so, counter to all commonsense, the photon was conceived to be a *wave particle*.

Another major step towards the advent of Quantum Theory involved experimental spectroscopy. In 1885, a Swiss secondary-school teacher, Johann Balmer, observed that the spectrum of light emitted by hydrogen gas forms an informational structure very similar to what we would now call a 'bar-code'. He was the first to produce a successful mathematical formula for the distribution of these spectral lines. Then, in 1890, the Swedish physicist Johannes Rydberg extended Balmer's work and discovered a general rule applicable to the spectral lines of many other elements. Stated in terms of the frequency of the light, the generalised Balmer-Rydberg formula may be expressed as

$$v(n_1,n_2) = c\alpha_N RN^2\left(\frac{1}{n_1^2} - \frac{1}{n_2^2}\right). \tag{5.2}$$

In this formula, v is the frequency of the light in cycles per second, N is the ordinal number of the element (*e.g.*, $N = 1$ for hydrogen), R is a constant, known as the *Rydberg constant*, n_1 and n_2 are natural (whole) numbers representing the fixed and running terms respectively, and α_N is a constant depending on the element, with $\alpha_N \approx 1$ [9]. In Balmer's original formula, $N = 1$, and $n_1 = 2$. For $n_1 = 1$, the formula gives the Lyman series and $n_1 = 3$, gives the Paschen series.

This formula was obtained *empirically*, so as to fit the observed spectral lines. It expresses no more than a fact of pure observation. Its constructors, Balmer and Rydberg, had no underlying *theory* as to *why* this formula is true [10]. It was not until 1913 that the first theoretical explanation emerged. This was put forward by Niels Bohr, who based his explanation on a mixture of classical mechanics and electrodynamical theory, plus the inclusion of the quantisation of angular momentum [11]. The spectral lines, Bohr supposed, were energies released by the elementary charged particles known as *electrons*, orbiting like planets around the *nucleus* of the atom. But unlike the continuous motions of the planets, these electrons changed orbits in discrete quantum jumps of energy, E, given by (5.1). In Bohr's model for the hydrogen atom, he supposed that the single electron was confined to certain discrete orbits only. For simplicity, he considered these orbits to be *circular*. Bohr postulated that the magnitude of the angular momentum of the electrons in these orbits was quantised, in discrete units of $\hbar = h/2\pi$ since the circumference of a circle of unit radius is 2π [12]. Thus, whereas h is the quantum of radiant energy as Einstein saw it, $\hbar$ is the quantum of angular momentum in Bohr's model. Angular momentum will be discussed at length in the following chapters, but for now it is sufficient to note that the magnitude of the angular momentum of a particle of mass m, travelling in a circular orbit of radius r about the centre at speed v is mvr. Bohr therefore postulated that the electron of mass m and speed v could occupy only a circular orbit of radius r which satisfied

$$mvr = \frac{nh}{2\pi},$$

(5.3)

where n is a natural (whole) number, *i.e.*, n = 1, 2, 3, ... Using a mixture of arguments from electrostatics and classical mechanics [8][13], Bohr deduced that the discrete energy levels, E_n, of the hydrogen atom must satisfy (in MKS units)

$$E_n = \frac{-\alpha_N m e^4}{8\varepsilon_0^2 h^2 n^2},$$

(5.4)

where $-e$ is the charge on the electron and ε_0 is a constant (the so-called *permittivity* of free space). It then follows that if an electron 'jumps' from orbit n_2 to orbit n_1, with $n_2 > n_1$, then the loss in energy is

$$\frac{\alpha_N m e^4}{8\varepsilon_0^2 h^2}\left(\frac{1}{n_1^2} - \frac{1}{n_2^2}\right),$$

which Bohr supposed was radiated as a single photon. Using (5.1), it follows immediately that the corresponding frequency is

$$v(n_1, n_2) = \frac{\alpha_N m e^4}{8\varepsilon_0^2 h^3}\left(\frac{1}{n_1^2} - \frac{1}{n_2^2}\right),$$

(5.5)

which is the Balmer-Rydberg formula (5.2) for hydrogen, with $R = m e^4/8 c \varepsilon_0^2 h^3$. This enabled the Rydberg constant to be determined from known constants and the result agreed with the experimentally determined value for R.

Modifications of Bohr's theory followed in quick succession. Finer spectral lines were discovered and then Pieter Zeeman showed that yet more lines appeared when the source of the spectrum was placed near a magnet. The extra spectral lines due to magnetic effects were eventually explained by Wolfgang Pauli and independently by George Uhlenbeck and Samuel Goudsmit [14]. The explanation was that the extra lines were due to hidden rotation, or spin, of the orbiting electron. With these and other theoretical modifications, the full informational contents of spectral lines were more or less explained on the basis of the hidden motions of these invisible elementary particles.

De Broglie extended the wave-particle concept of light to the motion of particles of any sort. These *De Broglie waves* were thought to be standing waves, which form harmonic patterns around the nucleus of an atom, at distances from the centre where the beginning and end of the wave-cycle are perfectly in phase. This concept of the underlying standing-wave was further developed by Erwin Schrödinger in 1926, by the introduction of a wave equation that satisfactorily described all quantum aspects of physical systems. Later that same year, Max Born subjected Schrödinger's wave-function to a probabilistic interpretation, describing it, not as a continuous wave but as a pure *probability amplitude*. In this interpretation, exactness of position and motion of elementary particles disappears at the quantum level. In 1927, Werner Heisenberg proposed his *Uncertainty Principle,* according to which observing the state of an elementary particle requires an energy-interaction with that particle, which alters its state. This means that so far as observation is concerned, the existence and state of particles on the ultimate quantum level is impossible to determine, since observing a particle inevitably alters whatever might be thought of as its 'unobserved' state. In these ways, what is now known as *Quantum Mechanics* slid further and further into the mystery we now associate with it [15].

5.3 The discrete nature of light-energy

As discussed in section 2.6, in our Normal Realist account of Relativity, light is to be thought of as *observational information*, rather than as particles or waves 'travelling at speed *c*'. Stripped of all its mechanistic precepts, light quanta are simply informational bits, in bar-code-like arrangements, out of which, ultimately, our knowledge of the world is constructed. What we observe is therefore a hologram-like presentation which the Peripatetic followers of Aristotle called a *species* [16].

According to Planck's relation (5.1), light (in the sense of all electro-magnetic radiation) is emitted and absorbed in discrete and irreducible units of Planck's constant, h, so if we wish to think of light as 'travelling' at speed c, then we have to think of these quantum bits, conventionally called photons, as all travelling at the same speed. But then, according to this interpretation, these photons have to possess mass, and Special Relativity has it, by (4.28), that at that 'speed' the observational mass of any travelling 'particle' becomes infinite. This is yet another argument against the interpretation that light 'travels' in the usual sense. In contrast, according to our NR philosophy, light, as energetic pixels of observational information, does not travel in this way but is simply a transfer of *disembodied energy* from one place to another in the phenomenal framework. We thus think of a 'photon', not as an inscrutable space-travelling entity, but as a quantum of transferable energy from one observational location to another.

This means that the Greek-based word 'photon', which Einstein used to describe the light quantum, is singularly inappropriate for our present purposes due to its unwanted 'space-travelling-particle' connotations. For this reason, we prefer the Latinised version, *photum* (plural, *phota*) to describe the Planck quantum insofar as it carries no mechanical overtones of the usual ballistic kind [17]. This dispenses with the apparent conflict of the 'wave' versus 'particle' theory of light and the consequent notion of light as a 'wave-particle'. It is to be noted that apart from its lack of the usual separatist, space-travelling connotations, the *photum* is the same in all other respects as the photon, both of which are variants of the name *quantum*. (Readers are alerted to this unfamiliar change of meaning by our italicising of the word *photum* wherever it appears in our Normal Realist context from here on.)

As discussed in section 3.5, far from having a 'speed', any incorporeal light interconnection is inherently proper time instantaneous. In this sense, energy transfer in light interaction is of a *potential* rather than a *kinetic* kind. Indeed, it has been called *quantum potential* by the Birkbeck group after David Bohm [18]. This purely potential nature of quantum interconnection is borne out by the well-known Thomas Young two-slit interference experiment, first performed in 1803. In this experiment, a light source is shone through a screen with two slits. This produces an *interference* pattern of alternating light and dark fringes on a plate behind the screen [19]. This pattern cannot be explained if light has particle-like characteristics, which led Young to deduce that in the experiment light 'travels' in waves. Interpreted as photons, the light quanta seem to 'know', ahead of time, how to 'avoid' those areas on the plate where their frequencies, if they 'landed', would be out-of-phase with one another and 'steer', instead, in correspondingly greater numbers for those areas where they would be in-phase. This is in such a way as to conserve (as though by telepathy from the 'travelling photon' point of view), the overall spread of illumination at the distant end. This mystery disappears when explained in terms of proper time instantaneous potential energy transfer, which does not induce us to think of light as travelling in the form of either waves or particles – far less of 'wave-particles' [20] [21].

Something else which is certain, from this point of view, is that the light-energy cannot 'set out' on some course in the vague hope of sometime in the future meeting either an absorber or a 'barrier' – or, perhaps, going on forever, meeting nothing at all. Conservation of energy demands that every quantum of interaction has to be an instantly consummated, double-ended affair, a one-ended quantum jump being as impossible to conceive as a one-ended coil of wire. The alternative, therefore, is to think of the atoms involved in the transfer as being in direct and reciprocal resonance. This is in accordance with Newton's Third Law of equal and opposite action and reaction in what has been called *quantum touching* [22]. (See Chapter 3, section 5.)

There is, then, no *time* separating whatever we may think of as the 'beginning and end' of a quantum interaction. The conceptual 'flip-over', which our approach requires, is to treat the photon (or *photum* as we are now calling it) as a single irreducible quantum event common to both the 'object' and the 'observer' [1][23]. Space and time, as we normally perceive it, therefore, cannot exist on that quantum level, any more than a video drama can exist at the level of the individual screen pixels. These dimensions of physical phenomena exist solely on the macrophenomenal level, optically projected, as we say, from informational patterns and sequences of these quantum 'pixels'. On the quantum-phenomenal level, the atoms of bodies interact by direct resonance, with nothing existing or happening in between. And if, on the ordinary macrophenomenal level, those resonances are between, say, the atoms of a distant galaxy and those in the eye of an astronomer or a photographic plate, then the distance of that object is an optical projection made from information-statistical numbers of those immediately perceived, intrinsically distanceless quantum events. This is in the same way that in some ultra-fine-grained pointillist painting, the length, depth and breadth of a landscape are optically projected from whole arrangements of paint-spots in a way which would be impossible from examining those paint-spots themselves.

In these purely information-sequential terms, how do we account for the observational delay in two-way signalling, as, for example, in Michelson's experiments to determine the 'speed of light' [24]? Our answer is as follows.

A single *photum* has no intrinsic spatial or temporal extension, so in itself, it cannot signify any measure of observational distance. Rather, the distance, s, of a source relative to an observer, O, is the manifestation of distributions of large numbers of *phota*, of which that particular atomic source is just one among many, all observed more or less together at O. Since all distances in observer-space are also times in the ratio of units c, the emitter and absorber of a *photum*, which are non-separated in quantum space and time, are separated in observer-time by the observational interval s/c. Thus, if A is a light-source and B a mirror situated a distance s from A, a *photum* originating at A, although seen instantly at B in the proper time of the *photum* itself, cannot reach B in O's extrapolated observer-time until the lapse of time s/c, shown in Fig. 5.1, below.

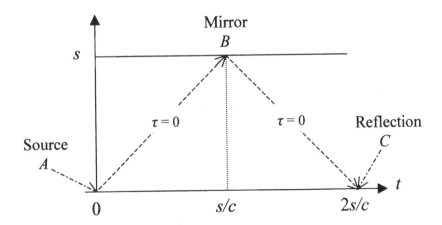

Fig. 5.1: A Two-Way *Photum* Interaction

Of course, the only signification A will receive at this stage that the *photum* has 'arrived' somewhere will be a 'jolt' consisting of the loss of that *photum* at A. This is because the jolt consisting of that loss of the *photum* by A and the gain of that same *photum* by B affects both A and B *simultaneously*.

However, since B cannot both gain and lose a quantum of energy in the same instance, the response of a mirror at B, *i.e.*, its 'reflection', has to be another *photum* contact in which, in this instance, a quantum is lost by B and gained (again proper time instantaneously) at A. This involves another lapse of observational time s/c. Hence, the overall observational time recorded at A, for the signal transaction will be $2s/c$ (see Fig. 5.1). What we customarily call the 'transmission and reflection of the photon' is no more than the 'cinematographic' extrapolation, in A's observation, of the two separate, intrinsically instantaneous blips illustrated in the figure. We may summarise this situation by saying that each *one-way* leg of *photum* interaction is instantaneous, whilst all *two-way* *photum* interactions are time-retarded.

This analysis shows that the instantaneous to-and-fro linkages between *phota* into the sequences of which macrophenomenal time ultimately analyses, cannot be *transitive*. In other words, there cannot be – at least, not at the final microphysical level – any universal, or non-local, single present-moment in which all these instantaneous connections occur together. If there were, it would be a case of 'cosmic gridlock'.

In summary, the energy transfer in light interaction is proper time instantaneous in accordance, not only with the time-dilation formula, but also with conservation of energy. The time-delay which is usually associated with these phenomena is not a feature of the quanta themselves but only of their time-sequences in relativistic (macroscopic) observation [25] [26].

5.4 Causality at the quantum level

We maintain then, that there is no such thing as cause and effect at the quantum level of phenomenal analysis [27]. One quantum does not *cause* another, any more than one letter in this sentence causes the next in sequence. So, what does 'causality' mean in this informational context if it is not that of quantum events causing one another? On its most mechanical level, cause and effect is the transfer of energy from a body in a higher energy-state to another body in a lower energy-state, according to the Second Law of Thermodynamics. In the classical thermo-dynamics of Boltzmann, *et al.*, these transfers are conducted by material particles in the void or by waves in some kind of medium. Since the advent of Information Theory, however, with Shannon *et al.* [2], that Second Law (of entropy) has been redefined in terms of pure probability-statistics which apply not only to mechanical processes such as the transfer of heat from one body to another but also to all forms of *communication*. Like distance and time, therefore, cause and effect are a function of statistical numbers of quantum events occurring in vast and fine-grained profusion. These probability functions include not only those automatic processes we call mechanical but also communication between humans and similar organisms. Since this includes communication with nature in general on all the levels known to science, whether classified as organic or inorganic, it breaks down the traditional Cartesian dichotomy between 'Mind and Matter' [28].

Moreover, none of this excludes informational exchanges between things other than ourselves; exchanges that may take place beyond our reach and beyond our ken. This by no means makes the existence of these things 'mysterious' to us in any deep metaphysical sense. Their unseen and unknown character is a logically necessary extension of all that lies right there in front of us.

5.5 *Photum* interaction and conservation of four-momentum

In section 4.5, the four-momentum, **P**, of a material particle was given by

$$\mathbf{P} = m\,(1, \mathbf{v}),$$

where m is its relativistic mass and $\mathbf{v}$ is its three-velocity. It follows by Einstein's equation (4.43) for the equivalence of mass and energy, that if E is the total energy of the particle, then

$$\mathbf{P} = \frac{E}{c^2}(1, \mathbf{v}).$$

From this it follows that since any *photum* is essentially a quantum of energy, we may *define* the **four-momentum** of a *photum* by

$$\mathbf{P} = \frac{E}{c^2}(1, c\mathbf{n}), \tag{5.6}$$

where $\mathbf{n}$ is a vector of unit length in the direction of the emitting source. Using (5.6), problems in which material particles interact via *phota* can be solved by applying conservation of four-momentum, as in section 4.5 [29]. We provide a typical example of such a problem below. Once again, however, it is necessary to emphasise here that in our approach, a *photum* does not travel in the usual sense but is instantaneously emitted and absorbed in its own proper time as a discrete packet of energy E.

EXAMPLE 5.1

Let us assume that an elementary particle radiates electromagnetic energy in the form of a *photum* whilst at rest relative to some observer and that, as a result, the particle's rest mass is reduced by one fifth. We may calculate the particle's speed of recoil and hence the energy of the *photum*, in terms of the particle's rest mass, as follows.

Let m_0 denote the rest mass of the elementary particle and let the energy of the *photum* be E. Choose Cartesian coordinates such that the elementary particle travels in the x-direction after emission, relative to the observer. It then follows by using (5.6), (4.29) and conservation of four-momentum that,

$$m_0(1, 0, 0, 0) = \frac{E}{c^2}(1, c, 0, 0) + \frac{4}{5}\gamma(v)m_0(1, v, 0, 0),$$

where $\gamma = (1 - v^2/c^2)^{-1/2}$ (see (4.6)). Hence, by conservation of energy,

$$m_0c^2 = E + \frac{4}{5}\gamma(v)m_0c^2 \tag{5.7}$$

and by conservation of relativistic momentum,

$$0 = \frac{E}{c} + \frac{4}{5}\gamma(v)m_0 v. \tag{5.8}$$

Eliminating E from (5.7) and (5.8), it follows that

$$m_0 c^2 = -\frac{4}{5}\gamma(v)m_0 vc + \frac{4}{5}\gamma(v)m_0 c^2 \Rightarrow c = \frac{4}{5}\gamma(v)(c - v) \Rightarrow c^2 = \frac{16c^2(c - v)^2}{25(c^2 - v^2)}$$

$$\Rightarrow 25(c + v)(c - v) = 16(c - v)^2 \Rightarrow 25(c + v) = 16(c - v) \Rightarrow 41v = -9c.$$

The resulting particle's speed of recoil is therefore $9c/41$. Then, by (5.8), the energy of the *photum* is

$$E = -\frac{4}{5}\gamma(v)m_0 vc = -\frac{4}{5}(1 - 81/41^2)^{-1/2} \cdot \frac{-9}{41}m_0 c^2 = -\frac{4}{5} \cdot \frac{41}{40} \cdot \frac{-9}{41}m_0 c^2 = \frac{9}{50}m_0 c^2.$$

From this it can be seen that it is a fallacy to take the fact of 'photonic' recoil and transfer of momentum as 'evidence' of the ballistic or 'photonic' nature of the light-quantum, since this fact can be fully explained without ascribing any real velocity to that quantum. This example also demonstrates that different *phota* may have different energies. Traditionally, this fact is expressed by the Planck relation, (5.1), which states that the energy of a photon is proportional to its frequency.

5.6 The Normal Realist derivation of the Balmer-Rydberg formula

Since, according to Planck, electromagnetic radiation consists of a whole number of quanta of energy hv, this suggests that there is direct deductive connection between the energy released by an object in optical interaction and the discrete lines that are observed in atomic spectra, which are described by the Balmer-Rydberg formula, (5.2). Bohr provided one such connection, as outlined in section 5.2. However, as we shall demonstrate in this section, this is not the only possible derivation of (5.2). Consistent with the Normal Realist philosophy, our derivation, in contrast to Bohr's, does not involve any conception of 'hidden mechanisms' of electrodynamics, but rather is based on purely observational considerations.

It follows from the equivalence of mass and energy, discovered by Einstein, that if energy is discrete, then so is mass. This suggests that there is a natural, indivisible unit of mass in the phenomenon of electromagnetic radiation.

Since frequency is also discrete, it seems reasonable to suppose that there is also a natural indivisible unit of time in this context. These measures are effectively continuous on the macro-scale, so there is no contradiction in supposing that the standard relativistic formulae are ultimately *discrete* on the micro-scale.

Consider the standard mass-increase-with-speed formula, (4.28):

$$m = (1 - v^2/c^2)^{-1/2}m_0, \tag{5.9}$$

where m_0 is the rest mass of a particle, v is its speed relative to an observer O, and m is its relativistic mass, as recorded by O. Suppose that, in accordance with our previous reasoning, there is some indivisible natural unit of mass, m^* for the phenomenon in question. Then at the quantum level, $m_0 = Nm^*$ and $m = nm^*$ say, where N and n are natural (whole) numbers. Equation (5.9) then reads

$$nm^* = (1 - v^2/c^2)^{-1/2}Nm^* \Rightarrow v^2/c^2 = 1 - N^2/n^2. \tag{5.10}$$

Thus, at the quantum level, $(v/c)^2$ takes discrete values only. It should be noted, however, that at this level, $(v/c)^2$ is no more than a terminal abstraction of the process of reduction, so it makes no sense to think of v, here, as a speed in the ordinary sense, any more that it makes sense to thinks of m^* as an ordinary mass. The ultimately discrete values of v^2/c^2 may also be obtained directly from the time-dilation formula (3.2b) by supposing that there is some indivisible unit of time [30].

For heuristic reasons, to be justified in due course, to each discrete value of v^2 may be assigned a total energy $\alpha_N m^* v^2$ (compare Einstein's formula (4.43)). Then (5.10) indicates that allowable discrete losses of energy are given by

$$E(n_1, n_2) = \alpha_N m^* c^2 N^2 \left(\frac{1}{n_1^2} - \frac{1}{n_2^2} \right) \tag{5.11}$$

This formula implies that the traditional 'atom' is an accumulation of relativistic mass-energy in discrete amounts. In this sense, the atom may be thought of as a *quantum accumulator*. (Compare this formula with Bohr's formula (5.5), for frequency.) It follows by Planck's relation (5.1) that $m^* c^2/h$ is some natural limit of frequency which, empirically, is the Rydberg frequency constant cR. It then follows in (5.11) that

$$m^* = hR/c,\qquad(5.12)$$

so that the allowable losses of energy are given by

$$E(n_1, n_2) = \alpha_N\, hcRN^2 \left(\frac{1}{n_1^2} - \frac{1}{n_2^2} \right).$$

The Balmer-Rydberg formula, (5.2), then follows directly from (5.1). Using the currently accepted values [31] of $h \approx 6.626069 \times 10^{-34}$ J s, $R \approx 1.097373 \times 10^7$ m^{-1} and $c \approx 2.997925 \times 10^8$ m s^{-1}, (5.12) then gives $m^* \approx 2.425434 \times 10^{-35}$ kg. We may associate this value of m^* with the 'mass-equivalent' of the energy of a *photum* transition associated with the hydrogen atom, since Bohr supposed that energy losses are radiated as single photons. But we repeat that in this derivation, the *photum*, unlike the photon, is not a space-travelling entity but a purely observational quantum pixel.

It follows by the above discussion and (5.12) that the energy, E, of a *photum* transition from one atom to another is given by

$$E = m^*c^2 = hcR \approx 2.179872 \times 10^{-18} \text{ J.}$$

Conventionally, this is the energy equivalent of the 'electron charge', e, *viz.*:

$$E = I_0\, e,$$

where I_0 is the *ionisation potential*, that is, the kinetic energy required completely to remove the electron form the atom [32]. It must be borne in mind however, that in our approach, the electron is not conceived as a well-defined 'electrically charged particle'. Classically, a loss of energy must be produced by a movement of rest mass, m_0 say, so that according to (4.28) and the results of section 4.6,

$$(m - m_0)c^2 = (1 - (1 - v^2/c^2)^{1/2})mc^2 = m^*c^2,\qquad(5.13)$$

where v is the speed of the mass and m^* is our fundamental unit of mass. The currently accepted empirically determined value of the relativistic mass of the 'electron' in the hydrogen atom is [33]

$$m \approx 9.1093897 \times 10^{-31} \text{ kg}.$$

Substituting this value in (5.13), together with the calculated value of m^*, gives

$$v \approx 2.187676 \times 10^6 \text{ m s}^{-1},$$

which traditionally is the 'speed' of the electron in the Bohr atom. With these approximate values, it follows that

$$mv^2/2 \approx m^*c^2. \tag{5.14}$$

In this sense, the energy loss can be approximately equated with the classically conceived kinetic energy of the moving electron, independently of any path it may be assumed to be following.

These derivations necessarily contain some *ad hoc* assumptions. It is nevertheless significant that the parameters of Bohr's historical model of the atom, as well as the Balmer-Rydberg formula, can be reproduced in this way without any references to 'electric charges' and associated 'field' and 'force' postulates. In Chapter 7, we continue our investigation of the parameters of the hydrogen atom, again avoiding any reference to 'charges', by supposing that angular momentum in all its forms is always conserved and is ultimately quantised.

First, however, having demonstrated that the fundamental dimensions of physical phenomena, mass, length and time, are basically quantised – that is, discrete or 'digital' – we now turn our attention, in the next chapter, to the phenomenon of true physical motion, which, according to Newton is everywhere under the influence of the 'universal force of gravity', hence never truly rectilinear in the way that is assumed in SR. Taking account of this essentially *curvilinear* character of motion extends our NR agenda to include what is commonly known as General Relativity.

Notes and References

[1] Pope, N. V.: *The Eye of the Beholder: the Role of the Observer in Modern Physics* (**phi** Philosophical Enterprises, Swansea, 2004) Chapters 1 and 8.

[2] Shannon, C. and Weaver, W.: *The Mathematical Theory of Communication* (Univ. of Illinois Press, Urbana, USA, 1949).

[3] McGoveran D. and Noyes H. P: SCLAC-PUB-4526, 3 (1989).

[4] Pope, N. V.: 'From Analog to Digital: A Revolution in Modern Physics' (www.poams.org)

[5] This is the approach favoured by the founding members of ANPA (the Alternative Natural Philosophy Association) whose meetings are held annually at Wesley College, Cambridge. This approach is called the Combinatorial Hierarchies, and is described in Bastin, T. and Kilmister C. W.: *Combinatorial Physics* (World Scientific Press, 1995).

[6] Our use of the term 'sense-datum', here, must be carefully distinguished from its use by the Logical Positivists of the Vienna Circle era during the 1920s and in other Philosophical circles from then onwards. The term was introduced by the physicist-philosopher Ernst Mach, who saw true science as seeking the most simple and economical descriptions of our sensations in ordinary language. For Mach, the ultimate descriptions are incorrigible 'sense-data'. No underlying entities or causes of these sense-data are postulated. However, with the later followers of Mach – in particular, Bertrand Russell and (the earlier) Wittgenstein – these 'sense-data' became 'atomic propositions' in a purely 'logical' or *Linguistic* approach to phenomenalism which lost all contact with physical science as Mach had conceived it. Proving ineffectual in the face of developing science it was eventually abandoned.

[7] Taylor, J. G.: *Quantum Mechanics: An Introduction* (Allen and Unwin, London, 1970) pp. 37-38.

[8] Polkinghorne, J. C: *The Quantum World* (Penguin, London, 1986) pp. 6-7.

[9] $\alpha_N = 1/(1 + m/Am_p)$, where m_P is the mass of the proton, m is the mass of the electron and A is the atomic mass number. Then $\alpha_N m$ gives what is termed the *reduced mass* of the electron.

[10] *Op. cit.* reference 1, Chapter 4.

[11] *Op. cit.* reference 7, pp. 42 - 44.

[12] *Op. cit.* reference 8, p. 11.

[13] Eisberg, R. and Resnick, R.: *Quantum Physics of Atoms, Molecules, Solids, Nuclei and Particles* (Wiley, New York, 1985) pp. 85-123.

[14] Christy, R. W. and Pytte, A.: *The Structure of Matter: An Introduction to Modern Physics* (Benjamin, New York, 1965) p. 363.

[15] Although quantum theory appears to defy any sort of commonsense interpretation, physicists claim it is a very successful theory insofar as on a practical level, it makes predictions which agree with observations. Yet it remains true that, as Richard Feynman observed: 'No-one – but *no-one* – understands quantum physics.'

[16] From the Latin: 'appearance' (from *specere* to look); an outward appearance or form. For the Aristotelian physicists of the late Middle Ages, this signified an image or pattern, what German perception psychologists call a *Gestalt*.

[17] See the POAMS website http://www.poams.org which states: 'In place of the 'photon', POAMS proposes the word '*photum*' as signifying a quantum of pure interaction with no suggestion of its having any motion or any other properties of the sort traditionally conceived as 'mechanical'. The quantum interaction between a pair of distance-separated atoms, as POAMS conceives it, is like a collision between two vehicles in accordance with Newton's law of direct and reciprocal action and reaction. To report this collision as an accident involving *three* vehicles, the two vehicles plus

the *accident* itself, is the sort of confusion modern physics creates by talking about quantum *interactions* between particles as if they were also *'particles'* in the same sense.'

[18] David Bohm (1917-1992), an American born quantum physicist, worked closely with Einstein at Princeton University and with Oppenheimer on the Manhattan Project. His use of the phrase 'quantum potential' was part of his holistic approach to physics which is in many ways similar to the approach described in this book.

[19] *Op. cit.* reference 8, pp. 34-36.

[20] Pope, N. V.: 'The Tantalising Two-Slit Experiment' in Duffy, M. C. and Wegner, M. (eds.): *Recent Advances In Relativity Theory, 2, Material Interpretations* (Hadronic Press, USA, 2001).

[21] Pope, N. V: 'A Tale of Two Paradigms', in Pope, N. V., Osborne A. D. and Winfield, A: F. T. (eds.): *Immediate Distant Action and Correlation in Modern Physics: the Balanced Universe* (Edwin Mellen, New York, 2005) pp. 102-103.

[22] Lewis, G. N.: 'Light Waves and Corpuscles', *Nature*, **117** (1926) 256. See also the website www.vivpope.co.uk: *The New Quantum Touching: A Cinematic Model of Instantaneous Action-at-a-Distance* (April 2003).

[23] Pope, N. V and Osborne, A. D.: 'Instantaneous Relativistic Action-at-a-Distance', *Physics Essays*, **5** (1992) pp. 409-421.

[24] These experiments were first conducted in the Naval Academy, USA, in 1879 and again in Cleveland Ohio, USA in 1882. (See Preston, T.: *The Theory of Light*, ed. Joly, C . J. (Macmillan, 1901).) The results have, of course, been confirmed and refined by many other experiments since.

[25] *Op. cit.* reference 1, pp. 10-14.

[26] *Op. cit.* reference 21, pp. 71-73.

[27] Pope, N. V.: *Philosophia Mathematica* II, **4** (1989) pp. 23-28.

[28] Someone is bound to ask what happens when we shine a torch or direct a laser. In essence, this is the same as when we send out any other kind of light-signal. The atoms in the source lose energy to resonant atoms somewhere else. All this happens in statistical amounts of proper time-instantaneous contacts between the atoms concerned in the manner already described. Single atoms, however, cannot shed energy omnidirectionally in the way that macrophysical bodies do. Every quantum of energy emitted by an atom is particular and directional, according to the vector orientation of the atom's internal angular momenta (orbit, spin, *etc.*). Only in normal distributions of statistical numbers of these atoms within a light-source can the energy be shed spherically.

Insofar as those statistical distributions can be manipulated on the macrolevel, those orientations can be aligned in the same way that electron-spins are aligned in a magnet. In a laser, this alignment is achieved by stimulated emission of the atoms of some polarising *e.g.*, crystalline substance, so that the energy emitted by the source is concentrated, or beamed, in the one required direction. In a searchlight all avenues for the statistical emission are blocked by reflecting materials and/or lenses, which beam the emission in much the same concentrated, directional way.

All this is consistent with our Normal Realist view of causality as the function, on the macrophenomenal level, of statistical laws such as the Second Law of Thermodynamics (entropy) which cannot apply to single quantum events.

[29] See, for example, Lawden, D. F.: *Elements of Relativity Theory* (Wiley, 1985) pp. 69-70, 73-79.

[30] *Op. cit.* reference 21, pp. 85-87.

[31] Figures taken from 2002 CODATA available from the Internet.

[32] *Op. cit.* reference 14, pp. 292-297.

[33] This is conventionally called the 'rest mass' of the electron. See, for example, Millikan, R. A.: *The Electron: Its Isolation and Measurement and Determination of Some of its Properties* (Univ. Chicago Press, 1963).

CHAPTER 6

The Pope-Osborne Angular Momentum Synthesis

From our Normal Realist point of view, for the same reason that Einstein's 'light travelling *in vacuo*' is unempirical, so is Newton's *in vacuo* 'force of gravity'.

Our study of general particle motion began, in Chapters 2 and 3 of this book, with uniform relative motion. This is for no other reason than that uniform motion is the simplest type of motion to study. However, in contrast to Newton, we do not believe that all free motion is naturally uniform and so rectilinear but rather that it is naturally curved, or orbital. In this chapter, we investigate the agency whereby the motions of the planets and stars are naturally orbital, the agency which is conventionally explained in terms of 'gravitational forces'. For initial simplicity, throughout this chapter we shall ignore any relativistic effects and assume that the speeds of any objects considered are very much less than c. The relative effects of faster motions will be dealt with later, in Chapter 8. For now we compare and contrast two different ways in which the phenomenon of orbital motion can be explained. First is in classical terms of a balance between centrifugal force and the centripetal 'force of gravity' and, second, in NR terms of pure *angular momentum*. As we shall see, this latter does not require the classical concept of equally opposing and therefore cancelling invisible forces of 'gravitational attraction' and 'centrifugal acceleration'.

6.1 Newton's theory of gravitation

Before the time of Isaac Newton, the observed fact that dropped objects always fall towards the ground could not be explained. Another mystery was the strange influence the Sun seemed to exert on the planets to keep them in their apparently closed orbits. Johannes Kepler (1571-1630), a German mathematician and astronomer, had postulated, on the basis of observations and recordings, that the orbits followed by the planets were ellipses, but he could not explain why. Newton addressed these questions by adding to his three laws outlined in sections 2.1 and 4.5, another law called his Law of Gravitation which postulated an *in vacuo* gravitational force of attraction. This was formulated as follows:

> *Every object attracts every other object with a* **gravitational force**, **f**, *with magnitude*
>
> $$f = \|\mathbf{f}\| = GmM/r^2,$$
>
> *where m and M are the masses of the objects concerned, r is the distance between them and G is a constant, known as the* **gravitational constant**.

The view underlying this assumption was that of the observable universe as a self-sufficient three-dimensional Euclidean space, with time acting as a universal parameter (*i.e.* not observer dependent), together with an invisible *in vacuo* gravitational force which distorted the (assumed) natural straight line paths of objects to form orbital trajectories.

We shall now discuss the classical problem of how the motions of a pair of bodies orbiting each other in an isolated gravitational system are to be calculated. This so-called 'two-body problem' is the only problem concerning orbital motion that is mathematically soluble, because any more than just two bodies poses a problem that is notoriously intractable [1]. First we shall demonstrate how this two-body problem is solved in standard Newtonian dynamics; and then, for comparison, in section 6.3, we demonstrate our alternative, Normal Realist solution to this same problem without involving Newton's postulated *in vacuo* force.

6.1.1 The role of angular momentum

Let us now consider an isolated system consisting of a particle P of mass m under the influence of a body B of mass M, with m very much less than M, as in the case, for example, of the moon orbiting the earth or a planet orbiting the Sun. Let the centre-of-mass of the body B lie at the origin, O, of a set of Cartesian coordinates and let the position vector of the particle P, in relation to O, at any particular time t be $\mathbf{r}(t)$, as in Fig. 6.1 below.

According to Newtonian theory, the particle P is attracted towards the body B by a gravitational force, $\mathbf{f}$, of magnitude GmM/r^2, where $r = \|\mathbf{r}\|$, so that

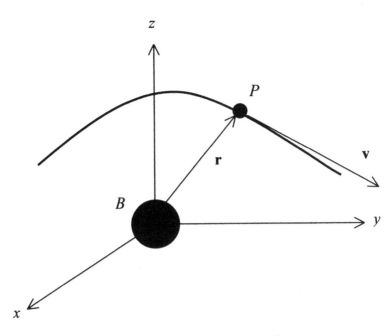

Fig. 6.1: The Two-Body Problem

by Newton's Second Law, the acceleration, $\mathbf{a}(t)$, of P, at any instant of time t, is

$$\mathbf{a}(t) = \frac{d^2\mathbf{r}}{dt^2} = -\frac{GM}{r^2}\mathbf{n}, \qquad (6.1)$$

where $\mathbf{n}$ is a vector of unit length in the direction of $\mathbf{r}$. Equation (6.1) provides an *equation of motion*, since it determines the possible paths of P relative to B. Note that from (6.1), $\mathbf{a}$ is parallel to $\mathbf{r}$. Here, the gravitational force is a particular example of a *central force*. Such a force always acts in the direction opposite to that of the position vector.

The concept of angular momentum plays a central role in the study of orbital motion. The angular momentum, $\mathbf{L}$, of the particle P relative to the chosen origin, O, is defined by

$$\mathbf{L} = \mathbf{r} \times m\mathbf{v} = \mathbf{r} \times \mathbf{p}, \qquad (6.2)$$

where $\mathbf{v} = d\mathbf{r}/dt$ is the velocity of P, which always lies tangentially to the path of P (as indicated in Fig. 6.1) [2], $\mathbf{p}$ is the (linear) momentum of P and '$\times$' denotes the vector product. It follows that the angular momentum of P is a vector that lies perpendicular to the plane containing **r** and **v**, and so gives information about the orientation of the path of *P* relative to the origin. Its magnitude is given by

$$L = \|\mathbf{L}\| = mvr\sin\varphi,$$

where $v = \|\mathbf{v}\|$ is the speed of *P* and φ is the angle between **r** and **v**.

Now in general, it follows by (6.2) and Newton's Second Law that

$$\frac{d\mathbf{L}}{dt} = \frac{d\mathbf{r}}{dt}\times m\mathbf{v} + \mathbf{r}\times m\frac{d\mathbf{v}}{dt} = \mathbf{v}\times m\mathbf{v} + \mathbf{r}\times m\mathbf{a} = \mathbf{r}\times\mathbf{f}, \tag{6.3}$$

where **f** is the force exerted on *P*. Here, $\mathbf{r}\times\mathbf{f}$ is the *torque* acting on the particle [3]. In the two-body case, the gravitational force **f** is parallel to **r**, so that

$$\frac{d\mathbf{L}}{dt} = \mathbf{0}$$

and hence **L** is a constant vector. It then follows that the trajectory of *P* relative to *B* lies in a plane and that *L* is constant.

Since the orbit of the particle *P* lies in a plane, it is convenient to describe it using plane polar coordinates *r* and θ, where $r = \|\mathbf{r}\|$ as before and θ is the angle between the radial vector **r** and some fixed radial axis [4]. The *angular speed* of *P* is then defined as $d\theta/dt$ and denoted by ω. Relative to plane polar coordinates, the position vector, **r**, of *P* is given by

$$\mathbf{r} = (x, y, z) = (r\cos\theta, r\sin\theta, 0) = r\mathbf{n},$$

where **n** is a vector of unit length in the direction of **r**, so that $\mathbf{n} = (\cos\theta, \sin\theta, 0)$. It follows that *P*'s velocity, **v**, is

$$\mathbf{v} = \frac{d\mathbf{r}}{dt} = \frac{dr}{dt}\mathbf{n} + r(-\sin\theta, \cos\theta, 0)\frac{d\theta}{dt} = \frac{dr}{dt}\mathbf{n} + r\omega\mathbf{m}, \tag{6.4}$$

where $\mathbf{m} = (-\sin\theta, \cos\theta, 0)$, another vector of unit length. The (orbital) speed, *v*, of *P* relative to *B* is then given by

$$v^2 = \mathbf{v}.\mathbf{v} = \left(\frac{dr}{dt}\right)^2\mathbf{n}.\mathbf{n} + 2r\omega\frac{dr}{dt}\mathbf{n}.\mathbf{m} + r^2\omega^2\mathbf{m}.\mathbf{m} = \left(\frac{dr}{dt}\right)^2 + r^2\omega^2. \tag{6.5}$$

Equation (6.4) also tells us that the acceleration, $\mathbf{a} = d\mathbf{v}/dt$, of *P* is

$$\mathbf{a} = \frac{d^2r}{dt^2}\mathbf{n} + \frac{dr}{dt}(-\sin\theta, \cos\theta, 0)\frac{d\theta}{dt} + \left(\frac{dr}{dt}\omega + r\frac{d\omega}{dt}\right)\mathbf{m} + r\omega(-\cos\theta, -\sin\theta, 0)\frac{d\theta}{dt}$$

$$\Rightarrow \mathbf{a} = \left(\frac{d^2r}{dt^2} - r\omega^2\right)\mathbf{n} + \left(2\frac{dr}{dt}\omega + r\frac{d\omega}{dt}\right)\mathbf{m}. \tag{6.6}$$

Finally, using (6.4), the angular momentum of P, in terms of polar coordinates, is given by

$$\mathbf{L} = r\mathbf{n} \times m(\frac{dr}{dt}\mathbf{n} + r\omega\mathbf{m}) = mr^2\omega(\mathbf{n} \times \mathbf{m}) = mr^2\,\omega(0, 0, 1),$$

so that its magnitude is

$$L = mr^2\omega. \tag{6.7}$$

Since L is a constant, $r^2\omega$ is a constant and so we have $2r\omega dr/dt + r^2 d\omega/dt = 0$. Then equation (6.6) reads,

$$\mathbf{a} = \left(\frac{d^2r}{dt^2} - r\omega^2\right)\mathbf{n}. \tag{6.8}$$

It is important to realise here that the results (6.4), (6.5), (6.7) and (6.8) *do not depend explicitly on the existence of an inverse square force of attraction* and are therefore independent of Newton's Law of Gravitation (6.1). These results follow whenever the angular momentum is constant, so that the orbit of the particle P lies in a plane.

6.1.2 The role of Newton's gravitational force

Returning now to Newton's postulate that there is a gravitational force of attraction from the particle P towards the body B and that (6.1) holds, it follows by comparing (6.8) with (6.1) and using (6.7), that

$$\frac{d^2r}{dt^2} - \frac{L^2}{m^2r^3} = -\frac{GM}{r^2}. \tag{6.9}$$

Once (6.9) is solved for $r(t)$, $\theta(t)$ may be determined from (6.7), i.e.,

$$\frac{d\theta}{dt} = -\frac{L}{mr^2},$$

so that P's trajectory about B may be found in the form $\mathbf{r}(t) = (r(t), \theta(t))$. Using (6.9) together with (6.7) we see that closed orbits of P about B are possible and that these closed orbits are ellipses [5]. We show this explicitly in the third section of this chapter. Notice that if the particle P has zero angular momentum, so that $L = 0$ in (6.9), then (6.9) reduces to

$$\frac{\mathrm{d}^2 r}{\mathrm{d}t^2} = -\frac{GM}{r^2},$$

which is the Newtonian equation for 'radial free-fall'. Note that it follows from (6.7) that in this case, $\omega = 0$, so that θ is a constant. Hence, in the ideal case of P and B being both non-rotating, the particle P falls towards the body B along a path which is rectilinear in the common, relatively stationary, reference frame of the two objects. This is what we would expect, since it is only its angular momentum that keeps P in orbit about B.

6.1.3 Conservation of angular momentum

We have seen that in the case of the two-body problem, the angular momentum of P is conserved. Although the multi-body problem is notoriously intractable, in the sense of determining equations of orbits, it is a simple matter to demonstrate that angular momentum is conserved under certain conditions. Consider an *isolated* system of n particles, *i.e.*, not subjected to any external influences. In order to constitute a system, the particles must interact in some way and in Newtonian theory all interactions are forces of some kind [6]. It follows by Newton's Third Law (of action and reaction) that if all the forces are central, *i.e.*, act along the line joining pairs of particles, then the angular momentum of the system is always conserved [6][7]. This may be demonstrated as follows.

Let the angular momenta of the n particles be calculated relative to some arbitrary origin. Let the position vector of the ith particle relative to this origin be $\mathbf{r}_i$, its (linear) momentum $\mathbf{p}_i$ and its angular momentum $\mathbf{L}_i$. Let the total angular momentum of the system be denoted by $\mathbf{L}$, the total force exerted on the ith particle be $\mathbf{f}_i$, and let $\mathbf{f}_{ij}$ be the force exerted on the ith particle by the jth. It follows by Newton's Third Law that $\mathbf{f}_{ji} = -\mathbf{f}_{ij}$. Then by definition and (6.3),

$$\frac{d\mathbf{L}}{dt} = \sum_i \frac{d\mathbf{L}_i}{dt} = \sum_i \mathbf{r}_i \times \mathbf{f}_i = \sum_i \mathbf{r}_i \times \left(\sum_{j \neq i} \mathbf{f}_{ij} \right) = \sum_i \sum_{j > i} \left(\mathbf{r}_i - \mathbf{r}_j \right) \times \mathbf{f}_{ij} = \mathbf{0},$$

since $\mathbf{f}_{ij}$ is parallel to $\mathbf{r}_i - \mathbf{r}_j$. Hence, $\mathbf{L}$ is constant, as required.

It is this constancy of angular momentum in general which provides one of the foundations of our angular momentum synthesis, presented in the next section.

6.2 The Pope-Osborne Angular Momentum Synthesis

Our general programme of Normal Realism for physics is to discern the best and most efficient way of interpreting observation with the least amount of theoretical elaboration. This minimalist approach makes much use of the method known as 'Ockham's Razor' for economising on unnecessary hypotheses. An example of such an unnecessary hypothesis, in our view, is Newton's idea of an invisible *in vacuo* 'gravitational force'.

When examined carefully, although it works well enough on a practical level and is able to produce, amongst other things, Kepler's laws, which are in agreement with observational evidence, Newton's theory of gravitation depends on the existence of an invisible force which can never be directly observed and is therefore unempirical. This is in much the same way as the classical wave theory of light depended on an undetectable luminiferous ether. According to Newton's First Law, all natural or free motion, *i.e.*, motion not subject to any kind of force, is rectilinear. However, such rectilinear motion is never observable in practice. All free motion we observe, from satellites to galaxies, is curved. Even apparently rectilinear motion on Earth is curved over a large enough distance, due to the shape of the planet. Newton therefore had to invent the idea of an *in vacuo* gravitational force of attraction to explain why all observable natural motion is curved and not rectilinear.

It is well known that one of the first to criticize Newton's theory of gravitation was his contemporary, the Irish philosopher and cleric, George

Berkeley. Berkeley argued that to make the vacuum a conductor of theoretical 'forces' of any kind was nonsense, and he went so far as to hint that perhaps what was involved might be some direct influence of a universal, *holistic* kind. Mach developed this argument and formulated his well-known principle, which, in essence, stated that the influence of distant matter in the observable universe may account not only for gravitational effects, but also for the local phenomena of inertia and momentum.

In our approach, Newton's manufactured and artificial *in vacuo* 'force of gravity' is eliminated by simply stating that any continuous free or natural (inertial) motion is always orbital in the way that the eminent empiricist, Aristotle, observed [8]. Here, the *natural* path of any particle is to be thought of as the path it describes when all restrictions on its motion are removed, that is, when the particle moves freely under the influence of nothing but its own angular momentum. The only 'unnatural' paths, in that sense, are those of bodies whose freedom to orbit as they otherwise should is constrained, such as when a body is in contact with the surface of a planet, or when an artificial satellite is accelerated by a booster rocket. In other words, for inertial or 'force-free' motion, all bodies seek to move, if allowed, in *orbits* with respect to one another, that is, in trajectories of the sort that we observe in astronomical space. So, in the same way that Normal Realism dispenses with any 'speed' interpretation of the constant c, it also dispenses with the interpretation of 'gravity' as a hidden *in vacuo* mechanism.

Since we claim that we do not require any 'gravitational forces' to explain how it is that freely moving bodies in the observable universe, such as stars and their planets, move in the way they do, the onus falls on us to describe what agency we propose as an alternative. Newton's mechanistic philosophy prevented him from seriously contemplating any holistic or non-local approach to gravitational interaction, of the sort envisaged by Berkeley. By contrast, in keeping with our underlying Normal Realist philosophy, our approach, following Berkeley and Mach, begins with the premise that the observable universe is in an *holistic* balance. Such a balance can be maintained only if the motion of each body in the system is *instantly* correlated with that of each and every other, in conformity with the various holistic conservation laws. Such unmediated instantaneous correlation-at-a-distance is supported by empirical evidence throughout the observable universe. We therefore concur with Phipps [9], Graneau [10] and Assis [11] in emphasising an urgent need to rethink our ideas of space, time and motion along more holistic lines.

Accordingly, in our approach, we choose holistic conservation of angular momentum as the agency whereby all natural force-free motions are instantaneously correlated. Angular momentum is clearly the measure to use in orbital motion, since it contains observational information about the fundamental empirical measures of spatial relations, mass, length and time as well as orientation. In addition, if we treat the observable universe as an isolated system, then, as shown in the last section, Newtonian theory tells us that angular momentum is holistically conserved. Then the Pope-Osborne Angular Momentum Synthesis agrees with both Newtonian theory and the Copenhagen interpretation of Quantum Mechanics (see section 3.5) insofar as in both these theories, angular momentum is instantaneously conserved.

The arguments for and against taking holistic angular momentum conservation specifically as the instantaneously correlating mechanism are well documented in some recent publications [12]. The other prime candidate that has been proposed for the instantaneously correlating agency is holistic conservation of energy. However, angular momentum provides more information than energy, being a vector rather than a scalar quantity. Moreover, conservation of angular momentum and conservation of kinetic energy do not imply each other. For example, in an elliptical natural orbit of constant angular momentum, the kinetic energy of the orbiting particle varies, hence is not conserved in the way that angular momentum is, and if the kinetic energy is conserved, then the angular momentum is not.

6.2.1 Felt and seen distant actions

Let us now consider the notion of inertia. This, according to Mach, is a *felt* connection. As he is reputed to have said, 'When the subway train jerks it is the fixed stars that throw you down' [13]. Changes in angular momentum imply, of course, changes in angular *inertia*. For this reason, these angular momentum connections may be described as *felt* connections [14]. However, just as in the case of any *seen* connection, we have to square the fact that these immediately felt (for example, visceral or sensational) connections are manifest to us instantly with the fact that in observational space their sources are separated from us by the distance-time c.

Now a space traveller orbiting freely around the earth does not feel the presence of the earth or the other bodies in and beyond the solar system whose existence and movements, in the angular momentum nexus as a whole, define his orbital trajectory. It is only when he either brakes or accelerates that he is immediately aware, by the sensations which he feels as soon as he takes the action, that the previous correlation between the motion of his own body and those other bodies has changed. This, of course, is what is commonly called 'inertia', except that this inertial trajectory is no longer rectilinear, as in Newtonian theory, but curvilinear, as befits its participation in an angular momentum system.

However, while the correlation between the space-traveller's motion-changing action and its accompanying visceral sensation are instantaneous and while his angular momentum connections with those bodies are also instantaneous (*i.e.*, proper time-instantaneous in both cases), any detectable distant reciprocal reaction will not be seen until the lapse of time s/c, as shown in Fig. 5.1 of the previous chapter.

According to our angular momentum synthesis then, these immediately felt connections, like the seen connections, are *proper time* instantaneous, although not *observationally* instantaneous, for those reasons described in Chapters 3 and 5. In other words, the felt and the seen are, unproblematically, all part of the same basic quantum-informational manifold [14]. So there is no 'EPR Paradox' associated with these instantaneously felt connections any more than there is with the seen. They are both manifestations of *action*, in ultimate units of Planck's action constant h, where action (the disembodied transfer quantity which is the product of energy and time) is 2π times the embodied angular momentum.

Now it should be noted that according to the Normal Realist philosophy, it is pointless trying to find some 'mechanical-causal' reason for *how* a change in angular momentum in one orbit-system produces a change in angular momentum in some other system somewhere else. This is like trying to find 'mechanical-causal' reasons for the fact that in thermal motion, the energies of the particles distribute themselves inexorably in the direction of maximum entropy applied to the system as a whole. So far as NR is concerned, all of physics is based, not on classical mechanical-causal determinism among the particles but on fundamental indeterminacy, governed by purely statistical laws like that of the Second Law of Thermodynamics, applied to the whole,

6.2.2 The postulates of POAMS

The fundamental postulates underlying the Pope-Osborne Angular Momentum Synthesis, known by the acronym POAMS [15], can thus be summarised as follows.

Postulate 1: *Natural (inertial) motion is always orbital, the natural path of any particle being the trajectory followed by the particle when it moves freely under the influence of nothing but its own angular momentum (angular inertia).*

Postulate 2: *Angular momentum (angular inertia) is holistically conserved.*

These postulates are combined in the following principle:

The Principle of Angular Inertia: *All bodies move angular-inertially. Angular inertia is the resistance of a body to any change in its angular momentum relations with other bodies and is the natural tendency of a body to follow the path of least resistance (i.e. least action) in accordance with the conservation of angular momentum.*

Our holistic approach to the agency behind the phenomenon of 'gravitation' was first proposed in a 1995 *Physics Essays* paper [16], and further developed in later papers and books [17][18]. Our approach takes the 'force of gravitation' out of metaphysical inscrutability and puts it where it truly belongs – that is, in actual physical reality – as the felt and measurable force required to *prevent* bodies from travelling in their otherwise naturally force-free (angular-inertial) orbits. The POAMS premise is that it is angular momentum which keeps bodies apart, and if angular momentum vanishes, then bodies automatically fall together in what orthodox astrophysics and cosmology describe as 'gravitational collapse'. In an angular momentum collapse there is no question of any 'vacuum forces' having anything to do with it.

One of the implications of POAMS is that all talk of 'attraction' and 'repulsion' between freely moving particles becomes redundant. There are only *degrees* of *relative* 'attraction' and 'repulsion' in the sense that a particle P_1 orbiting a body B at a mean radius r_1 can be considered more 'attracted' to B than a particle P_2 orbiting B at a mean radius r_2, if $r_1 < r_2$.

It is important to realise that, in complete contrast to Newtonian theory, POAMS makes no distinction between the observable universe on the macro- and micro-levels. Moreover, whereas Newtonian theory postulates an underlying continuum, in POAMS, as proposed in the previous chapter, the structure of the 'universe' at the microphysical level is ultimately discrete, with angular momentum quantised in discrete units of $h/2\pi$. As Peter Rowlands [12] points out, at this level, conservation of angular momentum implies that the three charges responsible for the electromagnetic, strong and weak interactions are separately conserved, so that what is customarily called 'charge' is essentially a representation of angular momentum. This idea is fully explored in the next chapter, where it is also indicated that applying POAMS at the quantum level and incorporating effects of *spin* may lead to the possible redundancy of the traditional 'field forces' not only of Newton, but also of Faraday and Maxwell. Energy may be regarded as a component of angular momentum at the quantum level, but not *vice-versa* and this is another reason why POAMS considers conservation of angular momentum more fundamental than conservation of energy.

Of course, POAMS is not the only approach to orbital motion which dispenses with *in vacuo* forces. Another, more well-known such theory is General Relativity (GR), which describes space-time by means of a mathematical model known as the Riemannian manifold. In GR, it is postulated that naturally orbiting bodies move in the way that they do, not because of the existence of *in vacuo* forces, but because they follow the geodesics, *i.e.* the curves of 'optimal length', in an underlying space-time continuum [19]. In other words, the agency for orbital motion in GR is the 'curvature of the space-time manifold'. It must be remembered here however, that this manifold is no more than a convenient mathematical structure and is not intended to be a model of actual physical reality. A global space-time continuum which predicts properties of the observable universe as a whole, *i.e.*, cosmological properties, can be contemplated in GR, and this represents a type of holism. But there is certainly no instantaneous unmediated correlation-at-a-distance in GR, which is bound by Special Relativity, according to which all physical interaction and information are delayed due to the universal 'speed limit' *c*. Moreover, no ultimate discreteness of the sort that POAMS embraces is contemplated in GR.

It must be emphasised here that POAMS is essentially a *synthesis* of apparently disparate physical theories. We must stress, once again, that it is not a new *theory* intended to replace, for example, Newtonian dynamics, Special and General Relativity or Quantum Mechanics [20]. Indeed, POAMS ultimately seeks to modify these theories to an extent that is no more than necessary to remove the logical contradictions between them and allow them to fit naturally together. In this way, whilst retaining some of the mathematical elements of existing theories, it dispenses with other elements regarded as unnecessary and, in some cases, provides a very different interpretation that is logically coherent and consistent with the Normal Realist philosophy.

Of course, the mere fact that angular momentum is universally conserved cannot be expected to supply, in itself, the reason why bodies move in the way they do. For instance, no conservation principle automatically provides an equation of motion. On the other hand, equations of motion can provide conservation. For example, as shown in subsection 6.1.3, in Newtonian gravitation, the existence of centrally directed forces in any isolated system ensures conservation of angular momentum. These forces do not have to be of an inverse-square kind, so Newton's inverse square law is not a consequence of conservation of angular momentum. However, supposing only that angular momentum is conserved provides more flexibility and produces not only the Newtonian field equations as a special case, as demonstrated in the next section, but also, by incorporating relativistic effects, provides General Relativistic equations of motion, as will be shown in Chapter 8.

We turn now, in POAMS, to the treatment of *constrained* (which we have called 'unnatural') trajectories. Such trajectories represent a state of motion in which a body is held, by a *real* measurable force, against its natural tendency to orbit freely. Had he been more of an empiricist, Newton might have based his formalism on the empirical fact that there are no forces manifest in natural orbital motion. His single gravitational assumption could then have been expressed as:

All bodies in natural force-free motion tend to orbit one another with constant angular momentum, such that the magnitude of the force required to remove any one of those bodies from that orbit is directly proportional to the product of the masses of the two bodies and inversely proportional to the square of the distance between them.

In this alternative interpretation, the true (*i.e.*, measurable) force is not concealed in the natural orbit of the body, but is *revealed* in the difference between that natural orbit and a constrained one. In effect, Newton's Second Law, which defines force as the rate of linear momentum, is replaced, here, by *torque*, defined as the rate of change of angular momentum. For example, in our approach, the weight with which a body presses on the surface of the earth is not the result of some unseen and mysterious 'pull of gravity'. It is because the body, where it stands on the rotating earth, has insufficient angular momentum to orbit freely (weightlessly), so that with the angular momentum it has, the force it exerts on a weighing scale is that of the reaction of the earth's surface preventing it from orbiting where it should, much closer to the earth's centre.

The central ideas of POAMS discussed in this section are made explicit in our alternative treatment of the two-body problem. This is in a way which does not involve Newton's *in vacuo* 'gravitational force' postulate, as may be seen in the following section.

6.3 The POAMS approach to the two-body problem

In this section, we return to the two-body problem consisting of a particle P of mass m orbiting a body B of mass M, with m very much less than M, but this time from the point of view of POAMS. All bodies in motion can be considered as part of such a paired system. Our approach is to use a combination of angular momentum conservation and empirical evidence to obtain the Newtonian equation of motion without any need for an *in vacuo* gravitational force. In this chapter, we shall assume that P and B either do not spin or that they spin very slowly, so that there is a negligible contribution from the spin angular momenta of P and B. The full incorporation of spin will be discussed in the following chapter. We shall also assume that the system is isolated, *i.e.* not subjected to any external effects. It then follows by Postulate 2 of POAMS that the angular momentum of P relative to B is always constant.

Since the angular momentum, $\mathbf{L}$, of P is constant in time, it follows, as in the first section, that the orbit of P lies in a plane and that $L = \|\mathbf{L}\|$ is a constant. Also, since $d\mathbf{L}/dt = \mathbf{0}$, it follows from (6.2) that

$$d\mathbf{L}/dt = d\mathbf{r}/dt \times m\mathbf{v} + \mathbf{r} \times m d\mathbf{v}/dt = \mathbf{v} \times m\mathbf{v} + \mathbf{r} \times m\mathbf{a} = \mathbf{0}$$

$$\Rightarrow \mathbf{r} \times m\mathbf{a} = \mathbf{0},$$

where $\mathbf{r}$ is the position vector of P, $\mathbf{v}$ is P's velocity and $\mathbf{a}$ is P's acceleration relative to O, the centre-of-mass of B. Note that $\mathbf{v}$ cannot be a constant in orbital motion (otherwise, the path of P would be rectilinear), so that $\mathbf{a} \neq \mathbf{0}$. Then, since $m \neq 0$, $\mathbf{r} \neq \mathbf{0}$ (otherwise P would be coincident with B) and $\mathbf{a} \neq \mathbf{0}$, the above result implies that $\mathbf{a}$ must be parallel to $\mathbf{r}$ and so, clearly, the acceleration of P is directed towards O.

Since the orbit of the particle P lies in a plane, we may employ plane polar coordinates, r and θ, to describe the orbit, whence (6.8) holds for the acceleration of P. (Recall that equation (6.8) depends only on the fact that the orbit of P lies in a plane.) It also follows, as previously, that the magnitude of P's angular momentum is given by (6.7), so that $r^2\omega$, i.e., $r^2 d\theta/dt$ is a constant [21].

In general, in order to determine all possible closed orbits of P about B, we require, of course, an equation of motion. Since the acceleration of P is directed towards B, this must take the form

$$\mathbf{a} = -h(r, \theta)\mathbf{n},$$

for some function $h(r, \theta)$, where $\mathbf{n}$ is a vector of unit length in the direction of $\mathbf{r}$, i.e., $\mathbf{n} = \mathbf{r}/r$. Equation (6.8) then provides our general equation of motion. However, there are two main reasons why we discount the case in which h is an explicit function of θ. Firstly, the angle θ is, in a sense, arbitrary on P's trajectory, since it is measured from an arbitrary radial line. Hence, it does not make physical sense for the acceleration $\mathbf{a}$ to depend on θ. Secondly, we wish equation (6.8) to provide circular orbits as a special case. For the circle of radius k, i.e., the circle with equation $r = k$, to be a solution of (6.8) it has to be that

$$\frac{L^2}{m^2 k^3} = h(k,\theta),$$

so that h cannot depend explicitly on θ.

It follows that POAMS' most general equation of a motion of P about B is

$$\frac{d^2 r}{dt^2} - \frac{L^2}{m^2 r^3} = -h(r), \tag{6.10}$$

for some function $h(r)$, which, of course, provides the Newtonian equation (6.9) as a special case. It is easily checked that the first integral of (6.10) is

$$\left(\frac{dr}{dt}\right)^2 + \frac{L^2}{m^2 r^2} = 2H(r) + C,\tag{6.11}$$

where $dH/dr = -h(r)$ and C is a constant. Note that from (6.5) and (6.7), the kinetic energy, K, of P is

$$K = \frac{1}{2}mv^2 = \frac{1}{2}m\left(\left(\frac{dr}{dt}\right)^2 + \frac{L^2}{m^2 r^2}\right),$$

so that (6.11) reads

$$K = mH(r) + \frac{Cm}{2}.$$

It then follows, by the conservation of energy (see section 4.6), that the potential energy of the orbit is $-mH(r)$ [22] and the total energy $E = Cm/2$ is a constant. For the moment, we shall ignore the special case of 'radial free-fall' for which, as we have seen, $L = 0$ and θ is a constant. Then multiplying (6.11) by $(1/\omega)^2 = (dt/d\theta)^2$, using the chain rule and (6.7) gives

$$\left(\frac{dr}{d\theta}\right)^2 + r^2 = \frac{2m^2}{L^2}H(r)r^4 + \frac{2Em}{L^2}r^4.$$

Finally, it is more convenient to work in terms of $u = 1/r$, so that $dr/d\theta = (-1/u^2)du/d\theta$. Making this substitution, and letting $\beta = L/m$ together with $k = 2Em/L^2$, gives

$$\left(\frac{du}{d\theta}\right)^2 + u^2 = \frac{2}{\beta^2}H(u) + k.\tag{6.12}$$

In theory, given $H(u)$, this equation may be solved to provide the equation of P's trajectory relative to B in the form $u = u(\theta)$.

In general, POAMS does not require that all orbits of P given by (6.12) have to be closed. In fact, it will be shown in Chapter 8 that when time-dilation effects have been taken into account it is confirmed that the orbit of P about B is not necessarily closed. However, for now, we wish to compare POAMS with Newtonian theory and so require that (6.12) provides *closed* orbits which are *ellipses*, so as to agree with the approximate empirical evidence. It can be seen from a table of standard integrals that if $h(r) = ar^n$, where α is a constant and n is an integer, then $u(\theta)$, given by (6.12), is expressible in terms of a trigonometric function and so may provide a closed orbit only if $n = 1, -2$ or -3 [23]. If $n = -3$, then $H(u) = \alpha u^2/2$ in (6.12) and it is easily checked that the general solution to (6.12), in this case, is

$$u(\theta) = 1/r(\theta) = a\sin \lambda(\theta - \theta_0),$$

where θ_0 is a constant, $\lambda^2 = 1 - \alpha/\beta^2$ and $a^2 = k/\lambda^2$. This equation does not represent a closed curve since as $\theta \to \theta_0$, $r \to \infty$. Hence, this case can be eliminated.

If $n = 1$, then $H(u) = -\alpha/2u^2$ in (6.12) and the general solution to (6.12) in this case can be verified to be

$$u^2(\theta) = 1/r^2(\theta) = k/2 + A \sin 2(\theta - \theta_0),$$

where θ_0 is a constant and $A^2 = k^2/4 - \alpha/\beta^2$. It is easily seen that, for certain values of the constants, this equation represents a closed curve that is ellipse-like in character in the sense that it is symmetrical about a major and a minor axis, but it does *not* represent an ellipse. Note that in this case, since $h(r) = \alpha r$, it follows that $\|\mathbf{a}\| = \alpha r$, so that $\|\mathbf{a}\|$ takes its maximum value at the point on the orbit of P *farthest* from O, which makes no physical sense and does not agree with empirical evidence. Therefore, this case may also be eliminated.

The only case that remains is then $n = -2$, *i.e.*, $h(r) = \alpha/r^2$. In this case, $H(u) = \alpha u$ in (6.12) and the solution is

$$u = \frac{1}{r} = \frac{\alpha}{\beta^2} (1 + e\cos(\theta - \theta_0)),$$

where θ_0 and e are constants, with $e^2 = 1 + k\beta^4/\alpha^2$. This is the equation of a conic section and represents an ellipse if $e < 1$, a parabola if $e = 1$ and a hyperbola if $e > 1$. A closed orbit of P around B is therefore possible, in the form of an ellipse, but only if $e < 1$, in which case, the total energy $E < 0$. The special case of a circle is obtained only when $e = 0$. Hence, altogether, if $h(r) = \alpha r^n$, then (6.12) provides closed orbits when and only when $h(r) = ar$ or $h(r) = a/r^2$. This result is a special case of Bertrand's theorem [24], which states that if we require (6.12) to include *closed* orbits then $h(r)$ must take one of these two forms. Recall that the former case has been discounted.

In summary, then, bearing in mind the Normal Realist basis of POAMS, if *closed* orbits are required, then the only remaining choice for $h(r)$ that agrees with observational and empirical evidence is $h(r) = a/r^2$. Consequently, in POAMS the equation of motion for P in a closed orbit about B is

$$\frac{d^2r}{dt^2} - \frac{L^2}{m^2r^3} = -\frac{\alpha}{r^2},$$

(6.13)

which, as in the Newtonian case, is to be used in conjunction with (6.7). This includes the special case of 'radial free-fall' when $L = 0$ so that θ is a constant. Since we wish to compare (6.13) with the corresponding Newtonian equation of motion, (6.9), we shall re-label α as GM, where G is simply a new constant, introduced for the sake of convenience. Then (6.13) is exactly equation (6.9) and the standard results of Newtonian theory follow. However, it is important to note that (6.9) has now been derived with no reference to arguments involving *in vacuo* forces. This is in radical contrast to Newtonian theory in which (6.9) is derived by equating the centrifugal force, $m\mathbf{a}$, on P with the artificially introduced 'gravitational force' $-(GmM/r^2)\mathbf{n}$ induced on P by B.

The simplest closed orbits provided by (6.9) are, of course, *circles*, when r is constant. In this case, (6.9) gives $L^2 = GMm^2r$. Also in this case, (6.5) gives $v = r\omega$, so that (6.7) then gives

$$L = mvr.$$

(6.14)

It then follows by (6.9) that natural circular orbits satisfy

$$v^2 = \frac{GM}{r}.$$

(6.15)

Note that there is only *one* such natural *circular* orbit for any given radius.

Recall that, according to the POAMS thesis, the true (*i.e.* measurable) force on the particle P is not concealed in its natural orbit but is revealed in the difference between that natural orbit and an 'unnatural' one, that is, some state of motion in which the particle is held by a *measurable* force, of magnitude F. Specifically, let us consider a closed orbit of P about B which is constrained in some way, but for which angular momentum is constant. In this case, P's equation of motion necessarily takes the form (6.13). (Of course, in general, a particle P may be artificially made to follow any 'unnatural' orbit about B and so may not have an equation of motion of the form (6.13).) In general, then, we may let $\alpha = G'M$ where G' is a constant with the same dimensions as the Newtonian gravitational constant G but equal to G only in any natural (unconstrained) orbit of P. Then the measurable 'gravitational' force on P in any constrained orbit (in the sense just described) has magnitude, F, given by

$$F = \left| G - G' \right| mM/r^2. \tag{6.16}$$

Otherwise, in a natural 'force-free' orbit we have $G' = G$ and $F = 0$.

We now demonstrate how this approach works in practice. For a particular constrained orbit of P of the type just described, the parameters $r(t)$ and $\omega(t)$ are known observational measures. Since from (6.13) and (6.7) we have, in this case

$$\frac{d^2 r}{dt^2} - r\omega^2 = -\frac{G'M}{r^2}$$

where the mass M of body B is known, the constant G' for this orbit can be calculated. The magnitude F of the measurable force exerted on P in its constrained orbit is then given by (6.16). In the context of the sorts of constrained orbits we have been considering, the obvious and most useful case to consider is the case in which P is fixed to the surface of a rotating body B, such as the earth, and so 'orbits' the centre-of-mass, O, of B, where the mass M of B is considered to be concentrated at O. In this case, P's constrained orbit is a circle with centre O. It follows from (6.15) that in this special case

$$G' = rv^2/M, \tag{6.17}$$

where v is the 'orbital' speed of P in its constrained circle of radius r.

In general, if P orbits B in a constrained orbit for which L is constant, then since $r(t)$ and $\omega(t)$ are known, L may be calculated from (6.7). This makes it possible to calculate any natural orbit of P, with the same magnitude of angular momentum L, where the orbit of P is not constrained. Let the particle P, in any natural force-free orbit, with magnitude of angular momentum L, have angular speed $\omega_0(t)$ and radial coordinate $r_0(t)$. Then by (6.9),

$$\frac{d^2 r_0}{dt^2} - \frac{L^2}{m^2 r_0^3} = -\frac{GM}{r_0^2}.$$

Knowing L, G, M and m, this is a second order differential equation for $r_0(t)$, and, with a given set of initial conditions, can be solved to give $r_0(t)$. Then $\omega_0(t)$ may be calculated from (6.7), *i.e.*

$$\omega_0(t) = \frac{L}{m r_0^2(t)}.$$

Notice that any natural orbit of P is not unique, since it depends on a given set of initial conditions. However, given a constrained orbit of P with constant magnitude of angular momentum L, there is a unique *circular* natural orbit for P, with the same constant magnitude of angular momentum, with parameters r_0 and v_0, where v_0 is the orbital speed of P. So it follows by (6.14) and (6.15) that

$$v_0 = \frac{GmM}{L} \tag{6.18}$$

and

$$r_0 = \frac{L}{mv_0}. \tag{6.19}$$

EXAMPLE 6.1

Consider a particle P of mass 1 kg, say, situated somewhere on the earth's equator. The speed of the mass in this constrained circular orbit about the earth's centre, is the rotational speed of the earth, namely $v \approx 464.74$ m s^{-1}. The radius of this orbit is the earth's mean equatorial radius, given by $r \approx 6.372828 \times 10^6$ m. For this constrained circular orbit, G' is given by (6.17) where M is the mass of the earth. Notice that this is not exactly the usual figure quoted for M in Newtonian dynamics since in POAMS, according to (6.16),

$$M(G - G')/r^2 = g,$$

where g is the usual acceleration due to the earth's 'gravitational pull'. Hence, by (6.17),

$$gr^2 = M(G - G') = MG - rv^2 \Rightarrow M = r(rg + v^2)/G,$$

where $g \approx 9.81\text{m s}^{-2}$ and $G \approx 6.67259 \times 10^{-11}\,\text{N m}^2\,\text{kg}^{-2}$ [25]. Thus $M \approx 5.989 \times 10^{24}$ kg. It then follows by (6.17) that

$$G' \approx 2.298254 \times 10^{-13}\,\text{N m}^2\,\text{kg}^{-2}.$$

Note that this figure is independent of the mass of P. Since $G' \neq G$, the body P is *not* in a natural orbit about the earth's centre. It follows by (6.16) that the magnitude of the real, measurable force on P at the earth's equator is,

$$F = M(G - G')/r^2 \approx 9.81\ \text{N}.$$

This is the magnitude of the force with which a 1 kg mass presses on the earth's surface which prevents it from taking up its natural, force-free circular orbit. It is this *real* force that produces 1 kg weight on a weighing-scale. In general, if the mass of P is m kg, then it follows by (6.16) that $F = 9.81m$ N.

Since the motion of P in its constrained orbit is circular, the magnitude of its orbital angular momentum, L, is given by (6.14), so that

$$L \approx 2.961708 \times 10^9\ \text{kg m}^2\ \text{s}^{-1}.$$

With this relatively small amount of angular momentum, if we imagine the earth's radius shrunk to the size of a super-dense billiard ball, the natural orbital speed, v_0, of that kilogram mass, assuming its natural orbit to be circular around the earth's mass, is given by (6.18), so that $v_0 \approx 1.349294 \times 10^5\ \text{m s}^{-1}$. The radius, r_0, of this natural orbit is then given by (6.19), so that $r_0 \approx 2.195 \times 10^4$ m. This is approximately 1/290th of the earth's true radius, so it follows that the mass would seek to orbit at 289/290ths of the distance down from the earth's surface to its centre. Note that, once again, the values of v_0 and r_0 do not depend on the mass of P [26].

EXAMPLE 6.2

In Example 6.1 we dealt with an object that is fixed on the surface of the rotating earth. Let us now consider a rocket-propelled road-vehicle, P, which is capable of travelling at a speed $V = 300$ m s^{-1}. The vehicle P has a mass, m kg. The value of m does not affect the following argument but, to be specific, let us take $m = 1400$. If, initially, P is at rest somewhere near the earth's equator, then it follows from the above example that P will press on the earth's surface with a force, of magnitude given by $F \approx 9.81 \times 1400$ N $= 13734$ N, and so weighs 1400 kg.

Now suppose that the vehicle P is set in motion and travels westwards along a track at speed $V = 300$ m s^{-1}. Then P counteracts the earth's rotational speed to some extent and, in effect, its constrained orbital speed relative to the earth's centre is $v \approx 464.74 - 300$ m s^{-1} $= 164.74$ m s^{-1}. From this it follows, by (6.17), that with $r \approx 6.372828 \times 10^6$ m and $M \approx 5.989 \times 10^{24}$ kg, we have:

$$G' \approx 2.887859 \times 10^{-14} \text{ N m}^2 \text{ kg}^{-2}.$$

This means, according to equation (6.16), that P would then press on the track with a force, of magnitude F given by

$$F = Mm(G - G')/r^2 \approx 13770 \text{ N}.$$

So the vehicle weighs *more* when it is moving westwards than when it is stationary relative to the earth's surface.

Now let us suppose that P travels in the opposite (*i.e.* easterly) direction along the track in the same direction as that of the earth's rotation, again at a speed of $V = 300$ m s^{-1}. The speed of P relative to the reference frame in which the earth is revolving is now $v \approx 464.74 + 300$ m s^{-1} $= 764.74$ m s^{-1}. In this instance, (6.17) gives

$$G' \approx 6.223082 \times 10^{-13} \text{ N m}^2 \text{ kg}^{-2}.$$

In this case, (6.16) shows that P would press on the track with a smaller force, of magnitude $F \approx 13647$ N. The vehicle now weighs *less* than when stationary relative to the earth's surface.

It is significant to note, here, that this decrease in the weight of the vehicle P when moving in the easterly direction, together with the rotation of the earth, fits the description of *levitation* of the vehicle with respect to the earth. This is the result of adding to the angular momentum of the vehicle due to the earth's rotation, the angular momentum of the vehicle itself due to energy supplied by its own engine. As a consequence of this addition of angular momenta the force between the two bodies is decreased.

These are rather commonsense examples of the fact that G is a variable, not a constant. Such changes in G due to rotational motion are manifest when a speeding car rides over humps, or when an airplane pilot moves between the top and bottom of a loop. Being so commonplace, these examples need no special experiment to confirm them. However, in the next chapter, we shall show that incorporating the effects of spin also has a significant effect on the value of G.

6.4 The POAMS analogue of Newton's Second Law

In the case of a particle P orbiting a body B of mass M, it follows by (6.9) that since there is no implied *in vacuo* 'gravitational' force determining a natural orbit of P, there is also no implied centrifugal force, $m\mathbf{a}$, felt by the particle P in such an orbit. In other words, although P has an acceleration $\mathbf{a}$, which is non-zero at each point of its orbit, any natural orbit of P is 'force free', so that the vector quantity $m\mathbf{a}$ is not a *force* in the classical sense. This implies that in POAMS, Newton's Second Law does not hold in its usual form, which commits us to formulating an amended version.

In POAMS, then, we require a new definition of acceleration, which is zero in any natural force-free orbit. The obvious course is to define the **natural acceleration**, **A**, for any orbit of the particle P in our two-body system as

$$\mathbf{A} = \mathbf{a} + (GM/r^2)\mathbf{n}, \qquad (6.20)$$

where $\mathbf{a}$ is the (classical) acceleration of P and $\mathbf{n}$ is a vector of unit length in the direction of **r**. It then follows by (6.9) that **A** = **0** along any natural orbit of P, whereas along any other orbit of P the natural acceleration is given by

$$\mathbf{A} = ((G - G')M/r^2)\mathbf{n},$$

and so will be non-zero. Notice that although there is no way of distinguishing between orbital (Newtonian) acceleration in natural and unnatural orbits, the above definition of natural acceleration does provide a way of distinguishing between the two types of orbit. Notice also that when $M = 0$, **A** = **a** = **0**. In this case, it follows by (6.9) that any natural orbit of P is a straight line, which means that in POAMS, rectilinear motion is a special case of orbital motion. This makes Newton's First Law a special case of the conservation of angular momentum, which implies also the conservation of linear momentum.

We may, then, define the **natural** or **intrinsic** force, **F**, felt by the particle P in any orbit about the body B of mass M by

$$\mathbf{F} = m\mathbf{A}, \tag{6.21}$$

where **A** is the natural acceleration of P. This is the POAMS analogue of Newton's Second Law. From this it follows that **F** = **0** in any natural orbit of P, also that **F** ≠ **0** on any other orbit. Notice that along any constrained orbit of P for which angular momentum is conserved,

$$\|\mathbf{F}\| = |G' - G|\, mM/r^2,$$

so that the magnitude of **F** is the real, measurable 'gravitational' force on P in any constrained orbit, which is given by (6.16).

In this chapter we have claimed that from the standpoint of Normal Realism, contrary to received opinion, the so-called 'gravitational constant G' is *not* a constant but a variable. We have shown that in NR terms the orbits of free-moving bodies are explained, both sufficiently and efficiently, in terms of angular momentum alone, with no need for the concepts of *in vacuo* 'forces' or the 'fields' customarily associated with them. In our next chapter we discuss, in the

124

same NR terms, the effect of spin on the orbital parameters of free-moving bodies and hence, on the value of G.

Notes and References

[1] Of course, such a pure isolated system does not occur in practice, but the model provides a sufficient approximation to the behaviour of, for example, a planet orbiting the sun.

[2] McCuskey, S. W.: *An Introduction to Advanced Dynamics* (Addison-Wesley, Reading, USA, 1959) pp. 1-2.

[3] McCuskey, S. W., *ibid*, p. 10.

[4] McCuskey, S. W., *ibid*, pp. 2-3.

[5] McCuskey, S. W., *ibid,* Chapter 3.

[6] Galeczki, G.: 'A Short Essay on Closed Systems, Hierarchy and Radiation', in Pope, N. V., Osborne, A. D. and Winfield, A. F. T. (eds.): *Immediate Distant Action and Correlation in Modern Physics: The Balanced Universe* (Edwin Mellen, New York, 2005) pp. 186-190.

[7] *Op. cit.* reference 2, pp. 14, 22-24.

[8] Pope, N. V.: 'A Tale of Two Paradigms' in Pope, N. V., Osborne, A. D. and Winfield, A. F. T. (eds.): *Immediate Distant Action and Correlation in Modern Physics: The Balanced Universe* (Edwin Mellen, New York, 2005) pp. 97-98.

[9] Phipps, T. E., Jr.: 'Should Mach's Principle be Taken Seriously?', *Speculations in Science and Technology* **1** (5) (1978) pp. 499-508.

[10] Graneau, P.: 'Far Action *Versus* Contact Action', *Speculations in Science and Technology* **13** (3) (1990) pp.191-201.

[11] Assis, A. K. T.: 'On Mach's Principle', *Foundations of Physics Letters* **2** (1989) pp. 301-318.

[12] Osborne, A. D.: 'Towards a Consensus' in Pope, N. V., Osborne, A. D. and Winfield, A. F. T. (eds.): *Immediate Distant Action and Correlation in Modern Physics: The Balanced Universe* (Edwin Mellen, New York, 2005) pp. 40-44.

[13] Phipps, T. E., Jr.: *Heretical Verities, Mathematical Themes in Physical Description* (Urbana, Illinois, 1986), p. 341.

[14] Pope, N. V.: *The Eye of the Beholder: The Role of the Observer in Modern Physics* (**phi** Philosophical Enterprises, Swansea, 2004) pp. 48-54.

[15] Our colleague Jon Blay gave our approach to orbital motion its current name, together with the acronym POAMS. There is now a dedicated website, www.poams.org. Jon Blay also formulated the Principle of Angular Inertia.

[16] Pope, N. V. and Osborne, A. D.: 'Instantaneous Gravitational and Inertial Action-at-a-Distance', *Physics Essays* **8** (1995) pp. 384-397.

[17] Osborne, A. D and Pope, N. V.: 'An Angular Momentum Synthesis of "Gravitational" and "Electrostatic" Forces', *Galilean Electrodynamics*, **14**, Special Issue 1 (2003) pp. 9-19.

[18] Pope, N. V and Osborne, A. D. in Pope, N. V., Osborne, A. D. and Winfield, A. F. T. (eds.): *Immediate Distant Action and Correlation in Modern Physics: The Balanced Universe* (Edwin Mellen, New York, 2005) Chapters 5, 9 and 11.

[19] D'Inverno, R.: *Introducing Einstein's Relativity* (Clarendon Press, Oxford, 1992) Chapters 8-10.

---

[20] Pope, N. V.: 'Newton's Dead...Long Live Newton', in Chubykalo, A. E., Pope, N. V. and Smirnov-Rueda, R.(eds.): *Instantaneous Action at a Distance in Modern Physics: Pro and Contra* (Nova Science, New York, 1999) pp. 3-17.

[21] Since $r^2\omega$ is a constant, it follows that equal areas are swept out in equal times by the orbit of P. In other words, this law due to Kepler does not depend on the existence of a Newtonian *in vacuo* gravitational force.

[22] This is supported by the fact that if $V = -mH(r)$, then $\nabla V = mh(r)\mathbf{n}$ where $\mathbf{n}$ is a vector of unit length in the direction of $\mathbf{r}$. Hence, in Newtonian terms, $-\nabla V$ is the 'gravitational force' from P towards B.

[23] *Op. cit.* reference 2, pp.79-85.

[24] Tikochinsky, Y.: *American Journal of Physics*, **56**, 12 (1988).

[25] The value of G is one of the most difficult physical constants to determine experimentally. The 2002 CODATA, available form the Internet, records its value as $6.6742 \pm 0.001 \times 10^{-11}$ N m^2 kg^{-2}.

[26] It follows by (6.14), (6.18) and (6.19) that $v_0 = GM/vr$ and then $r_0 = vr/v_0$.

CHAPTER 7

Angular Momentum and Spin

7.1 Introduction

In the previous chapter, we presented our alternative approach to natural motion, known as the Pope-Osborne Angular Momentum Synthesis (POAMS). Recall that POAMS begins with the premise that the observable universe is in an *holistic* balance, so that the natural or unrestricted motion of any body is (albeit in statistical numbers of sporadic quantum contacts) *instantly* correlated with that of each and every other body in the System. Recall also that or force-free motion in POAMS is not rectilinear but is naturally curved, or orbital. We postulate that the agency responsible for maintaining this holistic balance is nothing more nor less than the conservation of angular momentum. Also, in POAMS, the observable universe is ultimately discrete on the micro-phenomenal level, with angular momentum quantised (following Bohr) in discrete intransitive units of $h/2\pi$.

Our approach, therefore, makes no distinction between the macro- and micro-phenomenal levels so far as angular momentum conservation is concerned. All angular momenta, of whatever form, are part and parcel of the same holistic angular momentum nexus. Thus far, we have considered only the *orbital* angular momentum of a particle in relation to some fixed point of reference, particularly in relation to the centre-of-mass of some larger body. However, there is another and in some sense more fundamental angular momentum associated with any particle. This is the *intrinsic* angular momentum of *spin*. In POAMS, therefore, it is not just orbital angular momentum which is holistically conserved but, rather, the *total* angular momentum of a body, orbital plus spin. This commits us to predictions that are distinct from those of Newtonian dynamics. In particular, POAMS predicts certain relatively small but nevertheless measurable effects associated with macroscopic spinning bodies. In contrast, on the micro-phenomenal scale the proportion of spin to orbital angular momentum is much larger. Indeed, we show that by incorporating these spin angular momenta into the 'orbital' parameters of the 'electron' and 'proton' it is possible to obtain the accepted physical constants associated with the hydrogen atom without having to refer to the customary 'electrostatic forces' of Bohr's derivation. Our approach thus indicates that angular momentum considerations lead to the logical redundancy, not only of *in vacuo* 'gravitational' forces but also of 'electrostatic' forces. This POAMS approach to spin was first published in 1995 [1]. It was later developed for the 2001 Swansea Workshop and encapsulated in a 2003 paper [2].

7.2 Spin angular momentum

In the previous chapter, section 6.1, we defined the angular momentum, **L**, of a particle P of mass m relative to a chosen origin, O, as

$$\mathbf{L} = \mathbf{r} \times m\mathbf{v}, \tag{7.1}$$

where **r** is the position vector of P relative to O, and $\mathbf{v} = d\mathbf{r}/dt$ is the velocity of P. Remember that **L** is a vector that lies perpendicular to the plane containing **r** and **v**. In order to distinguish **L** from spin angular momentum, from now on we shall refer to **L** as the **orbital angular momentum** of P relative to O. In particular, we showed in section 6.1 that if the trajectory of P relative to O lies in a plane, then

$$L = \|\mathbf{L}\| = mr^2\omega,$$

where $r = \|\mathbf{r}\|$ and ω is the angular speed of P (see (6.7)). Here, the quantity mr^2, which gives information about both the matter content and the shape of the orbit of P, is the *moment of inertia, I,* of P.

In the same way, the magnitude of the **spin angular momentum, S,** of a spinning body depends on the body's moment of inertia and its angular velocity. In general, these measures are very involved [3] [4] and it is not the purpose of this section to reproduce an exhaustive treatment of these measures. Rather, we shall deal with only the simplest case, of an axially symmetric body spinning about a fixed axis, which is sufficient for the practical examples that follow. These examples will give an indication of why, according to POAMS, spin has an automatic and immediate influence on orbital motion in general.

Let us consider, then, a rigid *axially-symmetric* body, P, which is rotating (spinning) about its own fixed axis of symmetry. Instances of this include, (i) a sphere rotating about an axis through its centre, (ii) a circular disc spinning about an axis perpendicular to the disc and passing through the centre of the disc, and (iii) a cube rotating about any axis passing through its centre and the centre of any of its faces. In these cases, the **magnitude**, S, of P's **spin angular momentum**, (about the axis of rotation) is defined by

$$S = I\omega, \tag{7.2}$$

where I is the moment of inertia of P and ω is the angular speed of P about the rotation axis [5]. The moment of inertia, I, of P depends on the mass of P and its shape. We need not show, here, how I is calculated in general. All we need for our particular examples are, for a *sphere of radius r*,

$$I = \frac{2}{5}mr^2 \text{ [6]} \tag{7.3a}$$

and for a *circular disc of radius r*,

$$I = \frac{1}{2}mr^2 \text{ [7]}. \tag{7.3b}$$

The **spin angular momentum** of P is then the vector **S** defined by

$$\mathbf{S} = S\mathbf{n},$$

where **n** is a vector of unit length in the direction of the axis of rotation.

Because the moment of inertia of even an axially-symmetric body depends on its shape, it is often more convenient to express the spin angular momentum of such a body in terms of its rotational or spin kinetic energy. Equation (6.5) tells us that the kinetic energy, K, of a particle of mass m in a *circular* orbit of radius r, is

$$K = \frac{1}{2}mv^2 = \frac{1}{2}mr^2\omega^2 = \frac{1}{2}I\omega^2,$$

where I is the moment of inertia of P's orbit. It then follows that

$$L = \frac{2K}{\omega}. \tag{7.4}$$

By analogy, in general, the **spin** (or rotational) **kinetic energy**, K_s, of an axially-symmetric rigid body (about its axis of rotation) is defined by

$$K_s = \frac{1}{2}I\omega^2, \tag{7.5}$$

where I is the moment of inertia of the body and ω is its angular speed [8]. It then follows immediately from (7.2) that the magnitude of the body's spin angular momentum is

$$S = \frac{2K_s}{\omega}, \tag{7.6}$$

regardless of the shape of the body.

7.3 The incorporation of spin into orbital angular momentum in POAMS

In classical dynamics, Newton's laws are applied to any system containing spinning bodies by treating a spinning body itself as a system of many discrete and self-sufficient orbiting particles. In contrast, in POAMS, because of the holistic conservation of angular momentum, in which the motions of all bodies are immediately balanced with one another as a system, any effects due to spin are *instantly correlated with the total angular momentum*. POAMS accounts for this instantaneous correlation by postulating that the kinetic energy of an orbiting spinning particle depends on both its spin kinetic energy and the orbital kinetic energy it would have if it were not spinning. This implies that in orbital systems of constant angular momentum involving spin, the 'gravitational constant' G has to be replaced by a more general function, $\mathcal{G}$, of the orbital parameters.

For simplicity, we once again consider only the case of a freely moving particle, P, of mass m, in a closed orbit about a body B of mass M, with m very much smaller than M. If P spins on its axis while orbiting, then according to Newtonian dynamics, if the spinning body is perfectly spherical the spin situation is the same as that of the non-spin. In contrast, according to POAMS, since any orbital angular momentum is balanced against the total momentum of the system, introducing a spin at any one place has a direct and immediate effect on the system throughout. In other words, POAMS postulates that P's spin will cause it to take up a natural orbit different from that which it would describe if it were not spinning.

Suppose for the moment that P does not spin and follows a natural elliptical orbit about B, with radial coordinate $r_0(t)$, and with angular speed $\omega_0(t)$ at any time t. It follows by the results of the previous chapter and, in particular, (6.9), that in POAMS, just as in Newtonian theory, this natural elliptical orbit is determined by

$$\frac{\mathrm{d}^2 r_0}{\mathrm{d}t^2} - \frac{L^2}{m^2 r_0^{\,3}} = -\frac{GM}{r_0^{\,2}}, \qquad (7.7)$$

where L is the magnitude of P's orbital angular momentum. In order to distinguish between orbital and spin kinetic energy, we shall denote P's orbital kinetic energy by K_o. It then follows by (6.5) and (6.7) that

$$K_o = \frac{1}{2} m v_0^{\,2} = \frac{1}{2} m \left(\left(\frac{\mathrm{d}r_0}{\mathrm{d}t} \right)^2 + \frac{L^2}{m^2 r_0^{\,2}} \right),$$

where $v_0(t)$ is the speed of P in its natural orbit.

Assume now that P is axially symmetric and spins on its axis whilst orbiting the body B. POAMS postulates that the parameters of P's orbit will be directly affected by P's spin. Explicitly, when spinning, P follows a new closed natural orbit with parameters $r_s(t)$ and $\omega_s(t)$, for which $r_s(t)$ is determined by

$$\mathcal{K} = \frac{1}{2} m \left(\left(\frac{\mathrm{d}r_s}{\mathrm{d}t} \right)^2 + \frac{L^2}{m^2 r_s^{\,2}} \right), \qquad (7.8)$$

where $\mathcal{K}$ is P's new orbital kinetic energy. In this case, we postulate that $\mathcal{K}$ depends on both the orbital kinetic energy, K_o, of the orbit which P would naturally follow if it were not spinning, and its spin kinetic energy, K_s. In other words, P's spin kinetic energy is transferred directly to its new orbital kinetic energy, $\mathcal{K}$, such that the magnitude of the overall angular momentum is conserved. Once $\mathcal{K}$ is known, the parameter $r_s(t)$ of the effective orbit radius may be calculated, at least in theory, by solving the first order differential equation (7.8). It then follows by (6.7) that

$$\omega_s(t) = \frac{L}{mr_s^2} .$$
(7.9)

Since this 'new' closed orbit of P about B, as determined by its spin, is a natural force-free orbit, it must satisfy an equation of the form (6.13) so that in this case, (7.7) is replaced by

$$\frac{d^2 r_s}{dt^2} - \frac{L^2}{m^2 r_s^3} = -\mathcal{G} \frac{M}{r_s^2} ,$$
(7.10)

where $\mathcal{G}$ is a new factor which replaces the 'gravitational constant' G and depends on the orbital parameters r_s and ω_s. Note that this factor $\mathcal{G}$ reduces to G when and only when (7.10) describes any natural, spin-less orbit of P and so reduces to (7.7). In other words, $\mathcal{G} = G$ ($\approx 6.67259(65) \times 10^{-11}$ m^3 kg^{-1} s^{-2}) when and only when $\mathcal{K} = K_o$. Once the orbital parameters r_s and ω_s are known, the corresponding 'gravitational factor', $\mathcal{G}$, may be calculated from (7.10).

For a *circular* orbit of P this process is much simpler. In this case, it follows by the definition of orbital kinetic energy that the speed v_s of P in its natural orbit, adjusted for its spin (that is, *P's effective orbital speed*), is given by

$$v_s^2 = \frac{2}{m} \mathcal{K} .$$
(7.11)

Then r_s may be calculated using (6.14), *i.e.*,

$$r_s = \frac{L}{mv_s} .$$
(7.12)

Finally, in this case it follows by (6.15) that (7.10) reduces to

$$\mathcal{G} = \frac{r_s v_s^2}{M} .$$
(7.13)

Now although we have stated that the orbital kinetic energy, $\mathcal{K}$, in P's natural orbit, when spin effects are taken into account, depends on both P's spin kinetic energy K_s and the spin-less orbital kinetic energy K_o, we have not yet shown how $\mathcal{K}$ may be calculated from K_s and K_o. We shall consider only the case in which P is an *axially symmetric* particle in a *circular* orbit about the body B. Then the orbit of P is also symmetric. Not only is this the simplest case but also it is the most useful in practical examples, as will be seen later.

The maximum possible effects due to spin must occur when P spins in either the same or the opposite direction to that of its orbital motion. When P spins in the same direction as its orbital motion, its spin angular momentum vector, **S**, points in the same direction as its angular momentum vector, **L**. In this case, the magnitude $\|\mathbf{L} + \mathbf{S}\|$ of the total angular momentum is $L + S$ and the same is true for any multiples of **L** and **S**. In keeping with equations (7.4) and (7.6), we postulate that in this case, the total orbital kinetic energy is

$$\mathcal{K} = K_o + K_s. \tag{7.14}$$

Similarly, when P spins in the direction opposite to that of its orbital motion, **S** points in the direction opposite to that of **L** and, in this case, the magnitude of the total angular momentum $\|\mathbf{L} + \mathbf{S}\| = |L - S|$. We then postulate that in this case

$$\mathcal{K} = |K_o - K_s|. \tag{7.15}$$

In general, if P's spin angular momentum vector, **S**, is inclined at angle θ to its orbital angular momentum vector, **L**, *i.e.*, if P's axis of rotation is inclined at this angle to the normal of the orbital plane, then the magnitude of the total angular momentum is given by

$$\|\mathbf{L} + \mathbf{S}\|^2 = L^2 + S^2 + 2LS\cos\theta.$$

We then postulate, by analogy with (7.14) and (7.15), that in this general case,

$$\mathcal{K}^2 = K_o^2 + K_s^2 + 2K_oK_s\cos\theta.$$

In particular, if P's spin angular momentum vector lies in the plane of its orbit, so that **S** is perpendicular to **L**, then

$$\mathcal{K}^2 = K_o^2 + K_s^2. \tag{7.16}$$

With our hypothesis, this is clearly the minimum possible effect due to spin.

    To summarise this present section, the key difference between Newtonian dynamics and POAMS is that in POAMS, if the spin angular momentum and the corresponding spin kinetic energy are given as initial conditions within a system of *constant* angular momentum, then it is predicted that any change in the spin causes a change in the modified 'gravitational factor' $\mathcal{G}$, which replaces Newton's 'gravitational constant', G, in order that the holistic balance of the angular momentum of the system is maintained [9].

7.4 Summary of the incorporation of spin in POAMS: the simplest case

For the rest of this chapter, we shall consider only the simplest case of a freely moving particle, P, of mass m, in a *circular* orbit about a body, B, of mass M, with m very much less than M. In addition, P is *axially symmetric* and spins on its axis while orbiting B. POAMS then postulates that the speed, v_s, of P in its natural circular orbit, is given, as we have seen, by (7.11), *viz.*,

$$v_s^2 = \frac{2}{m}\mathcal{K},$$

where $\mathcal{K}$ is the orbital kinetic energy of P taking the spin of P into account. Then the radius, r_s, of P's natural circular orbit is given by (7.12), namely,

$$r_s = \frac{L}{mv_s},$$

where L is the magnitude of the constant orbital angular momentum. In this case, the 'gravitational factor', $\mathcal{G}$, associated with P's orbit satisfies (7.13), *viz.*,

$$\mathcal{G} = \frac{r_s v_s^2}{M}.$$

If P does not spin, then for the same constant L, these equations reduce to the equivalent Newtonian equations

$$v_0{}^2 = \frac{2}{m} K_o, \tag{7.17}$$

$$r_0 = \frac{L}{mv_0}, \tag{7.18}$$

$$G = \frac{r_0 v_0{}^2}{M}, \tag{7.19}$$

respectively, where v_0 is the speed of P in its natural, spin-less orbit, r_0 is the radius of P's natural spin-less circular orbit, G is the standard gravitational constant and K_o is the orbital kinetic energy of this spin-less orbit.

We postulate that when the particle P spins in the *same* direction as its orbital motion, then, as in (7.14),

$$\mathcal{K} = K_o + K_s,$$

where K_s is P's spin kinetic energy, and if P spins in the *opposite* direction to its orbital motion, then, as in (7.15)

$$\mathcal{K} = |K_o - K_s|.$$

Finally, since P is axially symmetric, K_s is as given by (7.5), namely,

$$K_s = \frac{1}{2} I\omega^2,$$

where I is the moment of inertia of P and ω is its angular speed. As stated earlier, for a *sphere* of radius r and mass m, according to (7.3a),

$$I = \frac{2}{5} mr^2,$$

and for a *circular disc* of radius r and mass m, as in (7.3b),

$$I = \frac{1}{2} mr^2.$$

For the most part, the equations summarised in this section are the only equations referred to in the rest of the chapter.

7.5 The effect of spin in POAMS: 'attraction' and 'repulsion'

In the previous two sections, we have indicated how, in an isolated two-body system of constant angular momentum, the parameters of a freely moving particle, P, in its natural closed orbit about a body B, are affected by its spin angular momentum and hence by its spin kinetic energy. It follows that in this case, P's spin affects either its relative 'attraction' or 'repulsion' towards B, depending on the orientation of its spin. Once again, we shall consider only the case in which P is axially symmetric and follows a natural circular orbit about B, such that the orbital angular momentum is constant.

In this case, it follows by (7.11) and (7.12) that if P is spinning, then the radius of P's natural circular orbit is

$$r_s = L/(2\mathcal{K}m)^{1/2}, \tag{7.20}$$

where m is the mass of P and $\mathcal{K}$ is the orbital kinetic energy. Hence, with constant L and m, r_s is proportional to $1/\mathcal{K}^{1/2}$. (For example, if $\mathcal{K}$ is quadrupled, then r_s is halved.) Recall that if P spins in the *same* direction as that of its orbital motion, (so that the spin and orbital angular momentum vectors are aligned) then POAMS postulates that its orbital kinetic energy, $\mathcal{K}$, is given by (7.14), so that $\mathcal{K} > K_o$. It then follows by (7.20) that an *increase* in P's orbital kinetic energy produces a *decrease* in the radius of P's natural orbit about B. Hence, in the Newtonian language of 'attraction' and 'repulsion', P is 'more attracted' to B when spinning compared to when it is not. The greater the spin kinetic energy of P, the smaller the value of r_s and so the greater the 'attraction' of P towards B. This makes physical sense if we note that in this case, P is spinning with its orbital motion and so is 'tumbling towards' B in its orbit.

If P spins in the direction opposite to that of its orbital motion, then the total orbital kinetic energy is given by (7.15). Now, in general, for macroscopic bodies, such as the planets of our solar system and natural and man-made satellites, K_o will be very much larger than K_s. So it follows in this case, by (7.15), that $\mathcal{K} < K_o$. Then by (7.20), the presence of P's spin kinetic energy produces an increase in the radius of P's orbit, so that P is 'less attracted' to B when spinning compared to when it is not. This makes physical sense if we note that in this case, since P is spinning in the direction opposite to that of its orbital motion, P is *resisting* its natural spin-less orbit in some way. Of course, in general, the effect of the spin of a macroscopic object on its natural orbit will be tiny. However, where K_s is very much larger than K_o, as seems to be the case on the microphenomenal scale (see section 7.6 following), it follows that the differences between the effective free orbital kinetic energy $\mathcal{K}$, given by (7.15), and K_o are so pronounced as to be distinctly measurable. In addition, in this case it follows by (7.20) that the result of any very large increase in K_s must necessarily decrease the orbit radius. This is *regardless* of the orientations of the orbital and spin angular momentum vectors where the effect of the first is swamped by that of the second.

It needs to be stressed that in both the cases discussed above, we are considering an idealised situation in which P is *spinning* in orbit about the centre-of-mass of B, where B is *not spinning*. These results should be compared and contrasted with Example 6.2 in the previous chapter, concerning the rocket-propelled road vehicle. Clearly, the situations discussed above are completely different from those discussed in Example 6.2, since there are no explicit spins involved in that example. However, the vehicle in that example could be considered as orbiting the earth which is slowly spinning. In this sense, Example 6.2 resembles a case in which the body B is *spinning* while the orbiting particle P is *not spinning* and so is essentially complementary to those cases discussed in this section.

In Example 6.2, it is the spinning earth which gives the stationary vehicle its angular momentum in its constrained orbit about the earth's centre. With this angular momentum, the vehicle's natural free orbit is much closer to the earth's centre and it is this difference between the constrained orbit and the natural orbit which gives the vehicle its weight. When the vehicle is set in motion either with or against the earth's rotation, its constrained angular momentum is changed, so that its weight is changed. Hence, the vehicle example also differs from the situation discussed in this section in the sense that the vehicle example investigates 'attraction' and 'repulsion' of an orbiting particle due to *changes* in angular momentum, whereas the present section compares the 'attraction' and 'repulsion' of an orbiting particle when spinning and not spinning, for the *same* angular momentum.

The effect of changes to the total kinetic energy on a natural, force-free orbit in a system whose angular momentum is constant, can be both compared and contrasted to the relationship between $\mathcal{K}$ and the 'gravitational factor' G, with which $\mathcal{K}$ is associated. Once again, in the simplest case of an axially symmetric particle P in a circular orbit about a body B it follows from equations (7.11) to (7.13) that

$$G = \frac{r_s v_s^{\,2}}{M} = \frac{L v_s}{mM} = \frac{L}{m^{3/2} M} (2\mathcal{K})^{1/2},$$

so that for constant m, M and L, G is proportional to $\mathcal{K}^{1/2}$. Thus G increases with increasing $\mathcal{K}$, in accordance with the fact that for constant L, as $\mathcal{K}$ increases, P is 'more attracted' to B.

To sum up this point, in POAMS the spin of a particle P in a situation of constant angular momentum affects its relative 'attraction' towards a body B in a way which it cannot according to Newton's thesis, where the addition of spin angular momentum has no effect on the parameters of the orbit.

It is to be noted that the cases we are studying here, of how the motions of particles are affected by their spin, are much simplified. This is because, for natural elliptical orbits in general, there is no such simple relationship between the orbital parameters and $\mathcal{K}$ [10]. In particular, r_s is not directly proportional to $1/\mathcal{K}^{1/2}$. Moreover, it must be remembered that in such an elliptical orbit, $\mathcal{K}$, r_s and v_s will not even be constant. Naturally, this makes the calculations for elliptical orbits far more complicated than those in our chosen examples. However, this does not invalidate our simplified examples any more than the simple principles of hydrodynamics are compromised by the practical difficulty of applying them to the motions of the individual water-molecules in, say, the Niagara Falls.

EXAMPLE 7.1

Let us first consider the simplest example of the effect of spin on orbital motion, namely that of a satellite P in a natural (force-free) circular orbit about the earth B. It should be appreciated at the outset that the figures and calculations quoted in this and following examples can be only approximate, and that the primary intention is to give qualitative results together with the order of magnitude of detectable effects. With that in mind, suppose that P orbits at a distance of 400 miles, $i.e.$, approximately 6.437376×10^5 metres, above the earth's surface, the mean radius of the earth from its centre being about 6.372828×10^6 metres. The radius of the satellite's orbit at that height above the earth's surface is then $r_0 \approx 7.0165656 \times 10^6$ metres. Suppose, also, that the mass of this satellite is $m \approx 7.52916642$ gm, $i.e.$, $m \approx 7.52916642 \times 10^{-2}$ kg. This just happens to be the mass of a quartz rotor, which orbits the earth at a distance of 400 miles in the proposed Gravity Probe B experiment run by a team of scientists at Stanford University [11]. However, the following considerations apply equally well to any satellite in a natural circular orbit about any body. Since it follows a natural force-free orbit, the speed, v_0, of P is given in accordance with (7.19) so that

$$v_0 = \left(\frac{GM}{r_0} \right)^{1/2} \approx 7.546790 \times 10^3 \text{ m s}^{-1},$$

(where M is the earth's mass, calculated in POAMS to be $M \approx 5.989 \times 10^{24}$ kg). Then the magnitude of the satellite's orbital angular momentum is, from (7.18),

$$L = mv_0r_0 \approx 3.986885 \times 10^9 \text{ kg m}^2 \text{ s}^{-1},$$

and its orbital kinetic energy is, from (7.17),

$$K_o = mv_0^2/2 \approx 2.144082 \times 10^6 \text{ kg m}^2 \text{ s}^{-2}.$$

Suppose now that this rotor P, treated as a spherical ball, spins while it freely orbits the earth in its unconstrained natural orbit. As in the proposed Gravity Probe B experiment, let us suppose that the diameter of the rotor is 3.81 cm and that it spins at 10,000 revolutions per minute. In other words, the radius of the rotor is 1.905×10^{-2} m and it spins at 166.667 revolutions per second. It follows by (7.3a) and (7.5) that the spin kinetic energy of any spinning sphere of uniform mass is given by,

$$K_s = \frac{1}{2}I\omega^2 = \frac{1}{5}m(r\omega)^2 = \frac{1}{5}mv^2,$$

where r is the radius of the sphere, ω (measured in radians per second) is its angular speed about its axis of rotation and v is its spin speed (measured in metres per second). The spin kinetic energy for the spherical ball in question is then

$$K_s \approx \frac{m}{5} \times (0.01905 \times 2\pi \times 166.667)^2 \approx 5.992721 \text{ kg m}^2 \text{ s}^{-2}.$$

It follows by (7.11) and (7.14) that if the rotor spins in the same direction and in the same plane as its orbit, then the rotor's orbital speed, v_s, in its natural orbit, accounting for effects due to its spin, is given by

$$v_s = (2(K_o + K_s)/m)^{1/2} \approx 7.546800 \times 10^3 \text{ m s}^{-1}$$

and so the radius r_s of the rotor's natural orbit while spinning is, by (7.12),

$$r_s = \frac{L}{mv_s} \approx 7.016556 \times 10^6 \text{ m.}$$

In this case, r_s is smaller than r_0, with $r_0 - r_s$ approximately 10 metres. Hence, POAMS predicts that the spinning rotor will follow a natural orbit approximately 10 metres *closer* to the earth than if it were not spinning. On the other hand, if the rotor spins counter to, but again in the same plane as its orbital motion, then it follows, by (7.11) and (7.15), that r_s is larger than r_0, with $r_s - r_0$ approximately 10 metres. In this case, then, POAMS predicts that the rotor will naturally orbit 10 metres *further away* from the earth than if it were not spinning.

It must be remembered that in this example, it is the *kinetic energies* that are added and subtracted, not the overall angular momentum, which is assumed constant; and, as already remarked, it is in this way that this example with the spinning rotor differs from that of the rocket-propelled road vehicle in the previous chapter, in which the angular momentum of the vehicle was added to (or subtracted from) that of the earth. However, we recall that in order to send the satellite into orbit, angular momentum has to be added, in the same way as in the example of the 'levitating' rocket-propelled vehicle, in which case, the effect on the satellite is the same as with that vehicle, where the overall angular momentum is not conserved. On the other hand, once settled into its free orbit, the satellite and the earth form a paired and balanced, *constant* angular momentum system, the effects of which are as described in this example of the free orbiting rotor.

In the actual proposed Gravity Probe B experiment, we understand that the satellite is equipped with four gyroscopic rotors, each of which spins on an axis which permanently points at a guide star on the earth's equatorial plane, while the satellite orbits the earth from pole to pole. Hence, the spin angular momentum vector of each rotor will be at right angles to the satellite's orbital angular momentum vector and there will be only a minimal effect of each rotor's spin on its orbit. In this case, it follows by (7.11) and (7.16) that the orbital speed of each rotor is given by

$$v_s = (2(K_o^2 + K_s^2)^{1/2}/m)^{1/2} \approx 7.546790485659 \times 10^3 \text{ m s}^{-1}$$

and so the radius of the spinning rotors' natural orbit is

$$r_s \approx 7.016565599986 \times 10^6 \text{ m}.$$

In this case, $r_0 - r_s$ is approximately 0.014 millimetres, so that the effect of spin will be negligible!

In the actual proposed experiment, the rotors will be permanently spinning, so that it is not possible to detect a difference between the natural orbit in the spin and no-spin cases. Also, there may well be a precession effect due to the spin orientations, which may affect any predictions that POAMS makes.

Finally, the experiment sets out to detect very different effects from those predicted by POAMS, in particular, the 'frame-dragging' predicted by General Relativity. Hence, on a purely practical level, we believe that terrestrial experiments such as those considered in the next example hold the most promise for verifying or disproving the predictions made by POAMS in relation to spin.

EXAMPLE 7.2

Our next example concerns the effect of spin on a body located on or near the earth's surface and travelling with the earth around the terrestrial centre. In effect, this example combines the ideas of both the previous example and Example 6.1 in the preceding chapter. As in the experiments performed by Hideo Hayasaka and his Japanese team at Tokai University, this example is concerned with a circular disc of mass $m = 175$ gm (*i.e.*, $m = 0.175$ kg), and of radius $r \approx 3.3286$ cm (*i.e.*, $r \approx 0.033286$ metres) [12] [13]. However, one significant difference between this example and the Hayasaka experiments is the requirement that the experiment in this prospective example be conducted somewhere on the earth's equator. In this case, the radius of the disc's approximately circular constrained orbit is the earth's mean equatorial radius, given by $R \approx 6.372828 \times 10^6$ metres, and its orbital speed is the rotational speed of the earth, namely $V \approx 464.74$ metres per second. It follows by (6.14) that the magnitude of the disc's orbital angular momentum in this constrained orbit is

$$L = mVR \approx 5.182989148 \times 10^8 \text{ kg m}^2 \text{ s}^{-1}.$$

Suppose for the moment that the disc is an inert mass which does not spin. It follows by (6.17), exactly as with the 1 kg mass in Example 6.1 of the previous chapter, that the 'gravitational factor' associated with the disc's constrained orbit is

$$G' = RV^2/M \approx 2.298254 \times 10^{-13} \text{ N m}^2 \text{ kg}^{-2},$$

where $M \approx 9.989 \times 10^{24}$ kg is the earth's mass. According to POAMS, this disc, if allowed, would follow its natural circular orbit with radius r_0, at orbital speed v_0, relative to the earth's centre. It follows by (7.18) and (7.19), *i.e.*, (6.18), that

$$v_0 = \frac{GMm}{L} \approx 1.349293731 \times 10^5 \text{ m s}^{-1},$$

and so by (7.18),

$$r_0 = \frac{L}{mv_0} \approx 2.195006185 \times 10^4 \text{ m}.$$

Recall that, in fact, these parameters are independent of the mass m. The orbital kinetic energy K_o of the disc, if allowed to follow its natural circular orbit, is

$$K_o = \frac{1}{2} mv_0^2 \approx 1.593019375 \times 10^9 \text{ Kg m}^2 \text{ s}^{-2}.$$

Suppose that now, as in the Hayasaka experiments, the disc spins at 18000 revolutions per minute. The disc's moment of inertia, I, is given by (7.3b), so that

$$I = \frac{mr^2}{2} \approx 9.694630715 \times 10^{-5} \text{ kg m}^2$$

and so its spin kinetic energy, given by (7.5), is

$$K_s = \frac{I\omega^2}{2} \approx (18000/60 \times 2\pi)^2/2 \times I \approx 1.722279059 \times 10^2 \text{ kg m}^2 \text{ s}^{-2}.$$

POAMS predicts that the disc's spin will have an effect on its natural circular orbit, so the present example proceeds along the same lines as Example 7.1. Suppose, first of all, that the disc spins in the same direction and in the same plane as its orbit around the earth's centre-of-mass. It then follows by (7.11) and (7.14) that the disc's orbital speed, v_s, in its natural circular orbit, if allowed to follow that orbit, is given by

$$v_s = (2(K_o + K_s)/m)^{1/2} \approx 1.349293804 \times 10^5 \text{ m s}^{-1}.$$

The radius, r_s, of that natural orbit, adjusted for spin, for constant angular momentum L, is then, by (7.12),

$$r_s = \frac{L}{mv_s} \approx 2.195006066 \times 10^4 \text{ m}.$$

Since $r_s < r_0$, it follows that the spinning disc, if allowed, would naturally orbit at a smaller distance from the earth's centre-of-mass than if it were not spinning, which is the same conclusion as reached in the previous example and in section 7.5. In other words, in its constrained orbit, the spinning disc is more 'attracted' to the earth's surface than if it were not spinning and so *weighs more*. Just how much more the disc weighs when it is spinning can be calculated as follows. It follows by (7.12), (7.13), (7.18) and (7.19) that the 'gravitational factor' $\mathcal{G}$, for the disc's natural circular orbit when spinning, is given by

$$\mathcal{G} = \frac{r_s v_s^{\,2}}{M} = \frac{L v_s}{Mm} = \frac{v_0 r_0 v_s}{M} = \frac{v_s G}{v_0}. \tag{7.21}$$

Hence, in this case,

$$\mathcal{G} \approx 1.000000054 G.$$

The weight of the disc, when not spinning, is, of course, 0.175kg. Using (6.16) and the technique of Example 6.1, this is the weight-equivalent of the force with magnitude F, where

$$F = mM(G - G')/R^2 \approx 0.175 \times 9.805865396 \text{ N} = 0.175 \text{ kg}.$$

On the other hand, the weight of the spinning disc is the weight equivalent of the force with magnitude $\mathcal{F}$, where

$$\mathcal{F} = mM(\mathcal{G} - G')/R^2 \approx 0.175 \times 9.805865927 \text{ N}$$

$$\Rightarrow \mathcal{F} \approx 1.000000054 \times 0.175 \text{ kg} \approx 0.17500000945 \text{ kg}.$$

It follows that the weight increase, due to the spin, amounts to approximately one hundredth of a milligram.

Suppose now that the disc spins in the direction opposite to that of its constrained orbit about the earth's centre-of-mass, and in the same plane. This time, the disc's speed, v_s, in its natural circular orbit, if allowed to follow that orbit, is given by (7.11) and (7.15), so that

$$v_s = (2(K_o - K_s)/m)^{1/2} \approx 1.349293658 \text{ m s}^{-1}.$$

The radius of that natural orbit is then, by (7.12),

$$r_s \approx 2.195006303 \times 10^4 \text{ m}.$$

In this case, the disc is 'less attracted' to the earth, in its constrained orbit, than when it is not spinning, so that the spinning disc weighs less. This time, (7.21) gives

$$g \approx 0.999999946G$$

and the weight of the spinning disc is the weight equivalent of the force with magnitude

$$\mathcal{F}' \approx 0.999999946 \times 0.175 \text{ kg} = 0.17499999055 \text{ kg}.$$

Hence, the spinning disc weighs about one hundredth of a milligram less than when it is not spinning.

Of course, in practice, it would be very difficult to measure the effect of spin on weight by using some sort of weighing scale. It is much more practical to record the effect of spin as what is conventionally perceived as the 'acceleration due to gravity' of a falling spinning disc, as in the Hayasaka experiments. As explained in Example 6.1, as far as POAMS is concerned, this acceleration of the freely-falling disc is due to the measurable reaction-force which ultimately prevents a body from following its natural force-free orbit way below the earth's surface.

For a circular disc of the same physical dimensions as the one already considered, it follows from the above calculations that if the disc is not spun and is dropped towards the surface of the earth at the equator, then its acceleration is F/m and so is approximately 9.805865396 m s^{-2}. On the other hand, if it is spun in the same direction and in the same plane as the earth's equatorial rotation and is then dropped, its acceleration, now $\mathcal{F}/m$, is increased by a factor of about 1.000000054. Similarly, if the disc is spun in the opposite direction and in the same plane as the earth's equatorial rotation and is then dropped, its acceleration is decreased by a factor of approximately 0.999999946.

In these calculations we have assumed that the spinning disc is situated at the equator for maximum effectiveness. In this case, the constrained orbit of the disc lies in a plane relative to the earth's centre-of-mass. It can be shown that if the disc were situated at latitude θ^o north of the equator, then the magnitude of its angular momentum relative to the earth's centre-of-mass is given by $L' = \cos\theta L$, where L is the figure calculated earlier in this example. The actual Hayasaka experiments were carried out at Sendai, which has the latitude of approximately 38° north of the equator. Replacing L by L' and performing the same sequence of calculations as above, shows that in this case the weight of the spinning disc varies between about one two-hundredth of a milligram more or less than if it were not spinning, so that the effect of spin, in the one way or the other, is predictably smaller than when the disc is situated on the equator. Note also that there may be inaccuracies in the generally accepted values we have assumed in this example. For instance, the accepted value of the Newtonian 'gravitational constant', G, was determined accurately by *terrestrial* experiments, and as such, may need a minor correction in POAMS. For this reason, our predictions may have to be taken as somewhat more qualitative than quantitative.

In the actual Hayasaka experiments, the circular disc was dropped from a fixed height and it was claimed that a difference in acceleration was detected when the disc was spun in a particular direction but not in the opposite direction. However, as far as we know, no account was taken of the vector-orientations of those spins with respect to the earth's rotation. Also, the difference in acceleration claimed was very much larger than we predict for a similar experiment performed at the equator. Indeed the effect claimed by the Tokai experiment is over 3000 times larger than our thesis predicts! Nevertheless, it is encouraging to note that these practical experiments suggest that there *is* a change in weight of an object if it is spun, even allowing for the differences outlined above.

The fact that our predicted changes in weight for Hayasaka-type experiments are extremely small accords with the findings both of Quinn and Picard [14] and of Jim Faller and his NIST team [15], who have claimed that the Hayasaka results are spurious. It is to be noted, in fairness, that Hayasaka has taken issue with this criticism [13]. In our view, in order properly to test the predictions made by POAMS, what is required is a set of consistent experiments involving the dropping, near the equator, of axially symmetric spinning objects which have a larger mass than Hayasaka's spinning disc. These experiments should take full account of the orientation of the spin in relation to the earth's rotation. Predictions of the results of such experiments involving a spinning spherical steel ball have been presented in other works [16].

Of course, we are far from being alone in our predictions of an effect on weight due to spin. For instance, General Relativity predicts that spinning bodies will not fall with the same acceleration as non-spinning ones. Peter Kummel has also claimed to have measured predicted changes in weight in the form of gravitational acceleration for spinning bodies. In his investigations, spins imparted to freely falling bodies produce anomalous 'gravitational' effects. Kummel's experiments involve the Fall Tower in Bremen, where the vertical is inclined at approximately 53° north of the equator [17]. In addition, Phillip Kanarev has argued that conservation of angular momentum changes the 'gravitational force' for rotating gyroscopes and hence their free-fall acceleration. He does not, however, provide any data for comparison and, like Hayasaka, does not take into account the orientation of the spinning object with regard to that of the earth.

7.6 POAMS at the quantum level

The departure of POAMS from Newtonian dynamics in relation to the effect of spin may appear unnecessarily radical for physics at the macroscopic level. As already remarked, the effect of spin on the motion of macroscopic bodies is relatively small, added to which, the experimental evidence for any such effects, as outlined in Example 7.2 with the spinning disc, is somewhat scanty and controversial. However, we shall demonstrate in this section that spin does play an essential role but mostly on the microphysical level. It must be remembered that in POAMS, conservation of all angular momentum applies every bit as much on the micro- as well as the macro-phenomenal scale, and that on the micro-scale, angular momentum is ultimately quantised in discrete units of $h/2\pi$. Our next example, Example 7.3, will show that the standard parameters for the hydrogen atom can be derived purely from considerations of angular momentum alone, by the incorporation of spin, without any need for the classical assumption of the existence of an *in vacuo* 'electrostatic force'. This following example will show that, at this level, in contrast to the macro-phenomenal level, the spin, or intrinsic angular momentum of 'particles' predominates over their orbital angular momentum.

The results of this Example 7.3 accord well with the fact that those elementary particles conventionally called 'electrically charged' are much more volatile in terms of the strengths of the classically conceived forces they exert on one another compared to those of 'gravity'. Indeed, so spectacularly different are the strengths of these forces that they have historically been imputed to 'powers' that differ not only quantitatively but also qualitatively from that of 'gravity'. This, we maintain, is why these powers have been allocated special units such as, for instance, 'coulombs' for 'electric charge'. All these forces are currently conceived as analogous to 'gravity' by the introduction of an inverse square law, such as Coulomb's law of electrostatics. Due to the underlying Normal Realist philosophy of POAMS, in the same way that the notion of an *in vacuo* 'gravitational force' has no place in POAMS, neither does the concept of an analogous *in vacuo* 'electrostatic force'. This section will demonstrate that just as 'gravity' (with its variations in G) is a manifestation of angular momentum, so are 'electrostatic attraction and repulsion'. In other words, as agreed by Peter Rowlands [18], angular momentum at the microphysical level is essentially a dynamical representation of the conventional static 'charge'. Although, in this section, we concentrate particularly on 'electrostatic forces', our ultimate thesis is that all the classically conceived different-strength forces may be explained in terms of angular momentum. In other words, consistently with our NR philosophy, as explained in Chapter 1, in our POAMS approach to the problem of the unification of the plethora of *in vacuo* field-forces in traditional physics is to dispense with these inscrutable vacuum forces altogether in favour of the real forces that can be actually felt and measured.

The reason why we concentrate on the hydrogen atom in this section is that it constitutes the simplest atomic system and is relatively easy to treat mathematically. As such, it has played a crucial role in the history of modern physics as a testing ground for atomic theories. As outlined in section 5.2 of Chapter 5, Bohr's model of the hydrogen atom supplied an explanation of the Balmer-Rydberg formula for the spectral lines of hydrogen, based on a mixture of classical mechanics and electrodynamical theory, plus the inclusion of the quantisation of angular momentum. In Bohr's electrodynamical approach, the behaviour of an electron in relation to a proton is explained by ascribing to each particle the purely static property called 'charge', of equal magnitude but of opposite sign. The resulting 'attractive force' between the two particles, by Coulomb's law, countered by the 'centrifugal force' exerted on the electron, then determines the orbit of the electron about the proton, by analogy with Newton's account of planetary orbits. In contrast, in POAMS the need to imagine such a counterbalance between opposing *in vacuo* forces becomes redundant. Instead, the hydrogen atom is conceived as an angular momentum system of automatically paired and balanced pure-mass equivalents of the conventional 'electron' and 'proton'. Our POAMS derivation of the standard parameters of the hydrogen atom builds upon Bohr's postulate of the ultimate discreteness of angular momentum and interprets the ionisation energy associated with this atom as being equivalent to the spin kinetic energy of the electron. In this way, we identify the conventional 'electron charge' with the spin angular momentum of the electron.

Now it must be stressed here that we are not attempting to resurrect the Bohr model of the hydrogen atom [19]. It is to be borne in mind that Quantum Mechanics predicts the same values of the standard parameters associated with the hydrogen atom as Bohr's model. The following example is therefore a viable logical demonstration of how our concepts of motion and distant interaction might have developed without postulating the existence of invisible vacuum-spanning intermediaries interlinking the parts of the atom and atoms themselves. Although our mathematical model is not intended to provide a true *physical* description of the hydrogen atom in any sense, this does not prevent us from associating vectors with the quantities involved, in the same way that vectors can be associated with the operators of Quantum Mechanics [20] [21]. Note also that the speeds of electrons in Bohr's orbits are of the order $0.01c$, so that atomic systems can be adequately described by non-relativistic theories.

EXAMPLE 7.3

Consider once again, a two-body system consisting of a particle P of mass m orbiting a body B of mass M, where now the masses are of micro dimensions. For simplicity, let P have a circular orbit about B, with $m \approx 9.1093897 \times 10^{-31}$ kg and $M \approx 1.6726231 \times 10^{-27}$ kg. For purposes of comparison, these masses have been chosen to match those of the 'electron' and 'proton' respectively, in the Bohr hydrogen atom. Of course, it must not be supposed here that we are implying that the electron physically orbits the proton in a circular orbit, or indeed in any continuous classical orbit. According to POAMS, at the ultimate microphysical level, the paths of the elementary particles are as discrete and indeterminate as the positions and motions of particles themselves.

If it is assumed that there are no spin effects present in this two-body system, then taking account of the orbital angular momentum of P alone provides natural orbital parameters for P and hence parameters for the hydrogen atom which are clearly nonsensical. For instance, assuming that P has the smallest magnitude of angular momentum available, $i.e.$, $h/2\pi$, about B, and that there are no spin effects present, then by (6.18) the speed of P in its 'orbit' about B is

$$v_0 = \frac{GmM}{L} = \frac{2\pi \, GmM}{h}. \tag{7.22}$$

Taking the known standard values of $h/2\pi \approx 1.054572749 \times 10^{-34}$ Kg m^2 s^{-1} and $G \approx 6.67259 \times 10^{-11}$ N m^2 kg^{-2}, (7.22) gives

$$v_0 \approx 9.6406267 \times 10^{-34} \text{ m s}^{-1}.$$

It then follows by (7.18) that the radius of the natural circular orbit of P about B is given by

$$r_0 = \frac{L}{mv_0} = \frac{h}{2\pi mv_0} \approx 1.2008313 \times 10^{29} \text{ m.}$$

In this scenario, the 'electron' orbits the 'proton' at a truly enormous distance, at almost zero speed, which clearly demonstrates that *orbital* angular momentum alone is not sufficient to explain the parameters of the hydrogen atom. The implication is that, in POAMS, the effects of spin become significant at the quantum level.

The hypothesis that the electron, considered as an elementary particle, has an intrinsic angular momentum, as though it were spinning, was first introduced by Uhlenbeck and Goudsmit in 1926 [22] [23]. This, of course, was not known to Bohr when he proposed his model for the atom in 1913. According to our approach, it is this spin angular momentum that provides the correct parameters for the hydrogen atom without assuming the existence of an 'electrostatic force'. Following the technique summarised in section 7.4, it is necessary to incorporate the intrinsic (spin) kinetic energy of the 'electron' P in the calculation of its orbital kinetic energy for its proper orbit about the 'proton' B. Our hypothesis is that this spin kinetic energy of the electron is the energy equivalent of the conventional 'electron charge' and so, as discussed in section 5.6 of Chapter 5, is given by

$$K_s = I_0 e = hcR \approx 2.179872 \times 10^{-18} \text{ J,}$$

where I_0 is the ionisation potential (*i.e.*, the kinetic energy required completely to remove the electron from the atom), e is the 'electron charge' and R is the Rydberg constant. This hypothesis is justified by the considerations discussed in section 5.6, and, in particular, (5.14), whereby K_s is the energy equivalent of a direct *photum* interaction between inter-resonating atoms.

Notice that the purely orbital kinetic energy, K_o, of the natural orbit of P about B, *without taking spin effects into consideration*, is

$$K_o = \frac{mv_0^2}{2} \approx 4.2332101 \times 10^{-97} \text{ J}$$

and so is negligible compared to K_s. This means that in following the technique summarised in section 7.4, we can take $\mathcal{K} \approx K_s$, where $\mathcal{K}$ is the orbital kinetic energy of the 'electron' P in its true 'circular orbit' about B, *independent* of the direction of its theoretical spin in relation to the plane of its theoretical orbit about B [24]. It then follows from (7.11) that for that same constant unit of angular momentum, $h/2\pi$, the orbital speed, v_s, of P in its natural orbit, *taking spin effects into account*, is

$$v_s = \left(\frac{2}{m}\right)^{1/2} \mathcal{K}^{1/2} \approx \left(\frac{2K_s}{m}\right)^{1/2} \approx 2.1876903 \times 10^6 \text{ m s}^{-1}.$$

This derivation of v_s should be compared to that of v given in section 5.6. Remember that in this first derivation, v was calculated from the mass of the electron using (5.13) and the energy of a *photum*, without any angular momentum considerations. The radius, r_s, of the natural orbit of P about B is then given by (7.12), so that

$$r_s = \frac{h}{2\pi m v_s} \approx 5.2917756 \times 10^{-11} \text{ m.}$$

These parameters v_s and r_s are the same as predicted both by Bohr's model [25] and by Quantum Mechanics [26] for the hydrogen atom. In POAMS, these parameters can be explained in terms of an equation of motion of the form (7.13) for some particular value of the 'gravitational factor' $\mathcal{G}$. For this 'natural orbit' of the 'electron', (7.13) gives

$$\mathcal{G} = \frac{r_s v_s^2}{M} \approx 1.5141713 \times 10^{29} \text{ N m}^2 \text{ kg}^{-2}.$$

In this way, Coulomb's law of electrostatics is replaced with what is virtually the Newtonian gravitational inverse square law, but with a different value of G [27]. It must be remembered however, that in POAMS, this is not due to some unseen force acting *in vacuo*. The reason, of course, for this huge increase in the value of G is the presence of the relatively enormous amount of the intrinsic spin kinetic energy of the 'electron', as compared with its orbital kinetic energy.

This example considers only the lowest, or ground-level state of the spinning 'electron'. It can be generalised to consider the case of an 'electron' in what is conventionally called an 'excited state' in the hydrogen atom [2].

It needs to be stressed again here that our aim in this example is simply to demonstrate philosophically how those parameters, calculated by Bohr in terms of a Newtonian dynamics laced with the electrodynamics of Faraday, Maxwell, Coulomb and others, could *logically* have been derived from Newtonian-type dynamics alone, simply by altering the value of the 'gravitational constant' G.

7.7 'Attraction' and 'repulsion' in the hydrogen atom

As discussed in sections 6.3 and 7.5, in POAMS, for a two-body system it makes good sense to talk of degrees of 'attraction' and 'repulsion' in relation to changes in the mean radius of the orbiting particle. In these terms the 'attraction' of the 'electron' to the 'proton' is so much larger than that supplied by 'gravitational' effects alone because of the enormous amount of intrinsic spin angular momentum associated with the 'electron'. In addition, since the orbital kinetic energy of the 'electron' in its natural, spin-free 'orbit' (around the so far assumed spinless 'proton' mass) is negligible compared to that of its spin kinetic energy, the arguments of the previous section imply that the relative 'attraction' of the 'electron' to the 'proton' is virtually independent of the direction of the 'electron's associated spin angular momentum with regard to that nuclear mass particle. In this final section we investigate further the rationale of this relative 'attraction' of the electron in the hydrogen atom by assigning a spin angular momentum to *each* of the conventional masses of the 'proton' and 'electron'.

Again, for convenience, we shall treat the 'electron' as orbiting the 'proton' in a circle, but once again it needs to be emphasised that our intention is far from being to provide a *physical* description of the hydrogen atom. As in Quantum Mechanics, we may associate with the 'electron' an intrinsic angular momentum of magnitude $h/4\pi$, assuming, by convention, that it behaves as if its spin angular momentum vector is perpendicular to the plane of its orbit [21][28]. Since the magnitude of the total angular momentum for the 'ground state' orbit of the 'electron' is $h/2\pi$, it is logical, in POAMS, to consider the hydrogen atom as if it were a two-body system consisting of a spinning mass P orbiting another spinning mass B, in which both masses have an associated spin angular momentum vector. It is important to appreciate here that this new situation is very different from the situations thus far considered in this chapter which concern only *one* orbiting spinning body. Here, *both* bodies are spinning in relation to each other. For simplicity, neglecting all other possible extraneous angular momentum effects, we may suppose that the total angular momentum is derived from the spin angular momenta of both the 'electron' and 'proton', each with magnitude $h/4\pi$. Since the magnitude of the total angular momentum is $h/2\pi$, the spin angular momentum vectors of the two masses must be considered as pointing in the *same* direction and hence are added. Theoretically, if the two vectors were pointing in opposite directions, then the magnitude of the total angular momentum would be zero, so that the whole atom would collapse. In this sense, these added angular momentum vectors give rise to a relative 'repulsive' effect, without the presence of which the atomic system could not exist.

The statement, then, in classical electrostatics, that 'like charges repel and unlike charges attract' is replaced in POAMS by concluding that the *magnitude* of the addition of the spin angular momentum of the 'electron' to that of its orbital angular momentum gives rise to a relative 'attraction' between the 'electron' and the 'proton' in the form of the classical Bohr atom. This classical atom does not collapse completely since there is also a relative 'repulsive' effect between the 'electron' and the 'proton' in the sense that their associated spins are alike. The POAMS conclusion, therefore, is that what provides the true picture of the phenomena of so-called 'electrostatic attraction and repulsion' is not that of static 'charges' in 'centrifugal' and 'centripetal' opposition, but the natural, automatic balance of particles in an overall conserved angular momentum system.

Our preceding analysis, then, of the hydrogen atom, which talks of particle spin as a replacement for the conventional 'charge', could be interpreted as an alternative, lateral-thinking approach to conventional 'electrostatics' based on and consistent with the neo-Machian philosophy of Normal Realism. In developing these ideas further, we propose that conventional 'magnetic' effects, also, can be explained in terms of angular momentum relations alone, without the introduction of some mysterious *in vacuo* 'magnetic force'. In classical electrodynamics, an orbiting electric charge produces a magnetic field, so that any electron generates a magnetic moment proportional to its orbital angular momentum. Analogously in POAMS, any spinning 'electron' possesses an intrinsic 'magnetic' moment proportional to its spin angular momentum. Any region of a piece of matter such as, say, iron, in which conventionally, a large number of electron-spins are vectorially aligned will therefore (in the sense previously explained) either 'attract' or 'repel' another similar piece of matter in which those electron-spins are statistically aligned in either the opposite or same directions, respectively.

We maintain, then, that in a manner similar to that in which POAMS presents an angular momentum paraphrase of 'electrostatic' orbits within atoms as that of spin-orbital relations between electron-masses and proton-masses, 'magnetic' effects can also be explained sufficiently in terms of the spin angular momentum relations between 'electrons' alone. Predictably, since the difference between the standard electron mass and proton mass is so huge (the mass of the proton being 1836 times that of the electron), the real, measurable force which it takes to resist these 'attractions' and 'repulsions' between electrons is much less than that required to separate the electron from the proton, as described in the case of the hydrogen atom. However, it must be remembered that in POAMS, this relative 'attraction' and 'repulsion' due to the directions of the spin angular momentum vectors which separate, or 'repel' 'electrons' from one another inside the higher order atoms is always holistically balanced with the relative 'attraction' between those 'electrons' and the nuclear 'protons' within the overall magnitude of the spin kinetic energies in any atom [29].

7.8 Conclusion

To conclude this chapter, we have furthered our demonstration of how our alternative, POAMS approach to natural motion may be applied to unify the various classically conceived 'gravitational', 'electrostatic' and 'magnetostatic' forces. This is by replacing them all with the concept of a single overall (*i.e.*, holistic) angular momentum nexus which includes spin along with natural orbital motion. All the usual metaphysical concepts of *in vacuo* 'fields' and 'field-forces' associated with the phenomena in question are thus made redundant. This is consistent with our Normal Realist programme of radical empiricism as applied to physics, based as it is on the concept of light as *what we see*, the fount of all physical information rather than as something 'travelling in space'. In the same way as light, angular momentum is a *phenomenon* consisting of the observed orbital behaviour of both free-moving and constrained objects, as opposed to the unseen and unseeable 'forces' of classical 'gravity', 'electricity' and 'magnetism'. The same applies to the metaphysical concept of 'electrostatic charge' which, in classical electrodynamics, is measured in conventional coulombs. By cashing out these 'coulombs' in ordinary mechanical units of joules, we translate these mysterious 'static charges' into real spin-energies, thus incorporating them into the overall angular momentum system. This solves the 'unification' of *in vacuo* 'fields' and 'field-forces' at a stroke, by dispensing with them altogether.

It is definitive, then of our Normal Realist, hence POAMS, approach to modern physics that in this overall-conserved, automatically correlated angular momentum nexus, everything links directly with everything else, from electrons and protons to galaxies. As a well-known poet puts it [30]:

> All things by immortal power,
> Near or far,
> Hiddenly
> To each other linked are
> That thou canst not stir a flower
> Without troubling of a star.

Notes and References

[1] Pope, N. V. and Osborne, A. D.: 'Instantaneous Gravitational and Inertial Action-at-a-distance', *Physics Essays*, **8** (1995) pp. 384-397.

[2] Osborne, A. D and Pope, N. V.: 'An Angular Momentum Synthesis of "Gravitational" and "Electrostatic" Forces', *Galilean Electrodynamics*, **14**, Special Issue 1 (2003) pp. 9-19.

[3] See for example, McCuskey, S. W.: *An Introduction to Advanced Dynamics* (Addison-Wesley, Reading, USA, 1965) Chapter 4.

[4] Kibble, T. W. B. and Berkshire, F. H.: *Classical Mechanics* (Addison Wesley Longman, Harlow, 1996) Chapter 9.

[5] Kibble, T. W. B and Berkshire, F. H., *ibid*, p. 161.

[6] Kibble, T. W. B and Berkshire, F. H., *ibid*, pp. 168-171.

[7] Jordan, D. W. and Smith, P.: *Mathematical Techniques* (O.U.P., 1997) pp. 271-274.

[8] *Op. cit.* reference 4, p. 162.

[9] This summary was first proposed by George Galeczki at the UIAAAD Workshop held in Swansea in July 2001. See N. Vivian Pope, Anthony D. Osborne and Alan F. T. Winfield (eds.), *Immediate Distant Action and Correlation in Modern Physics: The Balanced Universe* (Edwin Mellen, New York, 2005).

[10] Osborne, A. D, in N. Vivian Pope, Anthony D. Osborne and Alan F. T. Winfield (eds.), *Immediate Distant Action and Correlation in Modern Physics: The Balanced Universe* (Edwin Mellen, New York, 2005) p. 220.

[11] Details of the proposed experiment may be found on the website: http://einstein.stanford.edu/.

[12] Hayasaka, H. and Takeuchi, S.: 'Anomalous Weight Reduction on Gyroscope's Right Rotations Around the Vertical Axis on the Earth', *Phys. Rev. Lett.* 63 (125) (1989), pp, 2071-2704.

[13] Hayasaka, H.: 'Generation of Anti-Gravity and Complete Parity Breaking of Gravity', *Galilean Electrodynamics*, **11**, Special Issues 1, (2000) pp. 12-17.

[14] Quinn, T. J. and Picard, A.: 'The Mass of Spinning Rotors: no Dependence on Speed or Sense of Rotation', *Nature*, **343**, (16260) (1990) pp. 732-735.

[15] MacCullum, M. *New Scientist* (Feb. 1990) p. 30.

[16] *Op. cit.* reference 10, pp. 221-224.

[17] Kümmel, P.: *Schubdraller: Raumfahrtanteib durch ROTATIONS-AMG.* Handeloh (2001).

[18] *Op. cit.* reference 10, p. 45.

[19] However, as Sutton states: "Bohr's theory of atomic structure, whatever its limitations, is a good example of the application of basic physics principles." See Sutton, R. M., *Encyclopædia Britannica* **17** (1961) p. 871c.

[20] Christy, R. W. and Pytte, A.: *The Structure of Matter: An Introduction to Modern Physics* (Benjamin, New York, 1965), p. 371.

[21] The fact that we do not require quantum mechanics to study the hydrogen atom can be justified by Ehrenfest's theorem, which states that the expectation values of quantum mechanical operators behave in the same manner as do the corresponding systems in classical mechanics. See Ehrenfest, P.: *Z. Phys.* **45** (192) p. 455.

[22] *Op. cit.* reference 20, p. 363.

[23] In Quantum Mechanics, electron spin was originally introduced to explain empirical evidence concerning atoms with a larger atomic number than hydrogen. For example, the observed

ionisation energy of the element mercury is partially explained by the adoption of the Pauli Exclusion Principle, which states that only one electron can occupy a particular energy state. In applying this principle, the intrinsic angular momentum of the electron must be taken into account.

[24] According to Quantum Mechanics, there are only two possible spin states for the electron, which are conventionally labelled 'up' or 'down'. Analogously, in POAMS it is possible conventionally to assign an intrinsic angular momentum vector to the 'electron', which points either parallel to its orbital angular momentum vector or in the opposite direction. Since, from section 7.3, $\mathcal{K} = K_o + K_s$ in the first case and $\mathcal{K} = K_s - K_o$ in the second, $\mathcal{K} \approx K_s$ in either case, so that the direction of spin has no effect on the parameters of the orbit of P.

[25] *Op. cit.* reference 20, pp. 292-297.

[26] *Op. cit.* reference 20, Chapter 21.

[27] This value of g may be referred to as the *Coulombian*, as apposed to the Newtonian value of G.

[28] In the vector approach to quantum theory, the component of the spin angular momentum vector of the electron, perpendicular to the plane of its orbit, is taken to be $\pm h/4\pi$.

[29] This accords well with the traditional view, as expounded George Galeczki, who states, 'At very short distances, like those in the helium atom, two electrons form a "closed configuration" due to the attraction between anti-parallel spins, which seems to overcome the strong 'Coulomb repulsion' between the electrons" (here conceived, by Galeczki, in the conventional way as orbiting charges).

[30] From the 'Mistress of Vision' 1., by Francis Thompson (1859-1907).

CHAPTER 8

Orbital Time-dilation and Schwarzschild Space-Time

8.1 Introduction

In General Relativity, Einstein's conception of the light-quantum as a travelling particle, the so-called 'photon', leads to the further conception of an absolute space-time continuum in which those 'photons' travel, at the 'speed' c in paths like those of ships and aeroplanes constrained to follow the curve of the earth's surface. In our Normal Realist (NR) account of motion, this conception of an absolute space-time continuum makes no physical sense, especially in the context of our view of physical reality as an ultimately quantised angular momentum *discretum*. Nevertheless, an overall conserved and balanced nexus of instantaneous, discrete and intransitive quantum resonances between atoms does provide a continuum of sorts, which is as objective as needs be insofar as it is projected by a community of interacting 'observers' – where, by 'observers', we mean interagents of all kinds, animal, vegetable and mineral. These may be complex, like ourselves or rudimentary, such as molecules and atoms, all of which interrelate to constitute the physical world.

In general then, the same geometrical (or, rather, geometro-temporal) conditions apply to this angular momentum discretum as to the 'space-time continuum' of General Relativity (GR), as may be seen in the following sections. It is to be emphasised, however, that the mathematics in this chapter expresses measures pertaining to *phenomena*, which are essentially observational, *i.e.*, empirical, not to entities of esoteric conception, as in GR.

Earlier in this book, we were concerned with effects associated with high speed uniform motion, customarily called 'inertial'. In Chapter 3 we stressed the importance of the time-dilation formula, (3.2), for this kind of relative motion. Starting with a study of ideally uniform (rectilinear) motion, we were able to present our Normal Realist alternative to Special Relativity (SR). This lateral-thinking alternative to Einsteinian Relativity provides not only a more philosophically coherent account of relative motion, of which Mach would surely have approved, but also a derivation of all the standard results of SR in a more conceptually economical manner.

In that same neo-phenomenalist way we now turn our attention to General Relativity. That standard orthodox theory is customarily presented as an addendum to SR. By contrast, in Normal Realism, these two theoretically separate aspects of relative motion, the Special and the General – the 'rectilinear' and the 'curvilinear' – are integrated within a single, unified philosophical (*i.e.*, neo-Machian) approach to the phenomenon of motion. This is because this alternative approach is based on the empirical fact that nowhere is any absolutely rectilinear free motion, *in extensio*, ever observed [1]. In the Pope-Osborne Angular Momentum Synthesis (POAMS), all unconstrained motion is naturally curved, as fully explained in Chapter 6. Recall that the fundamental postulates of POAMS are, essentially, that all free motion is a manifestation of angular momentum and that angular momentum is, self-sufficiently, holistically conserved. This defines the POAMS alternative to the Newtonian theory of 'universal gravitation' as the cause of non-rectilinear motion. Such a radical shift in thinking clearly puts the onus on us to explain how the well-authenticated phenomenon of relativistic time-dilation applies to naturally curvilinear or orbital motion. This produces our POAMS unified alternative to Einstein's theoretical duo, Special and General Relativity. Like GR, our Synthesis now addresses the phenomenon of natural curvilinear motion which (unnecessarily, in our view) is commonly attributed to 'gravitation'.

In this chapter, then, we demonstrate that by incorporating time-dilation in the POAMS account of natural orbital motion, it is possible to derive an NR paraphrase of the esoteric 'space-time continuum' of General Relativity, as Karl Schwarzschild described it [2]. In this way, POAMS offers the simplest solution of Einstein's Field Equations of GR and so provides predictions concerning our solar system which are directly verifiable by experiment and observation [3]. We maintain, therefore, that our alternative derivation of the Schwarzschild solution is more conceptually economical than in GR (*pace* 'Ockham's razor'). This is because it does not require what we regard as anything like the theoretical over-elaboration of GR which stems from its demonstrably over-complicated mathematical infrastructure.

Having said that, the mathematics required for the arguments presented in this chapter are necessarily more advanced than those required for previous chapters. In order to guide the non-specialist mathematician through this chapter, a summary of the mathematical and conceptual results will be provided in the text where appropriate. In addition, a *résumé* of the conclusions so far is supplied at the end of the chapter.

8.2 Time-dilation in general motion

To summarise the time-dilation result, (3.2), of Chapter 3, if a clock X moves *uniformly* relative to an observer O, so that X follows a rectilinear path at constant speed v relative to O, then during the passage of time t, as recorded by O, X records a passage of proper time, τ, given by

$$\tau = \left(1 - v^2/c^2\right)^{1/2} t . \tag{8.1}$$

More generally, let the clock X move with a (not necessarily constant) velocity, $\mathbf{v}(t)$, relative to the observer O, and let $v(t) = \|\mathbf{v}(t)\|$ denote the speed of X relative to O. Then, as demonstrated in section 3.8, in the passage of time, t, as recorded by O, X records a passage of proper time, τ, given by

$$\frac{d\tau}{dt} = \left(1 - v^2(t)/c^2\right)^{1/2} . \tag{8.2}$$

Of course, equation (8.2) includes (8.1) as a special case and if the relative speed, $v(t)$, of X is constant, even if its velocity is not constant, then (8.2) reduces to (8.1). Remember that in any case, since the proper time, τ, is the passage of time recorded on a clock moving relatively to any observer, it serves as an observer-independent parameter, whereas the coordinate time, t, is dependent on the observer.

In terms of Cartesian coordinates, (x, y, z), the speed of a moving object relative to an observer recording coordinate time, t, satisfies

$$v^2(t) = \left(\frac{dx}{dt}\right)^2 + \left(\frac{dy}{dt}\right)^2 + \left(\frac{dz}{dt}\right)^2,$$

so that (8.2) may be written as,

$$c^2\left(\frac{d\tau}{dt}\right)^2 = c^2 - \left(\frac{dx}{dt}\right)^2 - \left(\frac{dy}{dt}\right)^2 - \left(\frac{dz}{dt}\right)^2$$

and hence,

$$c^2 d\tau^2 = c^2 dt^2 - dx^2 - dy^2 - dz^2. \tag{8.3}$$

This equation (8.3) is the well-known *metric* for Minkowski space-time, the underlying mathematical structure of Special Relativity, but in our approach it is the case that $d\tau^2 \geq 0$ only. Within this Minkowskian metrical structure, the natural paths of material particles, that is, of *freely moving* particles in the sense to be described presently, are straight lines. This is a reflection of the fact that in SR, the paths followed by freely moving material particles in physical space are assumed to be rectilinear. Hence, (8.2) is the formula for the time-dilation effect taking into account only constant relative speed. In this scenario, any path for which the velocity of the moving clock, X, is *not* constant (*i.e.* a curved path) represents a path along which X is not freely moving but is *constrained* in some sense.

Bearing this in mind, as a first (somewhat simplistic) attempt at integrating time-dilation effects into POAMS, let us apply (8.2) directly to the equations of motion determined in Chapter 6 [4]. Once again, we shall consider only the isolated two-body system consisting of a particle P of mass m following a trajectory relative to the centre-of-mass of a body B of mass M, with m very much smaller than M. As demonstrated in section 6.3, if P follows a natural path relative to B, then its most general equation of motion is

$$\frac{d^2 r}{dt^2} - \frac{L^2}{m^2 r^3} = -h(r), \tag{8.4}$$

for some function $h(r)$, where $r(t)$ gives the radial distance of P from the centre-of-mass of B at any time t, and L is the magnitude of P's angular momentum with respect to B, which is constant (see equation (6.10)). As demonstrated in that section, if it is a requirement that at least some of the solutions of (8.4) provide *closed* orbits, then $h(r)$ must take the form $h(r) = \alpha/r^2$ for some constant α. In this case, POAMS reproduces the Newtonian equation of motion, for which $\alpha = GM$, so that natural orbits of P are given by

$$\frac{d^2 r}{dt^2} - \frac{L^2}{m^2 r^3} = -\frac{GM}{r^2},$$

(8.5)

where G is simply a constant introduced for convenience. (As noted in Chapter 6, in practice, (8.4) or (8.5) is used in conjunction with (6.7) in order to study the orbit of P.) However, it is necessary to emphasise here that POAMS does *not* stipulate that the orbit of P has to be closed. Hence, the POAMS equation, (8.4), for natural orbital motion, is more general than the Newtonian equation (8.5).

Solving (8.5) in the standard way [5], as indicated in Chapter 6, gives $r(t)$, and then (6.5) and (6.7) show that the speed, $v(t)$, of P is given by

$$v^2(t) = \left(\frac{dr}{dt}\right)^2 + \frac{L^2}{m^2 r^2}.$$

(8.6)

Substituting (8.6) into (8.2) then gives the time-dilation along any natural orbit determined by velocity effects alone in the same way as in Special Relativity. The result is further simplified when we note that the first integral of (8.5) is

$$\left(\frac{dr}{dt}\right)^2 + \frac{L^2}{m^2 r^2} = \frac{2GM}{r} + C,$$

where C is a constant (see equation (6.11)). This result, when substituting (8.6) into (8.2), then produces

$$\frac{d\tau}{dt} = \left(1 - \frac{2GM}{c^2 r} - \frac{C}{c^2}\right)^{1/2}.$$

(8.7)

This equation (8.7) gives the proper time, τ, as recorded by a clock travelling with the freely moving particle P in its orbit about the body B, where t is that same passage of time as recorded by the local clock of an observer for whom the speed of P is given by (8.6), again taking into account only the effects due to relative speed [6]. In POAMS, all observations are relative to the 'alpha frame', *i.e.* Mach's 'fixed frame of the stars', for which r tends to infinity in (8.7). Hence, the relative time t in (8.7) can be regarded as the time recorded by an 'external observer' far distant from the orbit of P which, in GR, is usually termed 'coordinate time'. In POAMS, this datum time is called *deep space time* (DST) [7].

Note that the constant C in (8.7) is not completely arbitrary and depends on the total energy, E, of P's orbit [8]. As shown in section 6.3, $C = 2E/m$. Hence, for example, if P's orbit is *closed*, then, as shown in section 6.3, E is less than zero, so that C is less than 0 in (8.7).

Of particular interest is the case in which P follows a natural *circular* orbit about B. It follows from section 6.3 that the speed of P around such an orbit is given by

$$v^2 = \frac{GM}{r}, \tag{8.8}$$

where r is now the constant radius of the circle, so that v is also constant. In this case, substituting (8.8) into (8.2), which now reduces to (8.1), gives

$$\tau = \left(1 - \frac{GM}{c^2 r}\right)^{1/2} t. \tag{8.9}$$

Of course, this formula is just (8.7) where C takes the special value $C = -GM/r$. Once again, (8.9) gives the time-dilation determined by effects due to relative speed alone, but this time in a natural circular orbit. Here, τ is the proper time recorded on P's clock and, as previously, t represents deep space time (DST). It follows by (8.9) that the closer P is to the body B, the greater the time-dilation effect. In other words, clocks in natural circular orbits, as they are further away from the central body B run faster than clocks closer to B, relative to DST. Clearly, in (8.7) there is a necessary lower bound placed on r given by

$$1 - \frac{GM}{c^2 r} > 0 \implies r > \frac{GM}{c^2}.$$

This lower bound presents no problem in general, since it is much less than the radius of any planet or stable star. For example, for Earth, GM/c^2 is approximately half a kilometre!

Although at first sight, due to considerations of conservation of angular momentum, equations (8.7) and (8.9) seem to account for the fact that P is in a particular orbit around the body B, since these results depend, directly, only on the speed of P in its orbit, they would apply equally well if P were travelling in a straight line with the same speed v. Hence, as emphasised previously, these conventional results do not take into account, in the way POAMS does, the fact that natural orbits, *i.e.*, those followed by freely moving particles, are *not* straight lines. In POAMS, in order to determine the true time-dilation effect on natural orbits it is necessary to investigate the idea of geodesics in an observational space-time. The results of this investigation are described in the next section.

8.3 Geodesics in a space-time

A *geodesic* traced on any two-dimensional surface in Euclidean space may be thought of as the generalisation of a straight line in Euclidean space itself, in the sense that it is the curve amongst all the possible curves of shortest length joining two points on a given surface. For example, on a sphere such as, approximately, the surface of the earth, the geodesics are the lines of longitude and more generally, the arcs of great circles, which are of the utmost importance in terrestrial navigation. A two-dimensional surface can be generalised to a mathematical structure known as an *n-dimensional Riemannian manifold*, or *n-dimensional Riemannian space*. Essentially, such a structure consists of points which can be described by a set of n local coordinates, such that any transformation of coordinates is twice differentiable, possessing a *metric* or *line element* that gives some sort of measure of 'distance' [9]. Minkowski space-time is an example of a four-dimensional Riemannian space, with metric (8.3). It is to be noted, in passing, that there already exists a well-developed theory for the determination of geodesics on Riemannian spaces in general [10][11].

In our POAMS approach to true (*i.e.*, orbital) time-dilation, it is necessary only to determine the geodesics for one Riemannian space in particular and hence it is not necessary to involve this general theory. In order to treat the determination of geodesics as simply as possible, we present the ideas by the following initial example.

Consider the particular case of Minkowski space-time (MST) which, in terms of the standard coordinate system, consists of *events* of the form (t, x, y, z), together with the metric (8.3). This metric, in our treatment, is the formula for the proper time, τ, in terms of these standard coordinates (see Chapter 3, section 8). Our physical intuition tells us that paths followed by freely moving particles in MST are precisely the paths for which the minimum *proper* time is taken by the particle in moving from one event to another. In general, we shall define a *geodesic* as just such a curve.

Any curve in MST which represents the path of a material particle, can be described by a parametric equation of the form

$$\mathbf{R} = \mathbf{R}(\tau) = (t(\tau), x(\tau), y(\tau), z(\tau))$$

(see Chapter 4, section 4). Consider all such curves which join an event A, given by $\tau = a$, to an event B, given by $\tau = b$. It follows by (8.3) that

$$\left(\frac{dt}{d\tau}\right)^2 - \frac{1}{c^2}\left(\frac{dx}{d\tau}\right)^2 - \frac{1}{c^2}\left(\frac{dy}{d\tau}\right)^2 - \frac{1}{c^2}\left(\frac{dz}{d\tau}\right)^2 = 1,$$

so that the proper time taken between event A and event B on any such curve is given by

$$I = \int_a^b \left(\left(\frac{dt}{d\tau}\right)^2 - \frac{1}{c^2}\left(\frac{dx}{d\tau}\right)^2 - \frac{1}{c^2}\left(\frac{dy}{d\tau}\right)^2 - \frac{1}{c^2}\left(\frac{dz}{d\tau}\right)^2\right) d\tau. \qquad (8.10)$$

From all the possible curves joining A to B, we wish to find those which give the minimum proper time and so the minimum value of the integral in (8.10). The integral in (8.10) is a special case of the more general integral

$$I = \int_a^b T(y_1, y_2, ..., y_n, y_1', y_2', ..., y_n') d\lambda, \tag{8.11}$$

where y_1, y_2, ..., y_n are n coordinates, λ is a chosen parameter and a dash denotes differentiation with respect to λ. It can be shown that the curves which maximise or minimise the integral in (8.11) are given by the Euler-Lagrange equations [12]

$$\frac{d}{d\lambda}\left(\frac{\partial T}{\partial y_k'}\right) - \frac{\partial T}{\partial y_k} = 0, \, k = 1, 2, ..., n. \tag{8.12}$$

(Some technical conditions have to be placed on the possible curves in order for (8.12) to hold [13].) In the particular case of (8.10),

$$T = t'^2 - \frac{x'^2}{c^2} - \frac{y'^2}{c^2} - \frac{z'^2}{c^2},$$

where a dash denotes differentiation with respect to τ. Then the curves which minimise the integral in (8.10) are given by (8.12) with this particular T, i.e.,

$$\frac{d}{d\tau}\left(\frac{\partial T}{\partial t'}\right) - \frac{\partial T}{\partial t} = \frac{d}{d\tau}(2t') = 0 \Rightarrow \frac{dt}{d\tau} = \alpha_1, \frac{d}{d\tau}\left(\frac{\partial T}{\partial x'}\right) - \frac{\partial T}{\partial x} = \frac{d}{d\tau}\left(-\frac{2x'}{c^2}\right) = 0 \Rightarrow \frac{dx}{d\tau} = \alpha_2$$

and, similarly, $dy/d\tau = \alpha_3$, $dz/d\tau = \alpha_4$, where α_1, α_2, α_3 and α_4 are constants. It follows that the geodesics for MST, i.e. the paths of freely moving particles in MST, are given by

$$\mathbf{R} = \mathbf{R}(\tau) = (\alpha_1\tau + \beta_1, \, \alpha_2\tau + \beta_2, \, \alpha_3\tau + \beta_3, \, \alpha_4\tau + \beta_4),$$

where β_1, β_2, β_3 and β_4 are also constants. This is the parametric equation of any straight line and so the geodesics in MST are straight lines. In particular, the spatial coordinates x, y and z are linear functions of τ, confirming that the paths of freely moving particles in Minkowski space are rectilinear. This agrees with what we have reasoned in the previous section.

In general, then, our thesis is that for any space-time geometry given by a particular time-dilation formula, freely moving particles in space satisfy the geodesic equations for that space-time, the geodesics being the curves which minimise the proper time between any two events in that particular space-time [14].

8.3.1 Summary of section

In POAMS we postulate that freely moving particles in space follow geodesics in a phenomenologically relativistic space-time, which are the curves that minimise the proper time taken by a material particle in moving from one point-event to another. The geodesics in Minkowski space-time are straight lines so that with this structure, all freely moving space-travelling material particles describe ideally rectilinear paths. This follows from the fact that MST is a direct consequence of the time-dilation formula, (8.1), for linear motion in Special Relativity. It is incumbent on us, therefore, in our Normal Realist curvilinear-motion terms, to provide a replacement for MST which takes account of the fact that in POAMS, natural motion is *not* rectilinear. This requirement is addressed in the following sections.

8.4 True time-dilation in circular motion

Consider once again an isolated two-body system consisting of a particle P orbiting a body of mass M, whose centre-of-mass lies at the origin of a plane polar coordinate system, (r, θ), as in section 6.3. The key to understanding the true time-dilation effect for any natural orbit of P comes from consideration of the simple case of a circular orbit. If P is freely moving in its circular orbit about M, then it follows that the proper time, τ, as recorded by a clock travelling with P, relative to DST t, taking only velocity effects into account, is given by (8.9), *i.e.*,

$$\tau = \left(1 - \frac{GM}{c^2 r}\right)^{1/2} t \approx \left(1 - \frac{GM}{2c^2 r}\right) t,$$

using the binomial series, which is valid since $GM/(c^2 r) < 1$. We shall suppose that the mass M is spherically symmetric and static. Then any additional time-dilation effect can depend only on M and the distance, r, of P from M. From (8.9), it is reasonable to suppose that any such additional effect is proportional to M/r. Hence we postulate that the true proper time as recorded by P's clock relative to DST is given by

$$\tau = \left(1 - \frac{GM}{c^2 r} - \frac{aGM}{c^2 r}\right)^{1/2} t \, ,$$

(8.13)

where a is a constant to be determined. At least we know that (8.9) is included as a special case of (8.13), when $a = 0$. It is convenient to denote the constant GM/c^2 by $\mathcal{M}$. Then using (8.8), (8.13) becomes

$$\tau = (1 - v^2/c^2 - a\mathcal{M}/r)^{1/2} t \Rightarrow c^2 \left(\frac{d\tau}{dt}\right)^2 = c^2 - v^2 - a\mathcal{M}\frac{c^2}{r} \, .$$

Recall that the speed of P in its circular orbit satisfies $v = r(d\theta/dt)$, (see (6.5)), so that (8.13) now reads

$$c^2 d\tau^2 = c^2(1 - a\mathcal{M}/r)dt^2 - r^2 d\theta^2 \, .$$

(8.14)

Taken on its own, (8.14) is no help in determining the value of a, since it is a representation of circular motion only, so that the geodesics associated with this two-dimensional space-time are necessarily circles. Once again, the geodesics may be thought of as the curves which minimise the proper time taken by a material particle (as opposed to 'photons') in moving from one event to another. In this case, it follows by (8.14) that we wish to minimise the integral

$$I = \int_a^b \left((1 - a\mathcal{M}/r)\left(\frac{dt}{d\tau}\right)^2 - \frac{r^2}{c^2}\left(\frac{d\theta}{d\tau}\right)^2 \right) d\tau,$$

with respect to all curves joining $(t(\tau = a), \theta(\tau = a))$ to $(t(\tau = b), \theta(\tau = b))$. Using (8.12), the geodesics in this case are given by

$$\frac{d}{d\tau}\left(\frac{\partial T}{\partial t'}\right) - \frac{\partial T}{\partial t} = 0 \text{ (a)}, \quad \frac{d}{d\tau}\left(\frac{\partial T}{\partial \theta'}\right) - \frac{\partial T}{\partial \theta} = 0 \text{ (b)},$$

(8.15)

where now

$$T = (1 - a\mathcal{M}/r)t'^2 - (r/c)^2 \theta'^2$$

and a dash denotes differentiation with respect to τ. In this case, equations (8.15) give

$$\frac{d}{d\tau}(2(1 - aMr)t') = 0 \text{ (a)}, \quad \frac{d}{d\tau}\left(-2(r/c)^2\theta'\right) = 0 \text{ (b)},$$

that is,

$$\frac{dt}{d\tau} = \alpha(1 - aMr)^{-1} \text{ (a)}, \quad \frac{d\theta}{d\tau} = \frac{\beta}{r^2} \text{ (b)}, \tag{8.16}$$

where α and β are constants. These equations express simply the fact that t and θ are linear functions of τ, with r constant and so, as we already know, provide solutions which are circles, without determining the value of a.

However, we may treat the two-dimensional space-time with metric (8.14) as a special case of the more general three-dimensional space-time with metric

$$c^2 d\tau^2 = c^2(1 - aMr)dt^2 - B(r)dr^2 - r^2 d\theta^2, \tag{8.17}$$

in the special case when r is a constant. This equation gives the time-dilation on any general natural orbit in POAMS. For the moment, the coefficient of dr^2, i.e. $B(r)$, in (8.17) is unknown, but it must be a function of r alone, since the central mass M is assumed to be spherically symmetric and static. In order to determine the value of a, we require that natural circular orbits in POAMS, given by (8.8), are circular geodesics in the space-time with metric (8.17). Fortunately we do not require the specific form of $B(r)$ at this point in order to obtain a. The geodesics for the space-time with metric (8.17) are the curves which minimise the integral

$$I = \int_a^b \left((1 - aMr)\left(\frac{dt}{d\tau}\right)^2 - \frac{B}{c^2}\left(\frac{dr}{d\tau}\right)^2 - \frac{r^2}{c^2}\left(\frac{d\theta}{d\tau}\right)^2\right)d\tau.$$

Using (8.12), these curves are given by equations (8.15), together with

$$\frac{d}{d\tau}\left(\frac{\partial T}{\partial r'}\right) - \frac{\partial T}{\partial r} = 0, \tag{8.18}$$

where T is now

$$T = (1 - aMr)t'^2 - (r/c)^2\theta'^2 - (B(r)/c^2)r'^2 \tag{8.19}$$

and r is not, in general, a constant. Equations (8.15) still produce equations (8.16), but with r not a constant in general, and (8.18) provides the additional equation

$$\frac{d}{d\tau}\left(-2(B(r)/c^2)r'\right) - \left((aM/r^2)t'^2 - (2r/c^2)\,\theta'^2 - (B'(r)/c^2)\,r'^2\right) = 0,$$

where $B'(r)$ denotes the derivative of $B(r)$ with respect to r. This equation simplifies to

$$2\frac{d^2r}{d\tau^2} + (ac^2MBr^2)\left(\frac{dt}{d\tau}\right)^2 + \frac{B'(r)}{B}\left(\frac{dr}{d\tau}\right)^2 = \frac{2r}{B}\left(\frac{d\theta}{d\tau}\right)^2. \qquad (8.20)$$

Geodesics in the space-time with metric (8.17), which are circles in space, are given by (8.16) and (8.20) with r constant. In particular, (8.20) with r constant simplifies considerably to

$$(ac^2MBr^2)\left(\frac{dt}{d\tau}\right)^2 = \frac{2r}{B}\left(\frac{d\theta}{d\tau}\right)^2,$$

that is,

$$ac^2M\left(\frac{dt}{d\tau}\right)^2 = 2r^3\left(\frac{d\theta}{d\tau}\right)^2, \qquad (8.21)$$

a condition which is independent of B. It then follows from (8.21) that for any natural circular orbit, since r is constant and $v = r(d\theta/dt)$ in such an orbit,

$$\frac{v^2}{r^2} = \left(\frac{d\theta}{dt}\right)^2 = \left(\frac{d\theta}{d\tau}\right)^2\left(\frac{d\tau}{dt}\right)^2 = \frac{ac^2}{2r^3}M \Rightarrow v^2 = \frac{aGM}{2r}.$$

Comparing this equation with (8.8) it follows immediately that in order for these circular orbits to be the natural circular orbits in POAMS, $\underline{a = 2}$. Then (8.13) gives the true time-dilation effect in any natural circular orbit and the two remaining geodesic equations, (8.16), are automatically satisfied.

8.4.1 Summary of section

The time-dilation formula, (8.9), for circular orbits, does not take into account, in the way POAMS does, the fact that these are the natural circular orbits followed by 'freely moving particles'. In order to address this problem, we adjust (8.9) in the form of equation (8.13) and calculate the value of the constant a by postulating that the natural circular orbits of POAMS are the circular geodesics of the associated space-time, *i.e.*, the circular paths followed by freely moving particles in this phenomenological space-time. This gives $a = 2$. By (8.13), the true proper time (*i.e.*, relative to DST) recorded by the clock of a particle P in its natural circular orbit about a static and spherically symmetric body, taking into account not only the velocity effects, is then given by

$$\tau = \left(1 - \frac{3GM}{rc^2}\right)^{1/2} t.$$
(8.22)

This equation (8.22) is the formula predicted by General Relativity for time-dilation on a circular geodesic except that in this instance r does not measure exactly the radial distance from the origin [15]. Equations (8.22) and (8.9), taken together, form the basis of calculations which clearly demonstrate that clocks in the Global Positioning Satellites in orbit around Earth run faster relative to Earth clocks by an amount which agrees with observations [16].

This analysis shows that time is dilated even on a *relatively stationary* clock in the neighbourhood of a massive spherically symmetric static body. In this case, in (8.13) there is no effect from relative speed and so, with $v = 0$ and $a = 2$, this equation reduces to

$$\tau = \left(1 - \frac{2GM}{rc^2}\right)^{1/2} t$$
(8.23)

and gives the proper time recorded on a relatively stationary clock relative to DST. This equation may also be obtained from the general time-dilation formula (8.17), since, in this case, r and θ are constant and (8.17) reduces to

$$\left(\frac{d\tau}{dt}\right)^2 = 1 - aMr = 1 - \frac{2GM}{rc^2}.$$

Once again, (8.23) is the same equation as produced in GR [17] in which time-dilation is a consequence of 'gravitational effects' alone. In our POAMS rendering of these same equations, of course, all talk of 'gravitation', in whatever sense, is redundant.

8.5 General orbital time-dilation: Schwarzschild space-time

Once again, let us consider a particle P on a natural trajectory in the neighbourhood of a static and spherically symmetric body B. In the last section, we have shown that in POAMS the time-dilation formula for P's clock is given by (8.17) with $a = 2$, i.e.,

$$c^2 d\tau^2 = c^2(1 - 2M/r)dt^2 - B(r)dr^2 - r^2 d\theta^2. \qquad (8.24)$$

This includes the time-dilation formula, (8.22) for natural circular orbits as a special case. Remember that $M = MG/c^2$, where M is the mass of the body B. We now need to determine the explicit form of the function $B(r)$. Again, we may treat (8.24) as the metric for a three-dimensional space-time. The geodesics for this space-time are given by equations (8.16) and (8.20) with $a = 2$. It also follows from this metric that along any geodesic,

$$c^2(1 - 2M/r)\left(\frac{dt}{d\tau}\right)^2 - B(r)\left(\frac{dr}{d\tau}\right)^2 - r^2\left(\frac{d\theta}{d\tau}\right)^2 = c^2. \qquad (8.25)$$

It can be checked that differentiating (8.25) with respect to τ, and using equations (8.16) with $a = 2$, gives (8.20) with $a = 2$. Hence, in practice, the geodesics for the space-time with metric (8.24) are completely determined by (8.25) and equations (8.16) with $a = 2$, i.e.,

$$\frac{dt}{d\tau} = \alpha\,(1 - 2M/r)^{-1}\;\text{(a)}, \quad \frac{d\theta}{d\tau} = \frac{\beta}{r^2}\;\text{(b)}. \qquad (8.26)$$

Having noted in the last section that natural circular orbits do not determine the function $B(r)$, we now consider non-circular geodesics given by (8.25) and (8.26). Ignoring, for the present, the case of radial 'free-fall', in which θ is constant, it is more convenient to find the equations of non-circular natural paths in space in the form $u = 1/r = u(\theta)$, as in Chapter 6. The geodesic equations (8.25) and (8.26) have to provide an equation which approximates to the Newtonian equation, (6.12) with $H(u) = GMu$, for non-circular natural paths, since the solutions to this equation produce natural closed orbits, i.e., ellipses, in good agreement with the empirical evidence. Recall that it was shown in Chapter 6 that the more general

POAMS equation of motion, (8.4), also gives (6.12), so long as *closed* natural orbits are required.

Multiplying (8.25) by $(d\tau/d\theta)^2$ and using the chain rule gives

$$c^2(1 - 2Mr)\left(\frac{dt}{d\tau}\right)^2\left(\frac{d\tau}{d\theta}\right)^2 - B(r)\left(\frac{dr}{d\theta}\right)^2 - r^2 = c^2\left(\frac{d\tau}{d\theta}\right)^2.$$

Then using equations (8.26), this equation reduces to

$$\frac{\alpha^2 c^2 r^4}{\beta^2}(1 - 2Mr)^{-1} - B(r)\left(\frac{dr}{d\theta}\right)^2 - r^2 = \frac{c^2 r^4}{\beta^2}$$

$$\Rightarrow \frac{\alpha^2 c^2 r^4}{\beta^2} - B(r)(1 - 2Mr)\left(\frac{dr}{d\theta}\right)^2 - r^2(1 - 2Mr) = \frac{c^2 r^4}{\beta^2}(1 - 2Mr).$$

Letting $r = 1/u$, as in section 6.3, then gives

$$B(u)(1 - 2Mu)\left(\frac{du}{d\theta}\right)^2 + u^2 = k + 2M\frac{c^2 u}{\beta^2} + 2Mu^3, \tag{8.27}$$

where $k = c^2(\alpha^2 - 1)/\beta^2$. In POAMS, (8.27) describes any non-circular natural orbit (with θ not constant) of the particle P about the body B. Notice that the term $2Mu^3$ in (8.27) is almost negligible for planetary orbits or satellites orbiting planets. For example, a satellite may orbit Earth at a distance $r = 3 \times 10^7$ metres and in this case, $2Mu^3 \approx 3 \times 10^{-25}$. Hence, (8.27) is very nearly

$$B(u)(1 - 2Mu)\left(\frac{du}{d\theta}\right)^2 + u^2 = k + \frac{2MGu}{\beta^2}.$$

This equation reduces to the corresponding Newtonian equation, (6.12), with $H(u) = GMu$, i.e.,

$$\left(\frac{du}{d\theta}\right)^2 + u^2 = k + \frac{2MGu}{\beta^2}, \tag{8.28}$$

and so provides closed elliptical orbits if and only if $B(u) = (1 - 2Mu)^{-1}$. Hence, we claim that it is this particular function $B(r)$, which must appear in the time-dilation formula, (8.24), for natural orbits in general.

8.5.1 Summary of section

We have identified the time-dilation formula, (8.24), with the metric for a three-dimensional phenomenological space-time. The geodesic equations for this space-time provide equation (8.27), whose solutions represent the possible non-circular paths (*i.e.*, with θ not constant) of a freely moving particle P about a body B. Equation (8.27) must approximate to the corresponding Newtonian equation, (8.28), in order to agree with observational and empirical evidence. This is so if and only if $B(u) = (1 - 2\mathcal{M}u)^{-1}$. Then the space-time metric (8.24) must read

$$c^2 d\tau^2 = c^2(1 - 2\mathcal{M}r)dt^2 - (1 - 2\mathcal{M}r)^{-1}dr^2 - r^2 d\theta^2. \tag{8.29}$$

This is the metric for the 'equatorial plane' of Schwarzschild space-time as derived in General Relativity [18]. (Although Schwarzschild space-time is four-dimensional, it is spherically symmetric, so it is always possible for it to work in the equatorial plane with loss of generality [19].) In our approach, (8.29) gives the time-dilation formula for any natural orbit, *i.e.*, (8.25) with $B(r) = (1 - 2\mathcal{M}r)^{-1}$.

Hence, in the same way that the time-dilation formula, (8.1), for uniform motion leads to Minkowski space-time in SR, incorporating the fact that in POAMS the paths of freely moving particles are not straight lines, inevitably leads to the Schwarzschild space-time in GR. However, in contrast to GR, the POAMS derivation of (8.29) does not depend on the Einsteinian 'gravitational' Field Equations but only on the Euler-Lagrange equations, (8.12). Also, since (8.29) is dependent ultimately on the time-dilation formula for circular motion, *i.e.* (8.22), it follows that r is greater than $3\mathcal{M}$ in (8.29). Hence, again in contrast to GR, in POAMS it is not possible to extrapolate and apply (8.29) to 'gravitational collapse' to obtain esoteric 'space-time singularities' [20]. Whether this omission, on the part of POAMS, is regarded as an advantage or a disadvantage to modern physics and cosmology very much depends on one's attitude towards mystification as a means of popularising those subjects.

Moreover, with $B(u) = (1 - 2\mathcal{M}u)^{-1}$, equation (8.27), associated with the metric (8.29), for general freely moving particle motion, becomes

$$\left(\frac{du}{d\theta}\right)^2 + u^2 = k + 2\mathcal{M}\frac{c^2 u}{\beta^2} + 2\mathcal{M}u^3, \tag{8.30}$$

which, of course, is the same equation, hence with the same predictions for planetary motion, as in GR. It is this equation which provides a simplified model of planetary and satellite orbits, with the term in $2\mathcal{M}u^3$ predicting a perihelion shift in planetary motion, which agrees with all observational evidence [21]. This will be expanded upon in the next section.

It is to be stressed that POAMS does not begin by postulating that all natural orbits are closed. Rather, POAMS postulates that in all natural orbital trajectories of whatever shape or size, angular momentum is conserved. For the sake of initial simplicity, in Chapter 6 we required at least some of the solutions of the POAMS equation (8.4), to be closed orbits. The analysis presented in that chapter revealed that, in that case, the only possibility is that (8.4) reduces to the Newtonian equation of motion (8.5). However, once time-dilation effects are taken into account, POAMS predicts, just as in GR, that natural orbits are as described by equation (8.30). In this case, some of the natural orbits are approximately ellipses with a small perihelion shift and so are no longer closed. Hence, in POAMS, conservation of angular momentum together with consideration of time-dilation effects inevitably leads to the perihelion shift phenomenon, to which Newton's Law of Gravitation cannot apply. This, of course, signified the famous advance on Newtonian mechanics that was hailed by GR, and it seems fair to say that this advance is extended by POAMS in re-interpreting those same implications for planetary motion in a much simpler and more conceptually economical way.

The fact that Newton's inverse square law cannot apply can be seen from the equation (8.30). Letting $u = 1/r$, with $k = Km^2/L^2$ and $\beta^2 = L^2/m^2$ in (8.30), as in Chapter 6 (remembering that $\mathcal{M} = MG/c^2$) produces

$$\left(\frac{dr}{d\theta}\right)^2 + r^2 = \frac{Km^2 r^4}{L^2} + \frac{2MGm^2 r^3}{L^2} + \frac{2MGr}{c^2}, \tag{8.31}$$

where L is the constant magnitude of the angular momentum of the orbit. It follows that since $L = mr^2(d\theta/dt)$ on any planar orbit (see (6.7)),

$$\frac{dr}{d\theta} = \left(\frac{dr}{dt}\right)\left(\frac{dt}{d\theta}\right) = \frac{mr^2}{L}\left(\frac{dr}{dt}\right).$$

Hence (8.31) becomes

$$\left(\frac{dr}{dt}\right)^2 + \frac{L^2}{m^2 r^2} = K + \frac{2MG}{r} + \frac{2MGL^2}{m^2 c^2 r^3}$$

$$\Rightarrow \frac{d^2 r}{dt^2} - \frac{L^2}{m^2 r^3} = -\frac{MG}{r^2} - \frac{3MGL^2}{m^2 c^2 r^4}. \tag{8.32}$$

This equation (8.32) is a special case of the general POAMS equation of motion, (8.4), so that angular momentum is conserved, where now

$$h(r) = \frac{MG}{r^2} + \frac{3MGL^2}{m^2 c^2 r^4},$$

instead of $h(r) = GM/r^2$, as in the Newtonian equation (8.5). The second term in $h(r)$ here represents the correction term which takes time-dilation into account. (Of course, the preceding argument does not hold in the case of radial 'free-fall', for which θ is a constant, whence (8.30) does not hold in that case. However, the equation for radial 'free-fall' is provided by (8.32) as a special case when the magnitude, L, of the angular momentum is zero.)

8.6 Free particle motion in Schwarzschild space-time

Let us consider, once again, an isolated two-body system consisting of a freely moving particle P of mass m following a trajectory relative to a body B of mass M, with m very much smaller than M. The possible paths of P, taking time-dilation effects into account, can be determined from the geodesic equations associated with the metric for the 'equatorial plane' for Schwarzschild space-time, i.e.,

$$c^2 d\tau^2 = -ds^2 = c^2(1 - 2M/r)dt^2 - (1 - 2M/r)^{-1}dr^2 - r^2 d\theta^2. \tag{8.29}$$

Remember here that $M = MG/c^2$. These geodesic equations are

$$\frac{dt}{d\tau} = \alpha (1 - 2M/r)^{-1} \text{ (a),} \quad \frac{d\theta}{d\tau} = \frac{\beta}{r^2} \text{ (b)} \tag{8.26}$$

where α and β are constants, and (8.25) with $B(r) = (1 - 2M/r)^{-1}$, i.e.,

$$c^2(1 - 2M/r)\left(\frac{dt}{d\tau}\right)^2 - (1 - 2M/r)^{-1}\left(\frac{dr}{d\tau}\right)^2 - r^2\left(\frac{d\theta}{d\tau}\right)^2 = c^2. \tag{8.33}$$

It is important to appreciate here that the coordinate r no longer expresses exactly the radial distance of P from the centre-of-mass of B. (This agrees with the fact that, in our approach, $r > 3M$, in order for (8.29) to hold.) If t and r are constants, then (8.29) reads $ds^2 = r^2 d\theta^2$ and so gives the distance between two neighbouring points on a circle of radius r. In other words, as in Chapter 6, the equation $r = k$, where k is a constant, describes a circle in space, a fact made use of in section 8.3. However, for any radial line in space, t and θ are constant in (8.29) so that

$$ds^2 = (1 - 2M/r)^{-1}dr^2 \quad \Rightarrow R = \int (1 - 2M/r)^{-1/2} \, dr,$$

where R is the exact radial distance.

Before dealing with the motion of P about B in general, we shall briefly examine, in more detail, the special cases of radial 'free-fall' and circular motion.

8.6.1 Radial 'free-fall'

If P is in radial 'free-fall' relative to B, then θ is constant and r is not constant. Geodesic equation (8.26)(b) is then automatically satisfied with $\beta = 0$, in which case, (8.33) reduces to

$$c^2(1 - 2M/r)\left(\frac{dt}{d\tau}\right)^2 - (1 - 2M/r)^{-1}\left(\frac{dr}{d\tau}\right)^2 = c^2.$$

Then, using (8.26)(a), this equation produces

$$\left(\frac{dr}{d\tau}\right)^2 + c^2(1 - 2M/r) - \alpha^2 c^2 = 0.$$

Differentiating with respect to the proper time τ then gives

$$2\left(\frac{dr}{d\tau}\right)\left(\frac{d^2r}{d\tau^2}\right) + 2Mc^2/r^2\left(\frac{dr}{d\tau}\right) = 0 \Rightarrow \frac{d^2r}{d\tau^2} = -\frac{GM}{r^2}.$$

This equation is exactly the same as the POAMS and Newtonian equation for radial 'free-fall', as discussed in Chapter 6, but where the proper time τ is now the parameter and not the relative time t. This corresponds to the case in which P has zero angular momentum with respect to B.

8.6.2 Circular motion

If P orbits B in a circle, then r is constant, with θ not constant. In this special case, it is convenient to refer back to the geodesic equation (8.20), with $a = 2$. When r is constant, this equation reduces to

$$c^2 M \left(\frac{dt}{d\tau} \right)^2 = r^3 \left(\frac{d\theta}{d\tau} \right)^2. \tag{8.34}$$

Applying the chain rule, equation (8.34) gives

$$\left(\frac{d\theta}{dt} \right)^2 = \left(\frac{d\theta}{d\tau} \right)^2 \left(\frac{d\tau}{d\theta} \right)^2 = \frac{GM}{r^3},$$

so that the change in coordinate time for one revolution of a circular orbit is $2\pi (r^3/GM)^{1/2}$. This result is the same as in the Newtonian case and corresponds to Kepler's Third Law except that, now, r is not exactly the radius of the orbit. However, note that the distance travelled in one circuit is still $2\pi r$.

We have already noted that, in our approach, since the metric (8.29) is ultimately derived for the time-dilation formula, (8.22) for circular orbits, $r > 3M$. This condition may also be confirmed from the geodesic equations, since (8.33) with r a constant gives

$$c^2 (1 - 2Mr) \left(\frac{dt}{d\tau} \right)^2 = r^2 \left(\frac{d\theta}{d\tau} \right)^2 + c^2.$$

Hence, using (8.34), it is seen that circular orbits are possible only when

$$c^2 (1 - 2Mr) \left(\frac{dt}{d\tau} \right)^2 = c^2 Mr \left(\frac{dt}{d\tau} \right)^2 + c^2 \Rightarrow c^2 (1 - 3Mr) \left(\frac{dt}{d\tau} \right)^2 = c^2 \Rightarrow r > 3M,$$

as expected.

8.6.3 The perihelion shift phenomenon

The 'equatorial plane' of Schwarzschild space-time provides the simplest mathematical model of our solar system. This is because the masses of the planets are negligible compared to that of the Sun, so that to a good degree of approximation, any planet may be treated as a particle, P, orbiting the Sun, B, in a two-body system. Each planet is freely moving and so follows a geodesic associated with the metric (8.29). We have already shown in section 4 of this chapter that in the standard two-body system, any non-radial and non-circular trajectory of a freely moving particle P relative to a body B is given by

$$\left(\frac{du}{d\theta}\right)^2 + u^2 = k + 2M\frac{c^2u}{\beta^2} + 2Mu^3, \qquad (8.30)$$

with k and β constant, where $u = 1/r$ is not constant. As we have already commented, the term $2Mu^3$ in (8.30) is extremely small for planetary orbits, so this equation is very nearly the Newtonian equation

$$\left(\frac{du}{d\theta}\right)^2 + u^2 = k + 2M\frac{c^2u}{\beta^2}. \qquad (8.28)$$

In Chapter 6 we showed that the orbital solutions of (8.28) which are closed are ellipses. In other words, Newtonian theory predicts that the planets orbit the Sun in ellipses, which almost agrees with observational evidence. The presence of the extra term in (8.30) shows that the planets orbit the Sun in approximately elliptical trajectories which, after each revolution, shift in some way. On any planetary orbit, the point of closest approach to the Sun is known as the *perihelion*, whilst the point furthest from the Sun is the *aphelion*. The presence of the extra term in (8.30) causes the perihelion of any planet to shift after each revolution around the Sun. The magnitude of this 'rosette-patterned' kind of advance of the perihelion can be investigated by finding the approximate solution to (8.30). Since this result is fundamental, our derivation here expresses, in full, a standard derivation originally due to Møller [22]. This is the same derivation that appears in a number of textbooks on General Relativity [23].

Now let $2\mathcal{M}$ be denoted by ε, and remember that this is small when compared to values of r corresponding to planetary orbits. The perihelion and aphelion are turning points on a planetary orbit and so they occur when $du/d\theta = 0$ in (8.30), so that they are solutions of the cubic equation

$$\varepsilon u^3 - u^2 + \varepsilon \frac{c^2 u}{\beta^2} + k = 0.$$

This equation has three solutions, two of which are close to their Newtonian counterparts. Suppose that the root $u = u_1$ gives the aphelion while $u = u_2$ gives the perihelion, so that $u_1 \leq u \leq u_2$. It follows from the coefficients of u^3 and u^2 in this cubic equation that the sum of its roots is $1/\varepsilon$, which is large. The third solution, $u = u_3$ of this cubic equation then satisfies $u_3 = 1/\varepsilon - u_1 - u_2$. Equation (8.30) may now be written, in terms of these roots, as

$$\left(\frac{du}{d\theta}\right)^2 = \varepsilon(u - u_1)(u_2 - u)(u_3 - u) \Rightarrow \frac{du}{d\theta} = \left((u - u_1)(u_2 - u)\right)^{1/2}\left(1 - \varepsilon(u_1 + u_2 + u)\right)^{1/2}$$

Since ε is small, we may ignore powers of ε above the first to a good degree of approximation. Then expanding by the binomial series gives

$$\frac{d\theta}{du} \approx \frac{1 + (\varepsilon/2)(u_1 + u_2 + u)}{\left((u - u_1)(u_2 - u)\right)^{1/2}}.$$

In order to express the integral for θ in standard form, it is convenient to re-label the constants u_1 and u_2, as $u_1 = p - q$ and $u_2 = p + q$. Then if θ_0 denotes the angle between the aphelion and the next perihelion in the approximately elliptical orbit,

$$\theta_0 = \int_{u_1}^{u_2} \frac{d\theta}{du} du \approx$$

$$\int_{u_1}^{u_2} \frac{1 + (\varepsilon/2)(2p + u)}{(u - p + q)^{1/2}(p + q - u)^{1/2}} du = \int_{u_1}^{u_2} \frac{\varepsilon(u - p)/2 + (1 + 3\varepsilon p/2)}{(q^2 - (u - p)^2)^{1/2}} du$$

$$\Rightarrow \theta_0 \approx \left[(1 + 3\varepsilon p/2)\sin^{-1}((u - p)/q) - (\varepsilon/2)(q^2 - (u - p)^2)^{1/2}\right]_{u_1}^{u_2} = (1 + 3\varepsilon p/2)\pi.$$

Doubling this angle gives the angle between successive perihelions on any planetary orbit. Hence, in each circuit, the perihelion is *advanced* by approximately

$$3\varepsilon p\pi = 6M\pi(u_1 + u_2)/2 = \frac{3MG\pi}{c^2}\left(\frac{1}{r_1} + \frac{1}{r_2}\right),$$

where r_1 and r_2 are the radial distances from the centre-of-mass of the Sun at the aphelion and perihelion respectively.

8.6.4 Summary of the perihelion shift phenomenon

Descriptions of the orbits of planets in our solar system are solutions of equation (8.30), which is very nearly the Newtonian equation (8.28). This equation dictates that the planets move in ellipses, and the small additional term $2Mu^3$ in (8.30) also implies that the planets move in approximately elliptical orbits but with the difference that the perihelion is advanced after each circuit by

$$\frac{3MG\pi}{c^2}\left(\frac{1}{r_1} + \frac{1}{r_2}\right),$$

where M is the mass of the Sun and r_1 and r_2 are the radial distances from the centre-of-mass of the Sun at the aphelion and perihelion respectively.

The perihelion advance may be calculated for any planetary orbit using this formula, but clearly the effect is greatest for Mercury, which is closest to the Sun. The formula gives the perihelion advance of Mercury as 43.03 seconds of arc per century, which compares favourably with the observed advance of 43.11 plus or minus 0.45 seconds of arc per century. Predicted results for other planets also agree with the observational evidence [24]. These comparisons between predicted and observed values are not so straightforward as they first appear since, of course, in practice, the orbit of a planet about the sun is not simply a two-body system. All the planets have an influence on each other's orbits and so even Newtonian theory predicts that the orbits are only approximate ellipses. However, despite taking these effects into account, there still remains a perihelion advance which cannot be explained in Newtonian terms.

Before the advent of GR in 1916 [25] and the publication of Schwarzschild space-time [26] a few months later, the perihelion on Mercury's orbit had been observed to advance over time but no-one was able to develop a satisfactory theory which could predict such an effect. In 1845, Leverrier showed that such a rotation in Mercury's orbit would be produced if Mercury were being influenced by the presence of another planet between it and the Sun. Of course, we now know that no such planet exists. However, the planet Neptune was also predicted by Leverrier as a result of variations in Uranus' orbit, and the new planet was subsequently discovered as a result.

8.7 The 'bending of light'

When GR first appeared in 1916, as well as correctly deriving the observed perihelion advance in Mercury's orbit, it also made predictions concerning certain other phenomena which, at least in theory, were verifiable by observations of the solar system. The most famous of these predictions concerned the so-called 'bending of light' by a massive object, such as the Sun. General Relativity predicted that 'light deviates from a rectilinear path' near massive objects, a hitherto unobserved phenomenon. The prediction was that light emanating from distant stars would be 'deflected', near the Sun's surface, through a tiny angle of approximately 1.75 seconds of arc.

It is important to appreciate here, however, that the 'deflection of light' by a massive object was not a new prediction. Such a 'deflection' can also be predicted using Newtonian theory, but with only about half the angle predicted by GR. It is now known that such predictions were made in the late eighteenth century by Henry Cavendish and John Mitchell [27]. Einstein himself, in 1911, initially predicted a 'deflection of light' using only the Doppler formula from SR (see Chapter 3, section 6) [28]. Again, this was only about half the angle predicted by GR. However, a significant number of scientists claim that GR is not actually required in order to predict the observed 'deflection of light' [29].

The first observations to be carried out to verify the angle of the 'deflection of light' by the Sun were performed in 1919 by Sir Arthur Eddington and Andrew Crommelin [30]. The method involved photographing the apparent positions of stars in a neighbourhood of the Sun during a total solar eclipse and then comparing the positions of the same stars in photographs taken at a time when the Sun had moved away. A comparison of these photographs would show that the stars had apparently moved due to the 'deflection of light'. Three years elapsed between the prediction and this first experiment since Eddington and Crommelin had to wait for a suitable total solar eclipse to occur and for that they had to travel to Brazil and the Gulf of Guinea. There were severe difficulties performing such an experiment. For example, the photographs had to be very accurate in order to detect the very small effect, and similar conditions had to be ensured when the photographs were taken at different times. There was also the difficulty of coping with the stark contrast of bright sunlight to the semi-darkness produced during a total solar eclipse. The result of accurately comparing the photographs taken in the 1919 experiment apparently confirmed that 'light was deflected' by the Sun, the observed value of the angle being 1.98 plus or minus 0.16 seconds of arc. It was the result of this experiment, confirming, as it seemed, a prediction of General Relativity, that made Einstein famous in the public eye.

It was essential for Eddington, in his support of Einstein, to assume that his observations of the bending of starlight around the Sun during the 1919 eclipse were exactly in accordance with the predictions of GR. However, there have since been disputes over the validity of that famous experiment [31][32]. For instance, the description of that alleged 'bending' of light 'passing at a grazing angle' to the Sun's surface seems strange in view of the fact that the interface between the Sun's surface and surrounding space is not distinct like that of a steel ball. Its atmosphere is a relatively dense plasma, known as the *heliopause*, which extends far out beyond what might be regarded as the Sun's surface, into space well beyond the solar system. In that case, how could that bending that is ascribed to 'gravitational' effects, be distinguished from ordinary refraction through the Sun's dense and very extensive corona [33]?

Altogether, there have been seven such total solar eclipse experiments to date [34]. The results of some of these experiments, whilst being in qualitative agreement with Einstein's prediction, have differed considerably from the actual result derived in GR. However, more recently, other types of experiments, such as those which involve radio sources, have also been performed [35]. In 1991, such experiments carried out by Robertson and others, using VLBI (Very Long Baseline Interferometry), are claimed to have verified Einstein's prediction to an accuracy of 10^{-4} [36].

General Relativity is based, of course, on Einstein's corpuscular conception of light as consisting of particles, called photons. This corpuscular conception was discussed fully in Chapter 5. In that case, it is not difficult to appreciate why Einstein predicted the 'gravitational bending of light'. If one thinks of the light quantum as a travelling photon, then it must be possible for its 'trajectory', like that of any other material particle, to be affected by 'gravity'. In stark contrast to GR, in our Normal Realist approach, there is no such concept as that of the ballistic photon. As already explained in Chapter 5, in our approach the light quantum is an immediate (non-mediated), instantaneous and distance-less quantum jump in which a quantum of action is transferred, by direct inter-resonance, from one atom to another, with no sensibly describable 'in between' in which its passage can be 'bent' in the way Einstein envisaged.

In order, then, to address what is actually meant by 'light bending' in our NR approach, it is necessary to have an appreciation of the meaning of a 'ray of light' in this context. Such a 'ray' is a *phenomenon* consisting of a sequence, in observer space and observer time, of quantum illuminations, each one of which, in itself, is a proper time-instantaneous quantum touching between a pair of macroscopically distance-separated atoms. Prime examples of this sequence of illuminations are a beam of sunlight shining through a smoky room, or the rays of the setting Sun at the end of the day in a hazy sky. In such cases, what we see is not the light 'travelling'. The phenomenon analyses-out at the quantum level to a cinematic succession of illuminated particles, of dust, moisture or whatever, which creates an observational *impression* of continuity where, in fact, there is none.

In a transparent medium, such as air, water or glass, such mediating sequences are typically slowed or *refracted*, in comparison with the way these interactions take place *in vacuo*. Of course, refraction is a well known natural phenomenon, as witnessed in optical experiments with lenses and prisms and in commonplace instances like that of an oar seemingly bent in water. Since every particle in this mediating process has mass, then insofar as these particles are energised in the mediating process, it is reasonable to assume that they will undergo some measure of time-dilation due to their relayed energy, $E = h\nu$, where ν is the spectral frequency of the incident energy. (See equation (5.1).) This implies that a 'ray' mediated by these particles is *slowed* in some ratio c_1/c, according to its spectral frequency, where c is the usual constant space-time ratio *in vacuo*, and c_1 is the length-time ratio *via media*. The ratio $\eta = c/c_1$ is the (absolute) *refractive index* of the medium, so that the 'speed of the ray' in the medium is $c_1 = c/\eta$. In Normal Realism, it is the refraction of a light ray that causes it to appear bent.

The effect of time-dilation on this refraction of a light ray as it passes through the Sun's heliopause may be investigated by using the geodesic equations for Schwarzschild space-time, as discussed earlier in this chapter but now for material particles whose speed is less than, though very close to, c. From a mathematical point of view, this represents the refraction of the ray as discussed above. Hence, formally, we begin with the geodesic equations and let the proper time, τ approach zero. It must be stressed here that although, as far as the mathematics are concerned, this 'bending' is the same as predicted by General Relativity, from a physical point of view we certainly do not claim that 'the path of a photon is bent due to the gravitational force of the Sun', which would be anathema to our Normal Realist approach to relativity.

The mathematical argument given in the following subsection shows that due to refraction through the medium surrounding a star, a 'light ray' (that is, an observationally projected line of sight) will be deflected through an angle

$$\delta \approx \frac{4MG}{r_0 c^2},\qquad(8.35)$$

where M is the mass of the star and r_0 is the distance of closest approach to its centre-of-mass. Taking M to be the mass of the Sun and r_0 to be its radius, this formula predicts that the Sun will apparently deflect a 'ray of light' (line of sight) through an angle of 1.75 seconds of arc.

8.7.1 The mathematical details

The following mathematical derivation is essentially the same as a standard derivation given in some texts on General Relativity [37]. Once again, it is provided here for completeness. The path of a freely moving particle whose speed approaches c is described by the geodesic equations (8.26), where, now, τ has to be replaced by another parameter λ [38], since $d\tau^2 \to 0$ in the general time-dilation formula, (8.29). In this case, (8.29) gives the additional geodesic equation,

$$c^2(1 - 2M/r)\left(\frac{dt}{d\lambda}\right)^2 - (1 - 2M/r)^{-1}\left(\frac{dr}{d\lambda}\right)^2 - r^2\left(\frac{d\theta}{d\lambda}\right)^2 = 0.$$

Then multiplying by $(d\lambda/d\theta)^2$ and using the chain rule, gives

$$c^2(1 - 2M/r)\left(\frac{dt}{d\lambda}\right)^2\left(\frac{d\lambda}{d\theta}\right)^2 - (1 - 2M/r)^{-1}\left(\frac{dr}{d\theta}\right)^2 - r^2 = 0,$$

which reduces to

$$\frac{\alpha^2 c^2 r^4}{\beta^2} - \left(\frac{dr}{d\theta}\right)^2 - r^2(1 - 2M/r) = 0,$$

when equations (8.26) are applied. Finally, letting $r = 1/u$, as in previous sections, this equation becomes

$$\left(\frac{du}{d\theta}\right)^2 + u^2 = K^2 + 2Mu^3,\qquad(8.36)$$

where $K^2 = \alpha^2 c^2/\beta^2$.

Let u_0 denote the value of u at the point of closest approach of the 'light ray' to a massive body, so that $du/d\theta = 0$ when $u = u_0$. It is easily ascertained that the solution to (8.36) when there is no matter present, *i.e.*, when the mass of the body B is zero, so that $\mathcal{M} = 0$, is

$$u(\theta) = K\sin\theta = u_0\sin\theta,$$

without loss of generality. This is the equation of a straight line, L, which is at distance $r_0 = 1/u_0$ away from the origin of the radius at the point of closest approach to a star, that is, when $\theta = \pi/2$, as indicated in Fig. 8.1 below.

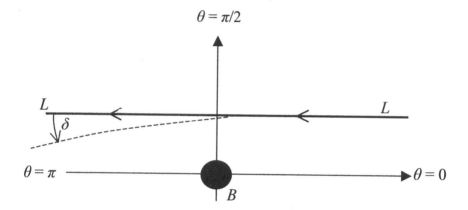

Fig. 8.1: The Deflection of a 'Light Ray' in the Presence of Matter

As in subsection 8.6.3, we let $2\mathcal{M} = \varepsilon$ in (8.36) and ignore powers of ε above the first, since ε is very small. In general, letting u_0 be the value of u at the point of closest approach to the body B, so that $du/d\theta = 0$ when $u = u_0$ as before, we may rewrite (8.36) in the form

$$\left(\frac{du}{d\theta}\right)^2 + u^2 = u_0^2\left(1 - \varepsilon\, u_0\right) + \varepsilon\, u^3. \tag{8.37}$$

We know that the solution to (8.37), with $\varepsilon = 0$, is $u = u_0\sin\theta$, so we try a solution of the form

$$u = u_0\sin\theta + \varepsilon v(\theta),$$

for some function $v(\theta)$ to be determined. Making this substitution in (8.37) and ignoring powers of ε above the first gives

$$2\cos\theta\left(\frac{dv}{d\theta}\right) + 2\sin\theta v(\theta) = u_0^2(\sin^3\theta - 1).$$

It can be checked that the solution to this equation for which $v = 0$ when $\theta = 0$ is

$$v(\theta) = \frac{1}{2}u_0^2(1 + \cos^2\theta - \sin\theta - 2\cos\theta).$$

It then follows that the approximate solution of (8.37) for which $u = 0$ when $\theta = 0$ is

$$u(\theta) \approx u_0(1 - \varepsilon\frac{u_0}{2})\sin\theta + \frac{1}{2}\varepsilon u_0^2(1 - \cos\theta)^2.$$

This solution shows that the 'ray' is deflected through a small angle δ, say, as indicated in Fig. 8.1. We then require that $u = 0$ when $\theta = \pi + \delta$, so that using $\sin(\pi + \delta) = -\sin\delta$ and $\cos(\pi + \delta) = -\cos\delta$, this solution yields

$$0 \approx -u_0(1 - \varepsilon\frac{u_0}{2})\sin\delta + \frac{1}{2}\varepsilon u_0^2(1 + \cos\delta)^2.$$

For small δ, $\sin\delta \approx \delta$ and $\cos\delta$ is approximately equal to 1, so that ignoring terms in $\delta\varepsilon$, the above result provides

$$0 \approx -u_0\delta + 2\varepsilon u_0^2 \implies \delta \approx 2\varepsilon u_0 = \frac{4MG}{r_0 c^2}, \tag{8.31}$$

as already stated.

8.8 Non-mathematical résumé of chapter

From the point of view of Normal Realism, the usual interpretation of Einstein's Field Equations of General Relativity as describing an underlying space-time continuum, is unnecessarily arcane. In this chapter we have demonstrated that the Schwarzschild solution of the Field Equations, the only solution whose predictions are directly verifiable by observation and experiment, can be derived from premises which require no unempirical postulates such as those of 'light travelling' and 'gravitational interaction' as processes taking place inscrutably *in vacuo* or in any other metaphysical substratum.

As we have fully explained in Chapter 6, in contrast to Newton's unempirical conception of all free motion as fundamentally rectilinear, POAMS perceives all free motion as naturally orbital *i.e.*, as a manifestation of angular momentum, and regards this angular momentum as universally conserved. This makes redundant any necessity for Newton's postulate of a universal *in vacuo* 'gravitational force' contrived to explain the fact that free moving bodies plainly do not travel in straight lines.

For these same reasons, Einstein's postulate of a 'gravitationally warped' underlying 'space-time continuum' is rejected in favour of observationally up-front studies of true natural motion. All that POAMS needs, therefore, in order to reproduce the valid and observationally confirmed consequences of General Relativity, is the constant c as a pure conversion factor interrelating the conventional units of observational distance and time, plus the postulate of overall-conserved and balanced angular momentum. In this present chapter we have taken these minimalist assumptions to their full logical and mathematical conclusions. These are seen to be virtually the same as those of GR but stripped of the usual intellectual overlay.

As we have demonstrated in Chapter 3, our Normal Realist synthesis begins with a direct approach to time-dilation in rectilinear motion based on Pythagoras' theorem. In Chapter 6, we extended the elementary formula, (3.2), from dealing with ideal (*i.e.*, unreal) rectilinear motion to include actual curvilinear motion, which is the only real force-free motion that can be observed. We have shown that this extension leads naturally to the Schwarzschild solution of GR as a replacement of Minkowski space-time in SR. It is the Schwarzschild solution that provides a description of the observed Spirograph-like motions of planets in solar orbits.

This seamless joining up of what are usually distinguished as 'Special' and 'General' Relativity has enabled us to dispense with, among other things, Einstein's ballistic interpretation of light-quanta as 'photons' that are pulled off their otherwise linear paths by *in vacuo* gravitation. In place of those various theories of hidden, or behind-the-scenes processes, POAMS presents a single, purely phenomenological, explanation in terms of the ordinary 'refraction' of lines of sight in the vicinities of massive bodies in the same way that, to an observer, an oar appears 'bent' in water. These lines of sight are 'refracted' in the neighbourhoods of bodies for the same reason that clocks are slowed in proportion to their distances from those same bodies.

Notes and References

[1] Pope, N. V.: *The Eye of the Beholder: The Role of the Observer in Modern Physics* (**phi** Philosophical Enterprises, Swansea, 2004), p. 41.

[2] Osborne, A. D. and Pope, N. V.: 'Orbital Time-dilation', *Galilean Electrodynamics* (to appear). Also available at www.poams.org.

[3] See for example, D'Inverno, R.: *Introducing Einstein's Relativity* (Clarendon Press, Oxford, 1992), Chapters 14 and 15.

[4] In the light of previous comments it may be appreciated that this will not provide the exact picture, but will, nevertheless, give an indication of the qualitative effect of incorporating time-dilation into orbital motion.

[5] McCuskey, S. W.: *An Introduction to Advanced Dynamics* (Addison-Wesley, Reading, USA, 1959), Chapter 3.

[6] According to Peter Rowlands, this analysis is no more than a 'bog standard' way of obtaining orbital time-dilation.

[7] *Op. cit.* reference 1, p.32.

[8] Osborne, A. D.: 'Further developments in the Pope-Osborne Angular Momentum Synthesis' in Pope, N. V., Osborne, A. D. and Winfield, A. F. T. (eds.): *Immediate Distant Action and Correlation in Modern Physics: The Balanced Universe* (Edwin Mellen, N. Y. 2005) pp. 277-278.

[9] See, *e.g.*, Spain, B.: *Tensor Calculus* (Oliver and Boyd, London, 1953) Chapters 1 and 2.

[10] Spain, B., *ibid*, Chapter 4.

[11] Kay, D. C.: *Tensor Calculus* (McGraw-Hill, New York, 1988), Chapter 7.

[12] Arthurs, A. M.: *Complementary Variational Principles* (Clarendon Press, Oxford, 1970).

[13] The curves under consideration are required to be at least twice differentiable, simple (without self-intersections) and smooth (with a continuously turning tangent).

[14] Essentially the same postulate occurs in General Relativity, which states that freely moving particles in any space-time follow geodesics.

[15] Foster, J. and Nightingale, J. D. *A Short Course in General Relativity* (Longman, New York, 1979) pp. 109-112.

[16] Alley, C. O and Van Flandern, T.: Briefing Document: 'Absolute GPS to better than one meter', available at http://metaresearch.org/solar%20system/gps/absolute-gps-1meter.asp

[17] *Op. cit.* reference 15, pp. 95-97.

[18] *Op. cit.* reference 3, pp.186-188.

[19] *Op. cit.* reference 15, pp. 105-106.

[20] *Op. cit.* reference 3, Chapter 16.

[21] *Op. cit.* reference 15, pp. 115-117.

[22] Møller, C.: *The Theory of Relativity* (Oxford University Press, Oxford, 1972) Section 12.2.

[23] *Op. cit.* reference 15, pp. 115-117.

[24] Dunscombe, R. L.: 'Relativity effects for the three inner planets', *Astronomical Journal*, **61** (1956) pp. 174-175.

[25] Einstein, A.: 'Foundations of the Theory of General relativity', *Annalen der Physik*, **49** (1916) pp. 769-822.

[26] Karl Schwarzschild was an astronomer who was the first person to discover the simplest non-trivial solution to the Einstein field equations.

[27] Rowlands, P.: *A Revolution Too Far: The Establishment of General Relativity* (PD Publications, Liverpool, 1994) pp. 107-120.

[28] Rowlands, P., *ibid*, p. 71.

[29] Rowlands, P., *ibid*, Chapter 5.

[30] Rowlands, P., *ibid*, Chapter 1.

[31] Rowlands, P., *ibid*, pp. 101-102.

[32] Hawking, S.: *A Brief History of Time* (Bantam Books, London, 1988) p. 32.

[33] 'HyperFlight', Internet: 'The bending of light is through optical interaction with matter comprising the sun's corona.'

[34] *Op. cit.* reference 15, pp. xiii-xiv.

[35] Riley, J. M.: 'A measurement of the gravitational deflection of radio waves by the Sun during 1972 October', *Monthly Notices of the Royal Astronomical Society*, **161** (1973) 11P-14P.

[36] Rindler, W.: *Relativity: Special, General and Cosmological* (O.U.P., Oxford, 2001), p. 249.

[37] *Op. cit.* reference 15, pp. 117-120.

[38] For which $dT/d\lambda = 0$, where T is given by (8.19), with $a = 2$ and $B(r) = (1 - 2M/r)^{-1}$.

CHAPTER 9

Some Aspects of Astrophysics and Cosmology

In this chapter, we shall critically review some scientific predictions made in the areas of astrophysics and cosmology. These predictions have so inspired the general public that they have now become part of popular culture. Specifically, we shall provide the POAMS approach to such questions as the existence of so-called 'black holes', the 'expansion' of the cosmos and the existence of 'dark matter' within the observable universe. The content of this chapter is necessarily more descriptive than previous chapters.

9.1 'Black holes'

An area of astrophysics which has attracted speculation and controversy alike over the last forty years is the study of stellar collapse. Some physicists allege that certain stars, at the end of their life, implode due to the 'force of gravity' to form a 'black hole', an astronomical body of extremely intense gravity from which nothing, not even light, can escape. In this scenario, the imploding star shrinks to a point of zero volume and infinite density, known as a 'space-time singularity'. This spectacularly bizarre prediction is far removed from any directly observable experience and so merits closer examination.

Theory and observation tell us that when stars reach the end of their lives, *i.e.*, when the nuclear fuel in their core is exhausted, many of them explode to form a *nova* or *supernova*. Such explosions are readily observable – the effects of one such supernova, which occurred almost a thousand years ago, can be seen as a cosmic nebula known as the Crab Nebula. However, theory and observation also tell us that it is possible for certain types of stars to implode at the end of their life and shrink in size. According to some theories, stars of a certain critical mass, M, continue to shrink to a radius corresponding to their *Schwarzschild radius*, $r = 2M = 2MG/c^2$ [1].

In General Relativity, Birkhoff's theorem [2] states that if a collapsing non-rotating, electrically neutral star is spherically symmetric, then its external space-time geometry is described by Schwarzschild space-time, the 'equatorial plane' of which was given as (8.29) in section 8.5.1 of the previous chapter, *i.e.*,

$$c^2 d\tau^2 = c^2 (1 - 2M/r) dt^2 - (1 - 2M/r)^{-1} dr^2 - r^2 d\theta^2. \qquad (8.29)$$

According to GR, it is possible for r to be less than $2M$ in (8.29) and in this case, mathematics tells us that r becomes a *time-like* variable. Since no physical effect can halt the monotonic increase of such a variable, the implication in GR is that once a star has collapsed through its Schwarzschild radius, it must continue to collapse to form a 'singularity' of the space-time at $r = 0$. In this way, GR predicts that the effect of such a collapsing star is literally to tear the fabric of space-time apart due to the enormous gravitational effects.

In General Relativity, with its interpretation of light travelling as 'photons', it is possible for light to be bent due to gravitational effects, as discussed in section 8.7 of the previous chapter. In this approach, the geodesic equations for Schwarzschild space-time, as discussed in section 8.7.1 of that chapter, can be used to investigate the paths of 'photons' in the vicinity of a collapsed star. The conclusion is that the paths of 'photons' are so bent by the enormous gravitational effects that any 'photon' within the region $r < 2M$, *i.e.*, within the Schwarzschild radius, cannot reach the region $r > 2M$. The physical consequence of this is that the collapsed star is invisible to any external observer. This is the reason why the term *black hole* was introduced to describe this final stage of stellar collapse [3].

The idea of a black hole as an astronomical phenomenon which can bend light to such an extent that it is effectively invisible, did not come with the advent of GR. In fact the idea is much older, first being mooted by Peter Simon Laplace at the end of the eighteenth century [4].

In the previous chapter, it was demonstrated, in section 8.4, how time is dilated in the neighbourhood of a massive spherically symmetric body. In the General Relativistic scenario of a black hole, as just described, the enormous 'gravitational' effects on time may be investigated by using the geodesic equations (8.26) and (8.33), for Schwarzschild space-time. The conclusion is that a space-traveller, according to his own clock, can reach the Schwarzschild radius surrounding a black hole in finite time and pass through. Once through $r = 2M$, the traveller suffers the same fate as the collapsed star and can never return to $r > 2M$. He will be crushed by the huge 'gravitational' effects long before he reaches the 'space-time singularity' at $r = 0$. On the other hand, according to the clock of an external observer who remains at a safe distance, the space-traveller can never actually reach $r = 2M$[5]. The upshot of this theory is that the existence of a black hole can never be verified directly by means of any physical experiment. Once an observer passes through the Schwarzschild radius to verify the existence of a black hole, he can never return to communicate his results! In this way, the 'space-time singularity' at $r = 0$ is surrounded by what is called an *event horizon* at $r = 2M$.

So far, of course, we have reported only on what General Relativity predicts when a non-rotating, spherically symmetric star collapses. The situation, as described above, is bizarre enough but for a rotating star, GR introduces a much more complicated space-time, known as the Kerr solution [6]. In this situation, theory predicts that it is possible for a space-traveller to avoid any space-time singularity after passing through two event horizons. It then allows for the possibility of the traveller being able to pass through a 'wormhole' in the space-time continuum, and to pop out somewhere else in the cosmos, perhaps light years from where he started! Some theorists have gone so far as to say that the existence of such a 'wormhole' in the fabric of space-time leads to the possibility of time travel!

When space-time singularities were first predicted by GR, some thought that they were simply a property of the Schwarzschild space-time metric or other specific solutions of the Einstein Field Equations. It was argued that these specific solutions were not adequate to describe such situations as stellar collapse and that in general, most space-times would be non-singular. However, the singularity theorems, first proved by Roger Penrose and Stephen Hawking in the 1960s and 1970s, show that, beginning with physically reasonable conditions, all space-times in GR will contain at least one space-time singularity [7].

General Relativity is certainly a very elegant mathematical theory, but we believe that many physicists have taken it well beyond its original role as a convenient description of physical reality. Nowadays, it seems that in many cases, it is the mathematical derivations and predictions of the theory which are given the top priority, whence it has lost its original purpose. In our view, what society needs to do is to stand back and, with a level head, examine any claims of the actual existence of black holes. The idea of a black hole is an enticing one since it makes our world (in the broadest sense) seem more exciting. It provides ready material for writers of science fiction and film directors alike. However, reality may be a lot more boring – can a star actually shrink to a point which tears the 'fabric of space' apart? Whatever the answer, with the present state of our knowledge, it is unacceptable for certain physicists to give the general public the strong impression that black holes do physically exist.

Certainly, it is possible to study a black hole as a purely mathematical object but there is no reason to suppose that it has any physical meaning. One of the dangers inherent in treating space-time singularities as physical objects, is that this leads to an 'anything goes' situation in which even the most fanciful and bizarre speculations are permitted. For example, the theoretical picture of the black hole keeps changing. Having started out as ever growing, cosmic vacuum cleaners, it now appears that they can merely evaporate away [8].

Schwarzschild space-time is derived in GR as a specific solution of the Einstein Field Equations. It provides a good model of our solar system in that it predicts physical effects which agree with empirical and observational evidence. It must be remembered however, that the same model is produced by POAMS, as described in the previous chapter. It is one thing to apply GR to derive such an accurate model of our solar system, but quite another to make a huge extrapolation to the situation of stellar collapse, however tempting that might be. Any process of extrapolation is fraught with difficulties and there is no reason to suppose that the theory is accurate where there are huge 'gravitational' effects. For example, the bizarre extrapolations of the consequences of the Hawking-Penrose singularity theorems are in sharp contrast to the physically reasonable assumptions needed to prove them [8][9]. As another example, General Relativity's description of space-time as a continuum may not be adequate on the micro-phenomenal level, as we have maintained in this book. If the predictions made by GR concerning stellar collapse can be extrapolated down to a small enough scale, then the effect of quantum fluctuations in the gravitational 'field' at that level may prevent a singularity from forming. In addition to these arguments there is another problem which remains unsolved. Despite many attempts, no-one has been able to find a solution of the Einstein Field Equations which provides a mathematical model for the *interior* of a collapsing star. Without this information, it is not realistically possible to speculate about the eventual fate of such a star.

It must be remembered that if a black hole did exist, then there could be no communication of any kind from within its event horizon. In effect, the event horizon 'covers' the singular core from observation in the rest of the universe. Thus, from the point of view of what can actually be observed, a black hole has no more than a metaphysical reality. The only observable facets are the effects a possible 'black hole' has on its surroundings, classically conceived as the effects of its 'enormous gravitational field' on nearby matter.

Certainly, there are phenomena in the observable universe which agree with the theoretical external effects produced by a 'black hole'. However, in these cases, of course, there are always other possible explanations. For example, the 'Holy Grail' for the believers in the existence of black holes lies in the binary star system, Cygnus X-1. This system consists of a star together with a 'dark' (invisible) companion, which is claimed to be a 'black hole'. If one star of such a binary system were a 'black hole', then it would accrete matter from its visible companion. Theory predicts that this would form a gaseous disc around the 'black hole', which would become hot enough to produce intense bursts of X-rays. In 1971, the Uhuru X-ray satellite detected rapid variations in X-rays emanating from Cygnus X-1 [10]. However, this so-called evidence has always been controversial [11] and, besides, there are other possible explanations of the data which do not involve a 'black hole' [12]. The 'dark' companion is certainly small and very dense and could be an object with properties similar to those of a 'black hole'. In fact, however, there is no qualitative difference between the Cygnus X-1 system and a binary system for which the 'dark' object is identified as a neutron star [13] (see below). Similarly, a 'black hole' is also thought to have been discovered at the centre of the giant radio galaxy M87, the 'black hole' being 5×10^6 times as massive as our Sun. This galaxy is surrounded by an X-ray cloud 10^6 light years across but, again, there are other possible explanations for the presence of this cloud [14]. Some astronomers believe that since 1994, the Hubble Space Telescope has provided 'conclusive evidence' for the existence of this 'super-massive black hole'. But clearly, any indirect evidence which is consistent with a particular theory does not imply that the theory is anywhere nearer the truth than a viable alternative.

There are many approaches to 'gravitation' which can be taken as alternatives to General Relativity and which avoid the presence of singularities. These do not predict the existence of black holes. For example, it is possible to construct other models which satisfy the experimental tests within the solar system but which do not contain singular solutions. The theory of Brans and Dicke [15] falls into this category. Other theories, such as the one studied by Stephenson [16], Kilmister [17] and Yang [18] generalise the Einstein Field Equations, whilst others, such as the one proposed by Muller [19] *et al.*, amend the Field Equations to avoid singularities. Of direct relevance to our approach in this book is that some authors have proposed that spin may avert 'gravitational collapse' [20][21]. Many physicists argue that a quantised version of General Relativity would perhaps prevent space-time singularities from occurring [22]. This is much in the same way that Planck's quantisation of black body radiation eliminated the ultraviolet catastrophe, as discussed in Chapter 5, and Bohr's quantisation of the atom prevented its classically predicted collapse. Another line of attack is, directly, to amend the geodesic equations which describe the paths of freely moving particles, so as to avoid any singular behaviour [23][24].

Clearly, a black hole as a physically meaningful object has no place in our Normal Realist philosophy, since it is a completely unempirical description of the endpoint of stellar evolution. Hence, POAMS rejects the notion of gravitational collapse, with its esoteric inferences as to the real existence of 'black holes', conceived as cosmic plugholes into which matter is sucked into oblivion. According to the paradigm we are exploring, we should look for explanations in terms of actually observable phenomena, not of pure mathematical abstractions clothed in the fanciful garb of quasi-materiality.

As explained in Chapter 8 and summarised in section 8.5.1, the POAMS derivation of the Schwarzschild metric, (8.29), depends ultimately on the time-dilation formula for circular motion, (8.22), so that $r > 3\mathcal{M}$ in (8.29). Remember that in POAMS, (8.29) amounts to the general time-dilation formula along the path followed by any freely moving material particle in the otherwise empty space surrounding a spherically symmetric body. Hence, in contrast to General Relativity, in which (8.29) is simply a solution to the Field Equations with no restriction on the value of r except that it cannot be negative, in POAMS, there is a built-in restriction to extrapolating (8.29) for use as a model of gravitational collapse. Also, POAMS implies that (8.29) does not provide an adequate mathematical model for $r < 3\mathcal{M}$, so that there is no reason to suppose that the Schwarzschild radius is reached in stellar collapse, let alone the predicted space-time singularity at $r = 0$. In short, there is no reason whatsoever for supposing that a star collapses to form a 'black hole'.

So, what explanation does POAMS provide for the observed phenomenon in the binary star system consisting of a star with a 'dark' companion such as the Cygnus X-1 system? One possible answer is that the 'dark' companion is the remains of a star which has come to the end of its life and which has imploded to form a very small and extremely dense object. The 'gravitational' effect of this object is so huge that it attracts matter from the visible star and so forms an accretion disc, which becomes hot enough to emit a burst of X-rays. In POAMS terms of course, the visible star and its 'dark' companion form an angular momentum system, with the paths of freely moving particles within the system being determined by an equation of motion which depends on the masses of the visible star and its 'dark' companion. In this case, the freely moving particles are those which come together to form the accretion disc around the 'dark' companion. In this way, it is possible to explain the observed behaviour of the accretion disc without even having to consider the formation of a space-time singularity. The reason why the 'dark' companion is effectively invisible is that it has simply expended all of its stellar energy so that it is what is known as a *cold stellar configuration*.

Certainly it is known that some stars, at the end of their evolution, contract to a *white dwarf* state, a star of approximately the same mass as the Sun with a radius of about 5000 kilometres and density of about 10^9 kg m^{-3}. Theoretically it is possible for certain stars to contract in size still further to form a *neutron star*, a star of around the same mass as the Sun with a radius of about 10 kilometres and density of about 10^{17} kg m^{-3}. Both of these are examples of stars in their final possible lowest-energy state with all heat expended and all angular momentum lost – a completely collapsed and merged, cold stellar configuration [25].

However, in any truly Normal Realist account of a binary system such as Cygnus X-1, we should not make *any* assumptions concerning the 'dark' companion since we cannot directly observe what is there. The explanation offered above provides only an indication of what the 'dark' companion *might* be. In NR terms, the explanation is simply that the binary system is a balanced angular momentum system for which the angular momentum is conserved. Within this system, the accreted particles move freely along paths determined by the total angular momentum.

In general, it is typical of angular momentum that for a pair of masses of comparable size, the centre of orbit for those bodies is located in neither of the masses themselves but in the void between. Although commonly called the centre-of-mass, this centre of the system has none of the characteristics normally ascribed to bodies. In particular, unlike the bodies themselves, it is completely invisible. In a relatively large compaction of objects each object tends to orbit each and every other, so that any angular momentum the compaction may possess as a whole is that of a swirling mass such as a spiral galaxy or a weather-system like a cyclone or hurricane. Typical of such a system is that at its centre-of-mass there is a void, like the 'eye' of a hurricane or storm. This has no existence as a material object but only as an empty barycentre for the matter swirling around it. It is 'dark' insofar as, in itself, it radiates no energy. Otherwise there is nothing singular or metaphysical about it. In our view, therefore, it makes no sense to explain the 'blackness' of an invisible centre of moment in a spiral galaxy, such as the X-ray nebula in M87, as being due to its 'gravitational entrapment' of the light it would otherwise emit.

As explained in Chapter 5, when a galaxy sheds energy, in the form of light for example, it sheds angular momentum, and when it sheds angular momentum it spirals inwards on itself towards its centre-of-mass in the way that spiral nebulae characteristically do. (Those galaxies which do not initially spiral in this way, such as widely dispersed primeval gas-clouds or globular clusters, inevitably condense by loss of angular momentum due to radiated energy and sooner or later begin to spiral inwards.) We may therefore, without logical contradiction, think of such a galaxy condensing inwards on itself, not into a 'black hole' residing at its centre, but rather into the void that is left pervasively *throughout the galaxy*. As the galaxy shrinks it rotates faster and faster, so this pervasive void between the stars and other bits of matter gathers towards its centre to form the typical vortex, like that of water-molecules approaching a plughole. Towards that vortex the stars and so on are continually drawn, not into some metaphysical sink but simply as the result of the galaxy's loss of angular momentum in the form of light emission to the colder and darker environment consisting of bits of intergalactic dust and other more or less evenly distributed light-absorbing objects [26].

To conclude, in the case of galaxies, POAMS finds no parallel with the idea of 'black holes' 'hoovering up' stars and other bits of matter into oblivion. Those bits of matter simply get closer and closer to a lower radial limit as they lose emitted energy and therefore angular momentum with respect to the common barycentre. Interpreted classically as a 'gravitationally attracting mass', that common barycentre, or emptiness, has to be conceived as a prodigiously dense body of some exotic kind, with imagined physical properties far removed from those of ordinary experience. As we have seen, in POAMS, there is no need for such speculation in interpreting the relevant phenomena.

9.2 The cosmological redshift

In 1929 the astronomer Edwin Hubble formulated his famous law relating the wavelength of light emitted by galaxies to their estimated distance. This law was based on observations carried out by his colleague, Vesto Slipher [27]. Hubble and Slipher noted that the light-spectra of the farthest galaxies are always shifted towards the red. This redshift in the wavelength of this light is defined by

$$ z = \frac{\lambda_o - \lambda_L}{\lambda_L}, \tag{9.1} $$

where λ_o is the observed wavelength and λ_L is the 'proper' wavelength, *i.e.* the expected wavelength. Hubble found that z is proportional to the estimated distance of any galaxy to a good degree of approximation. Since Hubble's first calculations, the majority of astronomers and physicists have interpreted the redshift as a Doppler shift due to a recession of the galaxies from ourselves and from one another at an appreciable speed, with the implication that the observable universe is expanding at the present time. The optical Doppler shift was studied in section 6 of Chapter 3. It is certainly an observed fact that when a light source is receding from an observer, its spectrum relative to that observer is shifted towards the red. However, it must be remembered that what is actually *observed* in the case of galaxies is simply that the lines in the light-spectra of those galaxies are shifted towards the red in proportion to their estimated distance. To assume that this necessarily implies that those galaxies are *receding* is a fallacy. The fact that all speeds of recession cause redshifts does not imply that in observing redshifts we are observing speeds of recession. This logical point was appreciated by Hubble if not by his followers [28].

Many scientists argue that since, in their interpretation, the universe is expanding at the present time, it has always been expanding at the same rate. Thus, extrapolating backwards into the past implies that some fifteen billion years ago, the whole universe of matter, space and everything that there is, exploded into being from something smaller than the size of a pea (sometimes known as the primæval atom)! This is the well-known 'Big Bang' theory according to which the whole of the universe was created from an initial space-time singularity and is seen by some as conclusive evidence for the existence of a God as the creator of the cosmos.

In General Relativity, one of the first space-time metrics to be studied, as an intended model of the universe as a whole, is the Robertson-Walker metric. This metric together with the Einstein Field Equations leads to the Friedmann models, which predict an expanding universe originating from an initial singularity [29][30]. According to these cosmological models, the universe can either continue to expand indefinitely or begin to contract at some stage. If the latter happens, theory predicts that the universe will collapse to another space-time singularity, representing the 'end of the universe'. The alternative to this fearsome extinction is a frozen waste as a result of continual expansion! More generally, the 'Big Bang' or initial space-time singularity is predicted always to occur, by the Hawking and Penrose singularity theorems, under reasonable physical assumptions, in all cosmological models produced by the Field Equations of GR. In general however, the initial singularity does not necessarily have the simple point-like structure predicted in the Friedmann models [31].

In our view, there can be no explanation of the redshift that is more absurd than the esoteric 'Big Bang' theory, to which there is no logical, philosophical or commonsense meaning. Even if the galaxies are receding from us at the present time, this does not necessarily imply that the universe was created from some initial space-time singularity at which the known laws of physics collapse. Once again, in GR this prediction follows from an extrapolation of the Field Equations by many orders of magnitude beyond the range for which its validity has been established. We have to be extremely dubious about a mathematical prediction based on such an extrapolation, and in no sense can anyone claim that this actually represents physical reality. The occurrence of such a space-time singularity, in our view, is more likely to be simply an indication of the limitations of GR or any other theory which attempts to model the universe. If the 'Big Bang' is accepted as a fact, then there is the even more bizarre question of what preceded it, to which of course, there can be no answer [32].

A large number of physicists argue that the 'Big Bang' theory is supported by observational evidence, such as the isotropic microwave background radiation, first discovered by Arno Penzias and Robert Wilson in 1965 [33][34]. This background microwave radiation apparently corresponds to black body radiation of about 2.7° K, which is supposed by many to be the remnants of the 'cosmic fireball' created by the 'Big Bang'. Although the presence of this radiation is consistent with an initial explosion, the 'experiment' is, of course, not repeatable. Moreover, to compute a *unique* path back to a singular origin, without any other 'fossil guide', is more in the realms of theological speculation than a scientific explanation. Besides, there are certainly other plausible explanations for the presence of the background radiation which do not involve a 'Big Bang' [35][36].

In any event, it is clear that in measuring galactic redshifts or the frequency of background radiation we are never actually observing either galaxies receding or space cooling with expansion after the 'Big Bang'. These, like all observations, are matters of interpretation and, on this cosmological scale of speculation, eminently diagnostic. Since the 'Big Bang' can *never* be *directly* observable, we would argue, especially from our adopted phenomenalist perspective, that it makes no sense to discuss it as though it were a physical phenomenon like, say, that of the Asian tsunami of 2004. As Fred Hoyle writes, in his *Nature of the Universe* (1950):

> I cannot see any good reason for preferring the big bang idea. Indeed, it seems to me in the philosophical sense to be a distinctly unsatisfactory notion, since it puts the basic assumption out of sight where it can never be challenged by direct appeal to observation.

In the following section, we show how the Friedmann cosmological models may be derived in POAMS, without reference to General Relativity. We go on to discuss problems involved with extrapolating these models to infer an initial space-time singularity. Then in section 9.4 we provide an alternative explanation of the Hubble redshift, which does not involve galactic recession. This is in terms of time-dilated periods in randomly moving bodies, in an overall-conserved angular momentum nexus where those random motions increase in proportion to their observational distance.

First, however, we need to point out that there are linguistic problems involved with claiming that the universe expanding. From the time of the Eleatic cosmologists, the word 'universe' has been taken to mean 'everything there is' in what they conceived as 'an everlasting and unchanging (*i.e.*, overall-conserved) unity, or whole' [37]. This meaning still persists today. So if it is claimed that the universe is expanding, then we have to consider the question of what that 'universe' is expanding into. Moreover, if the universe is defined as 'all there is', then against what may we presume to measure its expansion? From a Linguistic Analysis point of view, such misuses of language may be as catastrophic in science as in law. From that point of view, it is much safer and simpler, when talking about the 'universe' to employ that word according to what Ludwig Wittgenstein called its 'proper' meaning; *i.e.*, as an all-encompassing whole that always was, is and ever shall be.

According to the underlying Normal Realist philosophy of POAMS, rather than talking about 'the universe', it makes sense to talk only about the collection of the finite number of observed galaxies, the motion of any one galaxy being relative to all others. It is not only pointless but also hazardous to speculate beyond that, since no firm conclusion is to be gained by speculating about the unknown, especially since those speculations all too often take on a life of their own to become dogmas. Hence, in our approach, instead of talking about 'the universe expanding', we shall simply talk about *galactic redshifts*.

9.3 POAMS and the Friedmann equation

Consider, as in previous chapters, the case of an isolated system consisting of a particle P of mass m orbiting a body of mass M, with m very much less than M. As shown in section 3 of Chapter 6, in POAMS the equation of motion of P relative to O, the centre-of-mass of B, is

$$\frac{d^2 r}{dt^2} - \frac{L^2}{m^2 r^3} = -\frac{GM}{r^2}, \tag{9.2}$$

so long as the orbit of P about B is closed. Here, $r(t)$ is the radial distance of P from O at any time t, L is the magnitude of the orbital angular momentum of P about O and is a constant, and G is also a constant. This, of course, is the same equation as in Newtonian theory. In general, the constant L is given by

$$L = mr^2 \frac{d\theta}{dt}, \tag{9.3}$$

where $\theta(t)$ is the angle which the position vector of P makes with some fixed radial line from O at any time t, so that $d\theta/dt$ is the angular speed of P about O. As in Chapter 6, equation (9.2) can be integrated to give

$$\left(\frac{dr}{dt}\right)^2 + \frac{L^2}{m^2 r^2} = \frac{2GM}{r} + K, \tag{9.4}$$

where K is a constant. The orbital speed, $v(t)$, of the particle P is given by

$$v^2 = \left(\frac{dr}{dt}\right)^2 + r^2\left(\frac{d\theta}{dt}\right)^2 . \tag{9.5}$$

It then follows from (9.3)-(9.5) that

$$v^2 = \frac{2GM}{r} + K ,$$

and hence

$$\frac{1}{2}mv^2 - \frac{GMm}{r} = E , \tag{9.6}$$

where $E = Km/2$. In Newtonian language, (9.6) expresses the fact that the total energy, E, of P's orbit is constant, where $mv^2/2$ is the kinetic energy of P and $-GMm/r$ is the potential energy of its orbit. In this way, conservation of angular momentum implies conservation of energy. It must be remembered here however, that in POAMS, the constant G is merely a constant introduced for convenience and has nothing to do with the existence of any *in vacuo* 'gravitational force'. This equation arises simply because angular momentum is conserved and the orbit is closed.

With equation (9.6) in mind, consider a finite number, n, say, of observable galaxies,. For the moment, we shall assume that this collection is *homogeneous* (it has uniform density) and *isotropic* (the number of stars per unit solid angle is the same in all directions). This collection then satisfies the *cosmological principle* [38]. We shall also assume a simple model in which the galaxies orbit a common centre-of-mass. Since the cosmological principle holds, the existence of a commonly measured time coordinate, t, can be justified [39]. This time-coordinate is usually known as *cosmic time* in General Relativity. Let the kth galaxy have mass m_k and position vector $\mathbf{r}_k(t)$ relative to the common centre-of-mass. Then, because of the cosmological principle, any motion of the galaxies about this origin must be purely radial. It follows that the equation of motion of the kth galaxy is

$$\mathbf{r}_k(t) = r_k(t)\mathbf{n}_k,$$

where $\mathbf{n}_k$ is a unit vector in the direction of $\mathbf{r}_k$. Then the speed of the kth galaxy is

$$v_k = \left\| \frac{d\mathbf{r}_k}{dt} \right\| = \frac{dr_k}{dt}.$$

We shall simplify our model still further and treat each galaxy as if it were freely moving in orbit about each and every other. In other words, in this scenario, we take pairs of galaxies as closed isolated systems, apply conservation of angular momentum to each system and then calculate the total contribution of all these systems to the entire collection. In this way, we replace an intractable n-body problem into n two-body problems as an approximation. Applying (9.6) to each system and totalling in this way gives,

$$\frac{1}{2} \sum_{k=1}^{n} m_k \left(\frac{dr_k}{dt} \right)^2 - G \sum_{j,k=1}^{n} \frac{m_j m_k}{\left| \mathbf{r}_j - \mathbf{r}_k \right|} = E,$$

(9.7) where E is a constant. If the position of each galaxy is known at some fixed time, t_0, then the motion of each galaxy is determined by

$$\mathbf{r}_k(t) = R(t)\mathbf{r}_k(t_0), \tag{9.8}$$

where $R(t)$ is the same function for all galaxies due to the cosmological principle. In other words, the only motion relative to a fixed origin, compatible with homogeneity and isotropy, is that of uniform expansion or contraction [40]. Let

$$K_T = \frac{1}{2} \sum_{k=1}^{n} m_k \left(r_k(t_0) \right)^2, \quad P_T = -G \sum_{j,k=1}^{n} \frac{m_j m_k}{\left| \mathbf{r}_j(t_0) - \mathbf{r}_k(t_0) \right|}$$

so that, in Newtonian language, K_T is the total kinetic energy at t_0 and P_T is the total potential energy at t_0. It then follows by (9.8) that (9.7) reads

$$K_T \left(\frac{dR}{dt} \right)^2 + \frac{P_T}{R} = E,$$

and hence,

$$\left(\frac{dR}{dt}\right)^2 = \frac{C}{R} + \frac{E}{K_T}, \tag{9.9}$$

where $C = -P_T/K_T$. This equation (9.9) is the *Friedmann equation* for the 'expansion factor' $R(t)$, as derived from the Robertson-Walker metric in GR [29]. Newtonian theory provides the same equation by using (9.7) and the same arguments [40]. It also provides equation (9.9) if it is assumed that the collection of galaxies behaves like a fluid with no pressure [41], but the point here is to note that this equation can be derived in POAMS from considerations of angular momentum alone.

The Friedmann equation is easily solved to provide $R(t)$ for given values of the constants [42]. In all cases, $R(0) = 0$ without loss of generality. If the total energy E is positive or zero, then $R(t)$ continuously increases with time, whilst if E is negative, $R(t)$ increases to a maximum value and then decreases to zero. As stated in the previous section, these solutions, together with (9.8), imply that the galactic collection expanded from a single point in the past and that the galaxies continue to recede from one another. In addition, the galactic collection may or may not collapse again at some point in the future.

The derivation of the Friedmann equation, (9.9), presented in this section does one of two things. Firstly, it shows how this equation can be derived in POAMS without the need for General Relativity. Secondly, but more importantly, it highlights the problems with extrapolating the current interpretation of observational evidence into the past to obtain the 'Big Bang'. Certainly, *if* this equation provides an accurate model of the observable galactic collection for *all* time then the 'Big Bang' model must hold, and *if* the Hubble redshift is interpreted as showing that the galaxies are receding then this observational evidence supports the view that the Friedmann equation provides a good model at the present time.

However, there is no reason to suppose that the simple Friedmann equation does provide a reliable model for structures as complex as the observable galaxies. It must be remembered that we have introduced many simplifying features when deriving (9.9), and similarly simplifying features occur in the derivation in GR. In particular, the galactic collection may not satisfy the cosmological principle. It may be the case that the galaxies are clustered and that these clusters are clustered and so on [38]. In fact, more recent observational evidence suggests that the 'universe' is not homogeneous but fractal [43][44]. It may also be the case that the galaxies do not have a common centre-of-mass as such or do not behave at all like a collection of isolated two-body systems in the way that our model assumes. If any one of these conditions is dropped, then (9.9) need not follow.

Even if the galaxies are receding at the present time, the Friedmann equation does not necessarily provide an accurate model of the situation in the past. As in the case of the prediction of 'black holes', there are many theoretical alternatives to GR which do not support the presence of an initial singularity. Once again there are theories which generalise or amend the Field Equations to erase any possible singularities. In 1948, Bondi and Gold [45] and (independently) Hoyle [46] proposed a *steady state* model of the universe. In this model, it is supposed that the galaxies are receding, but that more matter is continuously created in order to maintain the constant density of the observable galactic collection [47]. Hence, although the galaxies may be continually receding, there was no initial singularity. Unfortunately, the predictions of this theory do not appear to agree with empirical evidence although the results are not yet conclusive.

Now a major problem with the standard Friedmann models of cosmology is that they give the density of the 'universe' as greater than its observed density, estimated on the assumption that its matter content lies principally in the galaxies. This discrepancy leads to the problem of the so-called 'missing matter' [48][49]. Some physicists have postulated the existence of hypothetical 'dark matter' to avoid any possible contradiction between the observed and predicted densities. It is suggested that this matter might take the form of an almost ethereal intergalactic gas, but searches for its existence so far have proved unsuccessful. We return to the idea of 'dark matter' and the search for its existence in section 5.

The main reason why the Friedmann equation is generally accepted as providing an accurate model for the motion of galaxies, at least in the present epoch, is simply because the majority of physicists interpret the Hubble redshift as being due to galactic recession. Soon after the advent of General Relativity, Einstein used his Field Equations to study the behaviour of a 'cosmic gas'. His Field Equations predicted that such a gas would continually expand whereas he firmly believed that the gas should be stable. He thus added an extra term to the Field Equations (involving the so-called *cosmological constant*) to avoid the prediction of expansion. Later, when the Hubble redshift was discovered, he too interpreted this as indicating galactic recession and deleted this extra term in the Field Equations. He later referred to his original decision to add this term as 'the biggest blunder in my life'.

Without the galactic-recession interpretation of the Hubble redshift, there is no reason to suppose that the Friedmann equation and the consequent extrapolation to an initial singularity, hold. The problem POAMS has with the implication that the galaxies are receding is that in POAMS, angular momentum is holistically conserved. In POAMS, the radial distance of the orbit of any free-moving body is a function of its angular momentum and speed. So if the Hubble redshift is due to the galaxies receding, then that implies that either the angular momentum of the galaxies is increasing or that we and those galaxies are moving along part of some great elliptical orbit. In the latter case, there are two difficulties. One is that the omnidirectional nature of the measured redshift is difficult to explain. The other is that for the effect to be so pronounced, the ellipse would have to be very narrow. In this case, any galaxies travelling in the opposite direction, on the opposite part of the elliptical orbit, must be close enough to be observed. But, of course, this is not so. On the other hand, if the angular momenta of all the galaxies are increasing with respect to one another, as *per* the former alternative, then that appears to break the rule of angular momentum conservation; that is, unless the angular momentum is accordingly redistributed elsewhere in the unobservable parts of the 'universe', which, from a phenomenalist perspective, is no less difficult to explain. Hence, in POAMS, we are obliged at least to consider alternative explanations of the Hubble redshift, which do not involve galactic recession, and this we do in the next section.

9.4 An alternative interpretation of the Hubble redshift

As we have already stated, since Hubble formulated his law relating the wavelength of light emitted by galaxies and their estimated distance, the redshift in wavelength has always been popularly interpreted as being caused by a Doppler effect due to the galaxies receding. This is certainly seen as the simplest and most obvious interpretation. If the redshift is interpreted in this way, then Special Relativity shows, as in section 6 of Chapter 3, that the speed of recession, v, is given by

$$\lambda_o = \lambda_L \left(\frac{c+v}{c-v}\right)^{1/2},$$

where λ_o is the observed wavelength and λ_L is the proper wavelength, as in (9.1). (See equation (3.6) and note that the wavelength is the reciprocal of the frequency.) In this interpretation, it follows from (9.1) that for v very much less than c,

$$z = \left(\frac{c+v}{c-v}\right)^{1/2} - 1 = (1+v/c)^{1/2}(1-v/c)^{-1/2} - 1 \approx (1+v/2c)(1+v/2c) - 1,$$

so that,

$$z \approx \frac{v}{c}. \tag{9.10}$$

The redshift parameter, z, is observed to be from approximately 1.835×10^{-4} to 3.3356×10^{-4} for galaxies at one megaparsec. We shall take the figure of 3.3356×10^{-4}, so that (9.10) gives $v \approx 100,000$ m s^{-1} at this distance. It then follows from (9.10) and Hubble's law (*i.e.* z is proportional to the distance) that

$$v \approx cz = H_0 r, \tag{9.11}$$

where H_0 is a constant, at least over a small enough period of time, known as *Hubble's constant* and r is the distance.

However, there is no *logical* reason why the redshift in wavelength need be interpreted as due to a speed of recession in this way. Admittedly, most of the alternatives to the 'galactic recession' interpretation of the Hubble redshift presented so far, have failed. Theories of 'tired light', or loss of energy due to 'travelling such enormous distances', have had to be rejected because any explanation involving 'light in transit' is like 'refraction' in that it entails a dispersion, or broadening, of the spectral bands. Of this there is little significant trace in the observed redshift. Likewise, explanations assuming that an accumulation of 'gravitational' and other contortions involving very large distances would have some dispersive effect on the light from distant galaxies, similar to the ways in which light is refracted through intermediaries such as glass or air. So these explanations also have to be rejected. However, one alternative to the galactic recession interpretation of the Hubble redshift that has so far not been logically eliminated is that it is the effect of *relativistic time-dilation* due to increasing *random* speeds with distance. Like the Doppler effect, time-dilation shifts the frequencies in a spectrum towards the red, uniformly and without dispersion. The radical difference is that unlike the Doppler shift, time-dilation applies not just to receding motion but to all motions in general.

On first impressions, it seems that such a speeding-up of motions with increasing distance runs counter to our normal expectations of angular momentum, because for constant angular momentum, as the distance between a pair of mutually orbiting masses increases, the slower becomes their orbital speed. However, the consequence of a slowing-down of speeds with distance applies only to a system involving just one pair of bodies sharing no more than just one common centre of motion. Angular momentum systems involving large numbers of bodies do not behave in that way, as, for instance, in the case of the great spiral nebulae. These are examples of free angular momentum systems involving many bodies, yet they do not rotate in the way that single pairs of bodies do. That is to

214

say, in the more uniformly packed regions of these galaxies, near their centres, the stars are as captive to one another as to their common centre, so that out to a certain distance from the centre, the rotational motion increases more or less uniformly, as for a rigid body, and it is only at their furthest reaches, of sparser density, that the speed of the stars decreases in the normally expected way [50].

For an angular momentum system then, of normally distributed stars and galaxies, the common 'centre of motion' is not central but may be indefinitely distributed. In that case, the further away a body may get from one local centre of motion, the nearer it may approach some other body. It follows from consideration of conservation of angular momentum that the nearer a body is to the major centre-of-mass of a system, the greater is its orbital speed. Hence, when the major concentration of mass is spread all around a given point in the system, the speeds of bodies relative to that point increase the further away from that point they get. In a sense, the further away a body is from any chosen point of reference, such as a terrestrial observatory, the 'nearer' it gets to the greatest (ubiquitous) accumulation of cosmic mass.

Our alternative hypothesis, then, is that the so-called 'recessional speeds' of the galaxies are due to the fact that they are getting 'nearer' to the greatest accumulation of cosmic mass. Let us assume that the relative speed, v, of recession of a galaxy increases statistically as the distance r increases, in compliance with equation (9.11), so that

$$v = kr, \qquad (9.12)$$

where k is a constant. We shall suppose formally, for simplicity, that the galaxies behave as if they were in a natural circular orbit relative to the 'central' mass – the accumulation of cosmic mass. This is not such a naïve assumption as it first appears. Roscoe has used a power-law description of *circular* velocities in idealised spiral discs and has found that this description is 'virtually perfect when applied to large ensembles' [44]. This description includes (9.12) as a special case. Under this hypothesis, it follows by (9.12) and (9.2) applied in the case of circular orbits (so that r is a constant and $L = mvr$) i.e.,

$$v^2 = \frac{GM}{r},$$

that this 'central' mass M is given by

$$M = (k^2/G)r^3. \qquad (9.13)$$

According to this formula, M is proportional to r^3, which is consistent with postulating that the universe has a homogeneous mass distribution. However, the obvious question now is: Why don't bodies seek to orbit that outside accumulation of mass in preference to their own local mass-centre? To this, one might reply that they do, but that being decentralised, that distant accumulation of mass is omnidirectional and therefore cancels itself out as a point centre of motion, leaving the local masses free to fulfil their main centring function with regard to each other in the way they do in the solar system and in spiral galaxies.

What remains, then, is to obtain a value for the constant k, in this ideal case, in terms of *time-dilation* for this increasing random motion as an alternative to Doppler-shifting due to recessional motion. If our hypothesis is correct, then the redshift parameter, z, is given by

$$z = \frac{t_R - t_P}{t_P} = (t_R / t_P) - 1, \qquad (9.14)$$

where t_R is the relativistically time-dilated period, t_P, of the oscillations, so that t_R and t_P are related by the standard time-dilation formula

$$t_R = (1 - (v^2/c^2))^{-1/2} t_P, \qquad (9.15)$$

where v is the relative speed (see equation (3.2a) of Chapter 3). It follows from (9.14) and (9.15) that for v very much less than c,

$$z = (1 - (v^2/c^2))^{-1/2} - 1 \approx v^2/2c^2,$$

so that,

$$v \approx (2z)^{1/2} c.$$

Using the figure of $z \approx 3.3356 \times 10^{-4}$ at one megaparsec, this equation gives $v \approx 7.7432 \times 10^6$ m s^{-1} at that distance. It then follows from (9.12) that our constant $k \approx 7.7432 \times 10^6$ m s^{-1}/megaparsec. This is about 77 times larger than the current figure for the Hubble constant. Since one megaparsec is approximately 3.08568×10^{22} m, it follows that $k \approx 2.5094 \times 10^{-16}$ s^{-1}, and then (9.13) gives $M \approx 9.437 \times 10^{-22}$ kg per cubic metre. This is as near as about one tenth of the theoretical density quoted in Haliday, Resnick and Walker [51] for what is described as 'the present estimated density of the universe', namely, 10^{-20} kg m^3. Taking the lower value of the redshift parameter, z, halves this figure, which puts it somewhat nearer to the value given in Dobson, Grace and Lovett [52], namely, 1.5×10^{-26} kg m^{-3}. Given these wide differences in the estimated mass-density of the universe, we may say that our hypothesis places the mass-density in the middle range of these textbook values and may therefore be regarded as quite reasonable. If so, then it supports our hypothesis that galaxies have very large *omnidirectional* speeds and corresponding time-dilations relative to us and to one another in proportion to their distance.

As noted earlier, recent observational evidence suggests that the mass distribution of the universe may not be homogeneous but may be fractal [43][44]. More precisely, clusters of galaxies are highly irregular but similar over small to medium distance scales. Observational evidence suggests that relative speed, v, of far-off galaxies in relation to their distance, r, is given by a power-law of the form [44]

$$v = kr^{\alpha}, \tag{9.16}$$

for some choice of constants k and α. If our Hubble-like law (9.12) is replaced by (9.16) then according to our previous arguments, the 'central mass' is given by

$$M = (k^2/G)r^{2\alpha + 1}.$$

Since recent observational evidence suggests that M is proportional to r^2 for galaxies in a certain range [43], this would give $\alpha = \frac{1}{2}$ in our arguments. In fact, Roscoe's analysis has led him to the conclusion that a globally inertial space and time can be associated with a non-trivial global matter distribution and that this distribution is necessarily fractal with dimension 2. However, whether the universe is homogeneous on a large enough scale is still very much an open question.

It must be appreciated that in this section, our figures are included only to support our logical arguments and, in practice, would depend on many different factors. For example, our analysis ignores any spin angular momentum that bodies have, which, for much of the cosmological material in the universe (such as, for example, pulsars) may be extremely large. According to POAMS, such spin angular momentum would have a considerable effect on the 'constant' G, as explained in Chapter 7. Very large spin kinetic energies in comparison with purely orbital kinetic energy entail correspondingly large increases in the value of G. The consequence of such increases in G due to spin is that the value of M in (9.13) reduces towards the value of the 'smoothed-out density of galactic material' supplied by Dobson, Grace and Lovatt. However, at the very least, our alternative interpretation of the Hubble redshift provides logical scope for us not to feel compelled to accept, without question, the current interpretation of galactic recession.

9.5 'Dark matter'

In Boulby, North Yorkshire, is Europe's deepest mine at the bottom of which is installed a laboratory containing scientific hardware on which millions of pounds have been invested for the purpose of answering what has been described as 'the biggest single challenge in physics today'. Led by Professor Tim Sumner, the aim of this team of scientists has been, for sixteen years, to discover evidence for the existence of what is popularly called 'dark matter' in the form of 'weakly interacting massive particles', called WIMPs. So far, however, the search has been completely unsuccessful.

Why, then, has this expensive research so doggedly continued when all the evidence seems to be against it? The reason is that, according to the majority of physicists, something *has* to be there to make up the 96% of our 'universe' that seems to be missing. In particular, conventional theories are unable to explain the observed motion of spiral galaxies, which according to these theories should fly apart when they rotate, in a way that they clearly do not. Recall also, as mentioned in section 3 of this chapter, that supporters of the Friedmann models for the 'expansion of the universe' say that there must be 'missing matter' due to the apparent discrepancy between the observed and predicted density of the known galactic collection. These ideas will be expanded upon in the following paragraphs.

In 1973, James Peebles and Jeremiah Ostriker were engaged in pioneering work with computer models of the galactic collection based on the known data obtained from astronomical observations. Their models of the cosmos did not compute since there was not enough matter to maintain stability. But no extra matter was to be found. It was decided that this inscrutable 'something' had to have mass but none of the other properties of ordinary matter, which is why it can be neither seen nor – so far – detected.

This theoretical prediction had been preceded, in 1933, by the observations of the astronomer Fritz Zwicky. His study of clusters of galaxies orbiting one another had revealed that on the basis of the known laws of physics, the forces holding those galaxies together were insufficiently accounted for in terms of the masses of the stars and so on that can be seen. He calculated that at least ten times more mass was required to account for the observed motions of the galaxies. Then, the astronomer, Vera Rubin, studying whole galaxies in the 1970s, reported that Newton's Gravitational Law does not hold for the rotations of these galaxies in the way it so clearly does for our solar system, where the ordinary rotation curve is an embodiment of the law of gravity. By measuring the Doppler shift of their H-alpha emission lines, she found that the rotation curves of the spiral galaxies are mostly flat, that they rotate like disks of stars held in place by something invisible that exerts extra gravity. From the POAMS point of view this, as we have seen, is only to be expected. In the sorts of galaxies Rubin studied, the stars, typically, are densely packed, to the extent that those stars and other bits of matter orbit one another in subsystems that orbit the centre-of-mass of the galaxy in the way our planets together with their satellites orbit the Sun. Indeed, it would be strange if all the stars in a system as densely packed as a spiral galaxy were found to orbit the centre-of-mass in the manner of free and dissociate single bodies. Even the bodies of our solar system do not orbit the Sun in that ideally dissociate way.

Riccardo Giovanelli, of Cornell University, using the huge radio telescope in Arecibo, confirmed Rubin's observations by reporting that even at the farthest reaches of the observable universe, the orbiting rate of interstellar gas is no slower than that of the stars. A study of spiral galaxies by Rubin and W.K. Ford suggested that there is matter outside the bulges of these galaxies which is invisible but exerts a gravitational force that increases the speeds of the gas clouds more than is to be expected from the known distribution of visible matter.

Earlier, in the 1920s, the astronomer Jan Oort had discovered that the orbital speeds of the stars in the Milky Way do not decrease with increasing distance from the galactic centre as Newton's laws demand. However, he did not conjecture the cause to be dark matter. Instead, he felt that the apparent anomaly would eventually be cleared up by further, more detailed observations of matter in the Milky Way. Since then, however, all the various theories and observations have seemed to fit together. Thus, despite the fact that there remains no hard evidence in support of its existence, in both professional and popular science a belief in the underlying reality of 'dark matter' has become highly fashionable.

This postulated 'dark matter', it was decided, is all around us, not in ordinary atoms but in some new, quasi-ethereal form of matter that has mass only, enough to account for the deficit of mass that is to be expected in terms of Newton's Gravitational Law. This is what led to Sumner's hunt for new particles that are alleged to fly straight through the earth and interact, if at all, only very weakly with ordinary matter. This, it is assumed, is why they have so far remained undetected, even by the best detectors in the deepest mines.

However, some scientists regard these searches for 'dark matter' as a waste of time. This is the view of Mordechai Milgrom who, in 1983, published his theory of Modified Newtonian Dynamics (MOND), based on varying gravity as a possible alternative to the 'missing matter' hypothesis [53][54]. But, he says, the research to detect 'dark matter' will continue and will stop 'only when the money stops' [55]. One of the reasons for this is that, at the time, any idea of varying gravity, no matter how well it fitted the data, was considered much too radical, and so Milgrom's theory went largely neglected. Other theories were regarded as much more sensible and less heretical. In particular, Saul Perlmutter, of the University of California, Berkeley, argued on the basis of the 'galactic recession' interpretation of the Hubble redshift that the expansion of 'the universe' is speeding up due to the existence of hypothetical 'dark energy'. Perlmutter hypothesised 'the universe' is made of 21% of 'dark matter' and 75% of 'dark energy', with only the remainder being ordinary matter. This idea, which is successfully adjusted throughout to fit all the known facts, has now become known as the *Standard Model* of cosmology.

It is to be noted that there are sceptics in the scientific establishment of this *ad hoc* model of cosmology [56]. In opposition to these sceptics, Carlos Frenk, on the basis of the 'Big Bang' theory, has defended the Standard Model by producing computer simulations of the cosmogony of 'the universe' by feeding-in the best of the known observational and theoretical data. These, pictorially speaking, are, to say the least, very convincing. The negative view of the Standard Model is also disputed by James Peebles, who claims to have indisputable evidence in favour of it.

It is the view of the many supporters of the Standard Model that it has now 'come of age'. This is despite the fact that all evidence of 'dark matter', 'dark energy', *etc.*, remains completely elusive. *Theoretically*, it all fits and that is sufficient for some. Others, however, are more in favour of alternative theories such as Milgrom's MOND.

Milgrom's approach implies that Newton's Law of Gravitation might have been wrong and that the sacrosanct 'gravitational constant', G, is not a constant but a factor that in some cases may be variable. This is precisely what is maintained by the authors of this book, as recounted in these chapters. According to POAMS what is 'missing' from the traditional account of the motions of the galaxies is nothing as mysterious as 'dark matter' or 'dark energy' but simply what might be called 'dark' *spin* ('dark' only because it has been neglected). In an angular momentum nexus, as opposed to a 'gravitational' one, all spin angular momenta (which are every bit as observable as orbital angular momentum) are an integral part of the overall balance of conserved angular momentum, being all part and parcel of the same equations of motion [57]. From this point of view, it is only to be expected that if this *spin* part of angular momentum is left out of account, then the astronomical data quite obviously will not agree with the theoretical predictions. Far from being invisible, mysterious and inscrutable, like 'dark matter' and 'dark energy', this missing spin angular momentum is all upfront and measurable, so long as our current classical precepts will allow it. Of course, to suggest that 'G changes' is thought in some quarters to be a heresy. But Rubin and others now also support Milgrom in this sacrilegious suggestion. More recently, Jacob Bekenstein has amended MOND in order to address its apparent clash with General Relativity. He claims his theory to be consistent with both GR and MOND [58]. The present authors' reasons for accepting the variability of G are even more sacrilegious, requiring a wholesale philosophical revision of our customary ways of thinking about matter, space and time.

Notes and References

[1] Misner, C. W., Thorne, K. S. and Wheeler, J. A.: *Gravitation* (Freeman, San Francisco, 1973) Chapter 24, pp. 618-635.

[2] Birkhoff, G. D.: *Relativity and Modern Physics* (Harvard University Press, Cambridge, 1923).

[3] Foster, J. and Nightingale, J. D.: *A Short Course in General Relativity* (Longman, New York, 1979) pp. 123-126.

[4] Hawking, S. W. and Ellis, G. F. R.: *The Large Scale Structure of Space-Time* (Cambridge University Press, 1973) Appendix A, pp. 365-368.

[5] *Op. cit.* reference 3, pp. 126-127.

[6] D'Inverno, R.: *Introducing Einstein's Relativity* (Clarendon, Oxford, 1992) Chapter 19, pp. 248-268.

[7] *Op. cit.* reference 4, Chapter 8, pp. 256-298.

[8] Hawking, S. W.: 'Breakdown of Predictability in Gravitational Collapse', *Phys. Rev.* D **14** (1976), pp. 2460.

[9] Carter, B.: 'Global Structure of the Kerr Family of Gravitational Fields', *Phys. Rev.* **33** (1970), p. 413.

[10] Thorne, K. S.: 'The Search for Black Holes', *Scientific American,* **231** (6) (1974), pp. 32-43.

[11] Rees, M. J.: 'Observational Effects of Black Holes', in Shariv, G. and Rosen, J. (eds.): *General Relativity and Gravitation* (Halsted, New York, 1975).

[12] Bahcall, J. N., Dyson, F. J., Katz, J. I. and Paczynski, B., *Astrophys. J. Lett.* **189** (1974) L 17.

[13] Rowlands, P.: *A Revolution Too Far: The Establishment of General Relativity* (PD Publications, Liverpool, 1994) pp. 197-199.

[14] Young, P. J., Westphal, J. A., Kristian, J., Wilson, C. P. and Landauer, F. P. 'Evidence for a supermassive object in the nucleus of the galaxy M87 from SIT and CCD area photometry', *Astrophys. J.* **221** (1978), pp. 721-730.

[15] Brans, C. and Dicke, R. H., *Phys. Rev.* **124** (1961) 925.

[16] Stephenson G., *Il Nuovo Cimento* **9** (1958), p. 263.

[17] Kilmister, C. W.: *Les Theories Relativistes de la Gravitation* (Centre National de la Recherche Scientifique, Paris, 1962)

[18] Yang, C. N., *Phys. Rev. Lett.* **33** (1974), p. 445.

[19] Muller, A., Heinz, B., Muller, B. and Greiner W., *J. Phys. A* **11** (1978), p 1781.

[20] Trautman, A., *Nature Phys. Sci.* **242** (1973), p 7.

[21] Prasanna, A. R., *Phys. Rev.* D **11** (1975), p. 2076.

[22] Isham, C., Penrose, R. and Sciama, D. (eds.): *Quantum Gravity* (Clarendon, Oxford, 1975).

[23] Osborne, A. D.: *Gravitation and Dynamical Systems*, Doctoral Thesis (City University, 1980).

[24] Osborne, A. D.: *Gravitation and the Problem of Space-time Singularities*, *Bull. I. M. A* **21** (1985)' pp. 123-129.

[25] *Op. cit.* reference 1, pp. 619-620, 624.

[26] Obviously, a void as such cannot absorb angular momentum. Only particles can do that. So a galaxy, like any other luminous body, can lose angular momentum only if there is matter in external space to absorb it. That is to say, it cannot shine or otherwise lose energy to a pure vacuum. This suggests an answer to Olbers' paradox. In an unlimited distribution of cosmical material there are always as many bits of matter absorbing light as there are producing it, with none of the light-quanta going unaccounted. So there is no preponderant accumulation or overplus of brightness to make the sky infinitely white in the way Olbers projected for the case of an infinitely extended static universe.

[27] See, for example, *Encyclopaedia Britannica*, CD-ROM (1994-2001).

[28] As Mayall notes in the entry in the 1961 *Encyclopaedia Britannica*, Volume 16, p.187Kd, "Hubble preferred the noncommittal term *redshift* and referred to his and his colleague Humason's results as the 'law of redshifts' ".

[29] *Op. cit.* reference 3, pp. 149-157.

[30] In fact, historically, the Friedmann models were derived by other means before the Robertson-Walker metric was known about.

[31] *Op. cit.* reference 6, p. 313.

[32] See, for example, reference 1, pp.769-770.

[33] Penzias, A. A. and Wilson, R. W.: 'A Measurement of Excess Antenna Temperature at 4080 Mc/s', *Astrophysics Journal*, **142** (1965), pp. 419-421.

[34] More precise measurements made by the Cosmic Background Explorer (COBE) satellite, launched in 1989, essentially confirmed the findings of Penzias and Wilson.

[35] Rowlands, P.: 'How To Get Something from Nothing', in Pope N. V., Osborne, A. D. and Winfield, A. F. T. (eds.): *Immediate Distant Action and Correlation in Modern Physics: The Balanced Universe* (Edwin Mellen, New York, 2005) pp. 257-262.

[36] Lerner, E. J.: *The Big Bang Never Happened* (Vintage, 1991).

[37] The Eleatic School flourished in Elea, Greece, in the 6th and 5th centuries BC. According to the Eleatics, the universe is an essentially changeless unity. (See, for example, Microsoft *Encarta Encyclopaedia Deluxe*, 2000).

[38] *Op. cit.* reference 6, pp. 312-314.

[39] *Op. cit.* reference 3, p. 150.

[40] *Op. cit.* reference 6, pp. 310-312.

[41] *Op. cit.* reference 3, pp. 158-160.

[42] *Op. cit.* reference 3, pp. 154-156.

[43] Graneau, N and Graneau, P.: 'The Evidence and Consequences of Newtonian Instantaneous Forces', in Pope N. V., Osborne, A. D. and Winfield, A. F. T. (eds.): *Immediate Distant Action and Correlation in Modern Physics: The Balanced Universe* (Edwin Mellen, New York, 2005) pp. 157-165.

[44] Roscoe, D.: 'A Perspective on Mach's Principle and the Consequent Discovery of Major New Phenomenology in Spiral Discs', in Pope N. V., Osborne, A. D. and Winfield, A. F. T. (eds.): *Immediate Distant Action and Correlation in Modern Physics: The Balanced Universe* (Edwin Mellen, New York, 2005) pp. 169-184.

[45] Bondi, H. and Gold, T.: 'The steady-state theory of the expanding universe', *Monthly Notices of the Royal Astronomical Society* **108** (1948), pp. 252-270.

[46] Hoyle, F.: 'A new model for the expanding universe', *Month. Notices Royal Astro. Soc.* **108** (1948), pp. 372-382.

[47] *Op. cit.* reference 6, pp. 344-347.

[48] *Op. cit.* reference 3, pp. 156-157.

[49] *Op. cit.* reference 6, pp. 341-342.

[50] Babcock, H. W., Aller, L. H. and Mayall, N. U., in their studies of M31 and M33 (1950).

[51] Haliday, D., Resnick, R. and Walker, J.: *Fundamentals of Physics* (Wiley, 2001, 6th ed.) p. 323.

[52] Dobson, K., Grace, D. and Lovett, D. (eds.): Physics, 2nd Edition, Series: Advanced Science (Harper Collins, 2002).

[53] Milgrom, M.: 'A Modification of the Newton Dynamics as a Possible Alternative to the Hidden Mass Hypothesis', *Astrophysical Journal*, **270** (July 15, 1983) 365-370. Note the acronym MOND (MOdified Newtonian Dynamics) signifying Milgrom's explanation for the gravitational anomalies of galactic rotation data usually attributed to dark matter.

[54] It is to be noted that, earlier than this, Anthony D. Osborne, in his 1980 Doctoral Thesis, *Gravitation and Dynamical Systems*, had hypothesised that '*G*' is not a constant.

[55] One is reminded, here, of a conversation that Viv Pope once had at CERN, in Geneva, with the late John Bell (of Bell's Inequalities fame). 'How can you be happy,' Pope asked him, 'with these sorts of impossible, purely *ad hoc* concepts of inscrutable particles?' 'Well,' Bell replied, waving his hand towards the sumptuous surroundings of CERN: 'It's much better, don't you think, than working down a mine!' Pope now thinks this conversation rather ironic in view of the fact that Tim Sumner has since extended the study of astronomical physics down to those very deepest mining levels!

[56] One such sceptic is Professor Michael Disney, an astronomer of the University of Wales, Cardiff. In his view, it is all 'wildly unrealistic', having no basis in Physics.

[57] Pope, N. V.: Part 1, Chapter 1 in Chubykalo, A. E., Pope, N. V. and Smirnov-Rueda, R. (eds.): *Instantaneous Action-at-a-Distance in Modern Physics: Pro and Contra* (Nova Science, New York) pp. 3-17.

[58] See issue 2483 of the *New Scientist*, 2nd January 2005, p.10.

CHAPTER 10

Résumé

Physics as we know it did not descend from the sky. It is the product of a long and complex history. Relics of that complexity are still with us in the way we think and speak about things today. The language of physics is therefore not only a record of our dealings with nature on the physical level, it is also a record of the tortuous trail that individuals have beaten through the dense jungle of the Unknown with their *ad hoc* theories and working hypotheses.

In the physics textbooks which those seeking proficiency in the subject have to study for their examinations, the vestiges of those theoretical meanderings remain. In the very words that are used, even in their most practical down-to-earth uses, that history is endemic. It is built-in, fixed and virtually ineradicable. Words like 'space', 'time', 'electron', 'charge', 'gravity', *etc.*, bespeak the historical twists and turns that physics took in reaching its present stage of development.

Nature and the way physics describes it may therefore be very different. The Ancient Greeks knew this. For them, nature as we describe it was *language*, and nature as it is in itself – whatever that might be – they called *logos*. For them, *logos* was the culminating point of achievement in the development of language. *Logos* was the *truth* towards the realisation of which natural philosophy aims and without which language would be meaningless.

The fact, then, that language evolves, that truth may be gradually sifted-out from error, signifies the existence of something beyond language towards which language aspires. Without that premium placed on the development of language there could be no such pursuit as science. Nowadays, the language of science is, of course, highly developed. However, being finite, it is far from being finished and replete. Moreover, from time to time this scientific language needs to be overhauled, purged of what might best be called theoretical waste – relics of working hypotheses which have served their time, surviving only to complicate and confuse. This is why the philosopher John Locke regarded it as his duty to serve as what he called an 'under-labourer to science', clearing up the swarf and general conceptual clutter from science's workshop floor, without which service science would soon grind to a halt.

Plainly, the objects and processes with which physics deals did not come ready classified, categorised and labelled by nature. It should be borne in mind that it is we, with our tentative and arbitrary linguistic devices, who do that. And since our efforts in that direction are essentially heuristic, there can be no preconceived specific goal towards which these efforts are directed. The language of physics has therefore to be examined from time to time and, if necessary, revised – perhaps radically in some instances. This means that there is always a philosophical dimension to physics, of the sort Locke envisaged as a clearing up of physics language.

The fact, then, that physical phenomena have been classified, divided and categorised in terms of 'vacuum', 'ether', 'light-speed', 'gravity', 'force-field', *etc.*, does not mean that these delineations are fixed forever. In zoology, the whale, which was once regarded as a fish, had to be reclassified as a mammal, and the virus particle confounded the natural history class-division between animal and mineral. Also, only fairly recently, in the context of Special Relativity, the separate and unrelated categories of 'space' and 'time' had to be merged into 'space-time'. A too conservative attitude towards maintaining the classifications of phenomena that our history has produced at any time may therefore do no more than inhibit progress in science. Indeed, physics itself cannot be guaranteed a fixture in its own academic category. This is why this book is a cross-disciplinary amalgam of physics, philosophy and mathematics. The result is a synthesis which some educators may regard as unclassifiable, hence as what, at one time, might have been regarded as a heresy, to be dealt with in the then customary manner. Presumably, these ancient strictures on scientific progress no longer apply, so that the consequences of stepping over the voodoo chalk lines drawn by the custodians of the norms may not, now, be so dire as in the days of yore. Nevertheless, one finds that this same resistance to change is as endemic in physics as it ever was, although, mercifully, tempered by political pressure towards democracy and the protection of human rights – and, it has to be said, public apathy towards the subject. To what extent this modifies modern academic physics is a moot point, perhaps to be tested by writings of this present sort. Plato's nephew, Speusippus, enshrined the results of his uncle's dialogues in what came to be called the Academy – which is, of course, the source of the word 'academic'. In that Academy, Plato's work was treated as sacrosanct. It was to be neither added to nor subtracted from. What Speusippus had established was therefore, one might say, the first 'university', in which examinations were intended, not so much to encourage free-thinking ideas about the nature of things as to make students show that they had grasped the ideas of those whose thoughts had set the standard of examinations for all students to follow. This academising, or fixing, of knowledge became the trend with universities everywhere, right up to the present time. This is why those scientists who most eminently thought for themselves had to 'buck the System' and work, for the most part, extramurally.

There is, of course, no sane way of thinking which can, entirely, 'go it alone', isolated altogether from the customary norms and standards of education, otherwise one would have to start a new language from scratch, which is inconceivable. So, somehow, progress in science has to steer carefully between the Scylla of Educational conformity and the Charybdis of anarchy, without falling foul of either.

Now one does not, of course, wish to change things just for change's sake. The reasons for change have to be clearly defined and justified. The first reason for change at the present time is, surely, the extent to which physics has become unempirical, that is to say, overweighted towards pure theory, rather than observation. From the point of view of common understanding, from microphysics to cosmology, there are already in circulation far too many altogether bizarre theories to be comprehended. So now is the time perhaps when it is propitious to free the stilted language of modern physics from the grip of the 'dead hand of the past'. Nature does not have, in itself, the guile to lie and create mysteries. Mysteries are the product of the human intellect alone. In science, this is often not appreciated. For instance, in reaction to the emphasis on theorising, modern physics is also bedevilled by 'Experimentalism', based on the notion that all theories and hypotheses can be dispensed with by just 'plain observation'. Observation in itself, these Experimentalists believe, cuts through all human subjectivity, automatically to reveal natural truth and reality. However, this ignores the fact that observations have to be *interpreted*, and it is these interpretations of physical phenomena that create the mysteries. Ideally, without artifice, physical phenomena should fit together naturally like bits of a jigsaw puzzle. This they cannot do if the pieces are conceptually misshapen or merely contrived to fit by the use of over-elaborate interpretation and misuse of language.

Observationism (classically called phenomenalism) and language go intimately together. It is the coherence or otherwise of language which dispels or creates mysteries. The test of linguistic coherence, hence of common understanding is, of course, logic. Logic is what systematically tests our perceptions and conceptions for consistency and integrity. This is by the gradual seeking out and eliminating of the fallacies which prevent phenomena, the pieces of the cosmic Jigsaw Puzzle, from fitting naturally and automatically into place.

Having said all that, we now return to the issue in hand, which is to summarise the results of the previous chapters. Our programme of conceptual catharsis begins with the convoluted interpretation of the dimensional constant c as the 'speed of light *in vacuo*'. This standard interpretation has created many conceptual chimeras. First of these was the 'luminiferous ether', in search of which physics was sent on the wild goose chase which led to the nineteenth century perplexity associated with Michelson and Morley, *et al*. All this was accompanied, of course, with a burgeoning of the jargon associated with what came to be known as 'electrodynamics'. As we have demonstrated, this historical rigmarole, illustrious and practically efficacious though it undoubtedly was at the time, strictly speaking, logically unnecessary.

Unnecessary also was the intellectual paraphernalia of Einstein's Special Relativity, with its customary explication in terms of electromagnetic radiation, light-signals travelling between observers, and so on. As we have seen, all this can be circumvented simply by re-interpreting the constant c as a dimensional *conversion factor*, which enables us to express the traditional three dimensions of observational space as measures in time-units of seconds. (This is in the same way that c^2 acts as a conversion factor between mass and energy in the formula $E = mc^2$.) Together with the dimension of observed duration, this makes the world of physical phenomena altogether *four*-dimensional, so that the distance and time dimensions of a speed become orthogonal *time* dimensions, to which the Theorem of Pythagoras applies in the same way as it did, originally, to just two and three dimensions. In this way, a 'speed' has a geometrical length, measured in seconds, equivalent to the relativistic time-dilation of Einstein, bypassing all the historical palaver associated with that discovery. Indeed, we have shown that, in principle, if the dimensional constant c had been available at the time of Pythagoras then relativistic time-dilation might have been, from those early days, an integral part of ordinary everyday geometry.

None of this, of course, detracts from the genius and fortitude of those who hacked their tortuous trails through the conceptual jungle. Only from the aerial elevation provided by a retrospective overview of the history of those heroic efforts can the truly logical connections between those discoveries be seen. There can be little doubt that those who forged those tracks would not wish all students of physics, thereafter, to follow exactly in their stumbling footsteps. As it is said, 'He thanks his teacher not at all who forever remains his pupil'. Any physicist worth his salt would therefore expect and approve any simplification of his findings, no matter how radical or revolutionary.

It is with this in mind that in this book we have subjected certain major concepts of physics, both ancient and modern, to the same logical scrutiny. Only those who, like Speusippus the Academic, would wish to enshrine the works of the pioneers in the name of 'physics' could possibly take exception to this programme of conceptual simplification. In that confidence, therefore, we have sought to translate the language of both classical and modern, 'God's-eye-view' absolutism, or 'Realism', into the radically empirical language of true relativism, or phenomenalism. This has meant, in some cases, melting-down the theoretical junk-heap relating to what are traditionally called 'light', 'gravity', 'electricity', 'force-fields' 'photons', 'black holes', 'galactic recession', and so on, to the bare empirical metal, skimming-off the dross and recasting the purified product into the new mould provided by the paradigm of phenomenalism supplied by Mach.

Perhaps the biggest advantage that this conceptual catharsis offers, apart from its automatic removal, as we have seen, of the current mystery of 'dark matter' by modifying the 'gravitational constant' G, is also the removal of the theoretical schism between those two main areas of modern physics, Relativity and Quantum Mechanics. In Relativity, both Special and General, motion is continuous, whence the quantisation of the phenomenon has to be no more than a conceptual appurtenance. In POAMS, all free motion is a manifestation of angular momentum, in ultimate units of $h/2\pi$, which is automatically quantised. Also, angular momentum includes the spin motions of bodies together with their orbital motions in the way that 'gravitation' cannot. This means that the spin which Goudsmit and Uhlenbeck ascribed to the 'electron' becomes an integral part of the overall angular momentum system instead of a supplementary *ad hoc* assumption. Moreover, as we have demonstrated, on the basis of POAMS, the effect of spin on the value of G, makes it predictable that the orbital parameters of spinning bodies will be different from those of non-spinning ones. This makes it at least plausible that the weight of a spinning disc will vary with the amount and orientation of the spin in the way that was envisaged by the likes of Peter Kummel and Hideo Hayasaka, in their different experiments with spinning bodies. As we have seen in Chapter 7, those experiments may be replicated with exact predictions of results more in line with the actual evidence than those that are variously claimed by these experimenters – that is to say, very much smaller than they have alleged.

All our arguments here, it may be recalled, relate to *phenomena*, not to the 'fundamental mechanisms' of classical physics. That is to say, our assertions are made on the basis of the observational *information* supplied by light – light, that is, as we directly *see* it, with our eyes and/or our instruments, not as it is imagined to travel in space. Moreover, as stated in the foregoing texts, for information to *be* information it has to be analysable into ultimately discrete elements. A continuum, with all its elements merged into one another, contains no information. It would be as though all the letters in a news-printer's font were fused permanently together. What sort of 'news' could that newspaper ever convey?

Phenomena therefore, *qua* observational information, are automatically discretised, or *quantised*. This, as we have seen, is into the quantum pixels we have re-named *phota* as the Normal Realist replacement for Einstein's space-travelling 'photons'. The paradigm shift, therefore, is from a physics based on analog projections of 'atomic mechanisms' into a physics that is based entirely on the logical interpretation of observational information. This conceptual shift is, surely, as revolutionary as it gets. However, it may be that nothing short of such a revolution will suffice to stem the runaway mystification of nature that has replaced logical coherence in modern physics, whose departments are currently being shut down at more and more universities, due to lack of student appeal.

This is scarcely surprising in view of what, in 1946, Bertrand Russell wrote in his popular book: *A History of Western Philosophy*:

> The philosophy appropriate to quantum theory...has not yet been adequately developed. I suspect that it will demand even more radical departures from the traditional doctrine of space and time than those demanded by the theory of relativity.

Now, more than half a century on, could POAMS possibly be Russell's long-awaited 'radical departure'? We leave it to the reader to decide.

BIBLIOGRAPHY

References to journal articles can be found at the end of each chapter.

Aharoni, J.: *The Special Theory of Relativity* (Clarendon, Oxford, 1959).

Arthurs, A. M.: *Complementary Variational Principles* (Clarendon, Oxford, 1970).

Assis, A. K. T.: *Weber's Electrodynamics* (Kluwer, Dordrecht, 1994).

Ayer, A. J.: *The Central Questions of Philosophy* (London, 1973).

Birkhoff, G. D.: *Relativity and Modern Physics* (Harvard University Press, 1923).

Blackmore, J. T.: *Ernst Mach, His Life, Work and Influence* (University of California Press, 1972).

Bohm, D.: *Wholeness and the Implicate Order* (Routledge, London, 1980).

Bondi, H.: *Assumption and Myth in Physical Theory* (Cambridge Univ. Press, 1964).

Christy, R. W. and Pytte, A.: *The Structure of Matter: An Introduction to Modern Physics* (Benjamin, New York, 1965).

Chubykalo, A. E., Pope, N. V. and Smirnov-Rueda, R. (eds.): *Instantaneous Action-at-a-Distance in Modern Physics: Pro and Contra* (Nova Science, New York, 1999).

Davies, P.: *Other Worlds* (Pelican, London, 1988).

D'Espagnat, B.: *Conceptual Foundations of Quantum Mechanics* (Benjamin, 1971).

D'Inverno, R.: *Introducing Einstein's Relativity* (Clarendon, Oxford, 1992).

Dobson, K., Grace, D. and Lovett, D (eds.): *Physics*, 2nd Edition, Series: Advanced Science (Harper Collins, 2002).

Eisberg, R. and Resnick, R.: *Quantum Physics of Atoms, Molecules, Solids, Nuclei and Particles* (Wiley, New York, 1985).

Foster, J. and Nightingale, J. D.: *A Short Course in General Relativity* (Longman, New York, 1979).

French, A. P.: *Special Relativity* (Chapman & Hall, New York, 1991).

Haliday, D., Resnick, R. and Walker, J.: *Fundamentals of Physics* (Wiley, 2001).

Hawking, S. W.: *A Brief History of Time* (Bantam Books, London, 1988).

Hawking, S. W. and Ellis, G. F. R.: *The Large Scale Structure of Space-Time* (Cambridge University Press, 1973).

Isham, C., Penrose, R. and Sciama, D. (eds.): *Quantum Gravity* (Clarendon, Oxford, 1975).

Kay, D. C.: *Tensor Calculus* (McGraw-Hill, New York, 1988).

Kibble, T. W. B and Berkshire, F. H.: *Classical Mechanics* (Addison Wesley Longman, Harlow, 1996).

Lawden, D. F.: *Elements of Special Relativity* (Wiley, 1985).

Lerner, E. J.: *The Big Bang Never Happened* (Vintage, 1991).

Marder, L.: *Time and the Space-Traveller* (Allen and Unwin, 1971).

McCuskey, S. W.: *An Introduction to Advanced Dynamics* (Addison-Wesley, Reading, USA, 1959).

Millikan, R. A.: *The Electron: Its Isolation and Measurement and Determination of Some of its Properties* (University of Chicago Press, 1963).

Misner, C. W., Thorne, K. S. and Wheeler, J. A.: *Gravitation* (Freeman, San Francisco, 1973).

Møller, C.: *The Theory of Relativity* (Oxford University Press, Oxford, 1972).

Muirhead, H.: *The Special Theory of Relativity* (Macmillan, London, 1973).

Phipps, T. E., Jr.: *Heretical Verities, Mathematical Themes in Physical Description* (Urbana, Illinois, 1986).

Polkinghorne, J. C.: *The Quantum World* (Pelican, London, 1986).

Pope, V.: *The Eye of the Beholder: The Role of the Observer in Modern Physics* (**phi** Philosophical Enterprises, Swansea, 2004).

Pope, N. V., Osborne, A. D. and Winfield, A. F. T. (eds.): *Immediate Distant Action and Correlation in Modern Physics: The Balanced Universe* (Edwin Mellen Press, New York, 2005).

Rindler, W.: *Relativity: Special, General and Cosmological* (Oxford University Press, Oxford, 2001).

Rowlands, P.: *A Revolution Too Far: The Establishment of General Relativity* (PD publications, Liverpool, 1994).

Sanders, J. H.: *The Velocity of Light* (Pergamon Press, Oxford, 1965).

Shankland, R. S.: *Atomic and Nuclear Physics* (Macmillan, 1961).

Shannon, C. and Weaver, W.: *The Mathematical Theory of Communication* (Univ. of Illinois Press, Urbana, USA, 1949).

Spain, B.: *Tensor Calculus* (Oliver and Boyd, London, 1953).

Taylor, J. G.: *Quantum Mechanics: An Introduction* (Allen and Unwin, London, 1970).

Taylor, J. G.: *Special Relativity* (Clarendon, Oxford, 1975).

INDEX